McGRAW-HILL PUBLICATIONS IN THE
AGRICULTURAL AND BOTANICAL SCIENCES
EDMUND W. SINNOTT, CONSULTING EDITOR

THE TRANSLOCATION OF
SOLUTES IN PLANTS

THE TRANSLOCATION
OF
SOLUTES IN PLANTS

*A Critical Consideration of Evidence
Bearing upon Solute Movement*

BY

OTIS F. CURTIS, *1888*

Professor of Botany, Cornell University

FIRST EDITION
SECOND IMPRESSION

McGRAW-HILL BOOK COMPANY, Inc.

NEW YORK AND LONDON

1935

Copyright, 1935, by the
McGraw-Hill Book Company, Inc.

THE MAPLE PRESS COMPANY, YORK, PA.

TO
L. W. C.

PREFACE

If one reads the literature dealing with problems relating to the translocation of solutes within plants, it soon becomes apparent that, relative to the importance of the subject, very little experimental evidence is available to which one can confidently turn for information and guidance. In fact, the available evidence has led to flatly contradictory conclusions. These contradictions obtain even with reference to such fundamental points as the tissues chiefly concerned in transport, and the mechanism of transport. One or both of these questions must be solved before any real progress can be made in an understanding of solute movement, or of the factors influencing the direction of movement, the rate of movement, or the final distribution of the materials. Any satisfactory explanation of the behavior of those plants which are differentiated into tissues and organs having differences in abilities to produce or absorb special substances, as for example differentiation into leaves which carry on photosynthesis and roots which absorb soil solutes or water, must involve also an explanation of conditions determining translocation of solutes from one part to another, because interchange of special solutes or their distribution within an organism has a profound effect upon its behavior. No higher plant could have developed or could even continue to exist without an effective conducting tissue and transport mechanism. ✓

Despite the importance of the subject, very few texts of general botany, or even of plant physiology, devote more than a paragraph or two to the subject of translocation, while many refer to the process very indirectly or only incidentally in the discussion of some other topic. My own investigations led me to disagree with some of the generally accepted interpretations regarding translocation and raised several interesting problems. A consideration of these findings, of the commonly accepted interpretations, as well as the investigations of Madam Birch-Hirschfeld and Professor Dixon led to a realization of the fact that the evidence bearing on translocation was incomplete and that much of that which has been published is directly contradictory. It was soon apparent that those favoring the xylem as the tissue chiefly concerned in solute transport based their conclusions almost exclusively on experiments involving movement of materials, either naturally present or introduced, after the conducting tissues were opened by cutting, while those favoring the phloem tissues as chiefly concerned in transport downward or upward or in both directions based their conclusion chiefly on ringing experiments. Since several writers apparently failed to recognize the relative significance of the different methods used and since no works have been published which bring together the various viewpoints and interpretations relating to solute translocation, I have attempted to bring some of this material together in the present publication.

No attempt has been made to refer to all papers dealing with translocation problems or in any sense to give a complete historical review of the subject. It will be clearly evident to the reader that a great deal of space has been devoted to a discussion of my own contributions. This is largely due to the fact that these contributions lead to an interpretation that has not been generally recognized or accepted. Perhaps insufficient space has been given to a presentation of the more recent findings of Mason and Maskell. This is partly due to the fact that the writing of several chapters of this book was nearly completed at the time their papers appeared and partly to the fact that many of their experiments repeat, under somewhat modified conditions, the experiments I had previously reported, and lead to the same conclusions. Where their data or interpretations differ from mine, I have discussed them at length. Their publications are really outstanding contributions to the subject and no one interested in translocation should fail to read their original papers. The extensive work of

Münch also gives a great deal of valuable material relating to translocation. A discussion of his contribution in the present publication is limited almost exclusively to his interpretations of the mechanism of transport. The original should be consulted for other valuable data bearing on translocation.

I have attempted to give a picture of the present situation regarding translocation and to evaluate the methods that have been used in studying problems relating to it, in the hope that those wishing to carry on with these problems will better appreciate the factors involved and the weaknesses as well as the strong points of the various methods of approach. I also hope this book will serve to make clear its own incompleteness, and, through raising more problems than it settles, serve to stimulate further investigations leading to an advance of our knowledge of these problems and their relation to plant behavior.

In several instances hypotheses are presented in some detail and criticized in spite of the fact that those who proposed them possibly no longer would uphold their earlier proposals. In several cases I have had no way of knowing whether the hypotheses had been dropped, but even if I had been certain that they had been discarded by their authors, I think it desirable to discuss them critically, especially in view of the fact that the same suggestions are frequently revived or reproposed with varying modifications but often without recognition of the underlying weaknesses. At the same time it is also possible that some of the conclusions which are now seemingly obvious may eventually be shown to be less acceptable than others which are here considered as untenable. I wish to emphasize that the criticisms in no case are directed toward individuals, but in all cases against the methods used or the interpretations of the data.

I am indebted to my father-in-law, Dr. F. E. Weeks, for his assistance in reading proof.

O. F. Curtis.

Ithaca, New York,
  April, 1935.

CONTENTS

xi

CHAPTER VII

TRANSLOCATION IN PLANTS

CHAPTER I

THE SIGNIFICANCE OF TRANSLOCATION AND EARLIER OPINIONS AS TO TISSUES INVOLVED

1. The Importance of Translocation.—The behavior of any given cell or tissue of a plant is largely determined by the kinds and amounts of materials present in that cell or tissue. In the simple types of organisms, especially the filamentous and unicellular forms, the kinds and amounts of materials present in cells are largely determined by the environment, which rather directly influences food manufacture in that particular cell or the absorption or loss of foods, water, salts, ions, gases, and such. With most of the higher plants, on the other hand, where there are much differentiation and specialization, certain types of materials are absorbed or manufactured in rather restricted tissues or organs. For example, carbohydrate manufacture may be restricted to the leaves, while water absorption may take place chiefly in limited regions of the roots, and salt or ion absorption also may be restricted to certain regions of the roots. There may be considerable specialization even in the salt absorption, whereby much of one element—the nitrogen, for example—may be absorbed chiefly by those roots near the surface, while other ions may be absorbed by the more deeply penetrating roots. Other tissues may serve largely as food-storage tissues, conducting tissues, or as mechanical support. One of the factors that determine the size and conformation of a plant may be the effectiveness of the translocation mechanism, for it is obvious that, to allow for the development of a plant with

1

its photosynthetic organs at a distance of from 10 to 100 or more meters from its mutually interdependent salt- or water-absorbing organs, it becomes imperative that some effective transportive system be at hand. An effective solute-transporting system is essential even for the development of the smaller herbaceous plants where distances between organs do not exceed a few centimeters or decimeters. In fact but few of the plants that now exist, except the unicellular and some of the filamentous forms, could have developed or could continue to exist if they had not developed and maintained an effective transport system.

It is evident that no one cell or tissue of a higher plant is self-sufficient, and that conditions determining the movement of materials from one region to another may profoundly influence the behavior of these different cells and tissues, and therefore the plant as a whole. For example, the behavior of a plant may be largely determined by what eventually becomes of the carbohydrates manufactured in a leaf; that is, whether they stay in the leaf, are carried to the apical shoot meristem or to the axillary meristems, or are carried to the stem cambium, the root apex, the root cambium, or to a storage organ, or to fruits. In a similar way the distribution of the materials, such as water and various salts or ions absorbed by the roots, may profoundly influence behavior.

Of the immense number of actual or potential growing points, as in that part of a tree which is above ground, only a few ever grow under what we call "normal" conditions. Yet in most plants any bud, except perhaps the flower bud, is capable of producing a shoot, and in many kinds of plants almost any meristematic cell is capable of producing either a shoot or a root. Though some investigators think that normal behavior as regards growth correlations is controlled largely through the transmission of influences or stimuli, it is equally possible that normal behavior is controlled largely through "normal" distribution of materials. By upsetting this distribution of materials, by cutting or otherwise interfering with the movement of solutes and perhaps water, though chiefly the former, one can greatly alter behavior of this sort, especially of regeneration phenomena. It is true that utilization in its broader sense has a distinct rôle to play in distribution. Therefore in one sense behavior partly determines distribution and yet, in the last analysis, distribution also controls behavior.

It is rather clear that a knowledge of how materials move about within a plant and what conditions determine this distribution are of fundamental importance to one attempting to explain many types of plant behavior. Considering its importance it would seem that much attention would have been directed toward a solution of the problems of translocation. Problems of major importance obviously involve the following: The tissues concerned in translocation, the mechanism of transport, factors determining the direction of transport, and factors influencing the rate of movement. It is true that a great deal of attention has been given to the problems of water movement within plants, but it is rather surprising how little attention, either in the general literature or in textbooks, has been given to solute movement. Lecomte, in 1889, stated that no problem is more important to the life of the plant than translocation and none has been more neglected by botanists. But neither his own valuable contributions nor his statement concerning the importance of the subject served to stimulate much interest in the subject.

The lack of attention given to these problems may have been due in part to a failure to appreciate that they are problems. In fact until recently it has been assumed that the tissues concerned in the movement and the method of movement, particularly that from the roots to the leafy parts, and the factors influencing the rate of movement were rather fully understood.

2. Older Ideas as to Tissues Concerned in Upward Transfer.—The absorption of large amounts of water by the roots, its passage through the wood to the leaves, and its loss from the leaves have been repeatedly observed since the time of Malpighi (1679) and Hales (1727). When it was recognized that essential mineral salts are absorbed from the soil solution, it was immediately apparent that absorption of water and its movement through the plant might account for both the absorption and the movement of these salts. Weight was added to the assumption that solutes are absorbed and carried with the transpiration stream, by the observations that, when cut stems are placed in solutions of dyes or other solutes, these are absorbed with the water and carried with it through the xylem. Among some of the earliest experiments dealing with the movement of water through stems are to be found experiments of this kind with dye solutions. Knight (1801) made use of colored solutions in tracing conducting tissues, and Pfeffer (1900, p. 217) speaks of Magnol in 1709 and De la Baisse in 1733 as having carried out such experiments. Indeed such experiments have been repeated innumerable times by beginning and advanced students in experimental botany as well as by investigators and have naturally led to the seemingly obvious conclusion that the upward movement of solutes takes place with the transpiration stream through the xylem. The amount of solute absorption and the rate and direction of its movement are, under these conditions, found to be determined by the amount, rate, and direction of water movement. Studies on transpiration and water absorption and conduction seemed therefore to help in solving the problems of the absorption and upward transfer of solutes.

It would be perhaps impossible and certainly impracticable to list all the papers which contain data of this nature dealing with the conduction of solutions through stems. Many have used dyes and have traced their movement macroscopically or microscopically. Others have used colorless salts and have traced the movement spectroscopically or chemically (iron, lithium, beryllium, caesium). Colloidal sols also have been used, both under conditions when the material was colored and easily observed, and when a microchemical test was necessary for demonstrating its presence, as when dilute solutions of starch have been used. Nearly all data from this type of experiment have clearly shown a close interrelation between solute movement and water movement. In fact, the one has often been used as a measure of the other.

Experiments with solute injection have seemed to confirm the conclusion that solute movement and water movement go hand in hand; for when the stem is not entirely severed but is left on the parent plant so that it can still obtain part of its water normally and is not forced to obtain all its water from the solution supplied, even then, if solutions of dyes or salts are introduced through incisions of various types, these solutions are carried almost exclusively through the water-conducting channels as in the completely severed stems. A number of investigators (Yendo, 1917; Birch-Hirschfeld, 1920; Rumbold, 1920; Dixon, 1922; MacDougal, 1925; and others) have observed that in such injection experiments the solutions may move not only toward the apex of the stem but also basally. These observations of backward movement in water-conducting tissues have been drawn upon, as evidence for a normal backward flow of solution through the xylem, to support the recently proposed hypothesis that not only upward movement but also movement of foods backward from the leaves occurs through the xylem. This will be discussed more fully in Chap. IV.

Though the xylem readily carries solutes in solution when they are introduced into it, this is no more than suggestive evidence that solutes are normally carried there. The finding of various solutes in the water exuding from cut stems, however, seems to offer rather convincing proof that solutes, both organic and inorganic, may be present there normally and that the xylem, therefore, may normally act as a channel for transport. Many plants have been found to "bleed" freely when the stem is severed. In those woody plants that show such bleeding the sap flow is most profuse in early spring before the buds break, and at that time also the sap contains the highest organic solute content. Jones, Edson, and Morse (1903) have published a valuable paper dealing with various aspects of the flow of sugary sap from maple and other trees. Sap flowing at that time of year from borings into the xylem of sugar maples (*Acer saccharum*) and closely related species (*A. nigrum, saccharinum, rubrum*) has commonly a sugar concentration of from 2 to 4 per cent, and concentrations up to 8 per cent have been reported. A rather extensive industry based on the collection of this sap sugar has developed in northern United States and Canada. According to the 1910 census, approximately 23 million kilograms of sugar are collected annually from these trees in the United States. A single fair-sized tree may produce 25 to 75 liters of sap and 0.5 to 3 kg. of sugar in a season. There is no doubt that this comes entirely from the xylem, and it is commonly assumed that the sugar solution is carried in the transpiration stream to the developing shoots. Many other kinds of plants also have been found to exude a sap more or less rich in organic and inorganic solutes. (Schroeder, 1871; Moreau and Vinet, 1923; Priestley and Wormall, 1925). The total solute concentration, however, or the concentration of any one solute, except sucrose as in the maple, butternut, hickory, *Ostrya*, and a few such plants, has been found to be rather low.

3. Older Ideas as to Tissues Concerned in Downward Transfer.—Even before anything was known about photosynthesis and before it was known that most of the organic matter is manufactured in the leaves, it was recognized that there was a movement backward from the leaves of some substance or substances which are necessary for the growth of the stem or roots, and that cutting the layers external to the woody cylinder prevented this backward movement. Malpighi (1679) considered that crude sap ascended through the wood to the leaves where it was in some way changed and then passed backward through these outer tissues to regions of storage or growth. He was led to these conclusions by ringing experiments. Hales (1727) carried out ringing experiments and observed increased swelling above rings and between rings if leaves were present, but no swelling if they were absent. He definitely states, however, that this increased growth is not due to a stoppage of the sap in its return downward. He demonstrated the possibility of a backward flow of water through the wood and suggested a flow and ebb of sap through the wood. Knight (1801) carried out a number of ringing experiments which showed that tissues below rings failed to grow unless a shoot or leaves were present. Parts of the stem isolated from the rest of the stem by rings showed growth in diameter if leaves were present but no growth if leaves were absent from the isolated portion. Knight found that colored solutions would readily move through the woody part of the stem but not through any tissue external to the wood. On examination of the bundles of tubes leading through the petioles of apple and horse-chestnut leaves, only some of them were found to be stained with these colored solutions. He traced the uncolored tubes backward and found them to lead through the petiole to the inner bark and not to the wood. He suggested that these were the tubes concerned in the backward movement of materials prepared by the leaves. Removal of leaves or a reduction of their area correspondingly reduced the growth of the tissue below their insertion. From experiments which showed that the removal of the pith—which also was not stained by the colored sap—did not hinder transfer, he concluded that it is not concerned in backward translocation.

Since these early observations many detailed studies have been made on the occurrence, structure, and arrangement of these tissues which are supposedly the principal channels for the backward translocation of foods. These tissues commonly consisting of several types of cells are usually spoken of as phloem tissues, although "bast" and "bark" are occasionally used as synonymous terms.

The large number of ringing experiments that have been carried out since the time of Malpighi seem to have proved that the phloem tissues are concerned in the backward transfer of foods from the leaves.   That cutting the phloem prevents this backward movement of foods has been repeatedly demonstrated not only by the lack of growth in stems, roots, or organs when separated from the leaves by rings, and by the failure of such organs to receive food, as indicated by measurements of dry weight as well as by chemical analysis, but also by the accumulation of these foods above the ring.   This has been made evident by the increased diameter growth of the stem, increased growth of fruits or other storage organs, and marked accumulation of organic materials as demonstrated by dry weight and chemical analyses.

It seems still more probable that the phloem is the tissue concerned in this backward transfer, from the observation that, when only the cortex tissues external to the phloem are removed, food transfer is not prevented, and this conclusion is still further supported by the observations (Hanstein, 1860; Weevers, 1928; and others) that those plants which have an internal phloem do not fail to transport foods backward even when all tissues external to the xylem are removed.

The fact that phloem tissues usually contain elongated cells which are connected in a continuous longitudinal series by pores or connections through sieve plates or fields has been cited as evidence that these tissues seem well adapted for food transport.   The presence of a high content of sugar and proteins within the tissues (Kraus, 1886; Zaccharias, 1884; Hartig, 1860) is added evidence that they may play a rôle in transport of these foods.   Since there are no other tissues that seem adaptable to backward movement, these observations, together with the fact that it is difficult to see how foods could move down through the xylem where water is rising, have led to the conclusion that backward movement of materials occurs through the phloem tissues.

Until recently, therefore, there was almost perfect agreement among botanists—indeed one of the few points in which there was such agreement—that upward movement of solutes occurs chiefly through the xylem, the rate and direction of movement being largely determined by transspiration, and that downward movement takes place almost entirely through the phloem. There was not agreement, however, as to the mechanism of this downward movement nor as to the exact cells concerned, whether sieve tubes, companion cells, or phloem parenchyma. Mangham (1910) discusses the evidence put forward by various investigators favoring or opposing specialization of transport in special cells of the phloem. There was also partial disagreement as to upward movement. Some have assumed there is no upward movement through the phloem (Reed and Halma, 1919a), while others (Hanstein, 1860; and Leclerc du Sablon, 1906) have thought some upward movement might occur through the phloem, especially movement into fruits and storage organs from which transpiration is low. Though Hanstein concluded that certain types of materials (freshly assimilated sap as well as the reserves stored in the bark) moved up almost exclusively through the phloem, he assumed that salts absorbed from the soil solution moved through the xylem. He seemed to think that reserve foods that had been stored in the xylem, especially sugars, are carried in the xylem but felt the evidence to be inconclusive. Leclerc du Sablon also thought some materials moved up through the phloem but assumed that nutrient salts were carried chiefly in the transpiration stream.

Atkins (1916, p. 187) is rather critical of botanical texts because they have failed to emphasize the importance of the xylem in carrying carbohydrates. He states (p. 201) that "the transference of carbohydrates can no longer be regarded as an occasional and accessory function of the vessels but is certainly a continual and principal function," and again (p. 214) he says, "The conveyance upwards of sugars, of which sucrose appears to be the most important, is a continual and primary function of the tracheae."

In 1920 I reported some experiments which led me to suggest that both upward and downward movements of sugars occur chiefly in the phloem and that probably very little upward transport takes place through the xylem. In the same year, 1920, Madam Birch-Hirschfeld published results of experiments which led her to think that the phloem was not adequate for carrying foods downward. A backward flow of introduced solutes readily took place through the xylem, however, and this tissue, she suggested, might serve for the backward movement of photosynthate from the leaves. In 1922 Professor Dixon read a paper at the British Association meetings in which he reemphasized the probable inadequacy of the phloem as a tissue for transport, and definitely proposed the hypothesis that the xylem is chiefly concerned not only in upward transfer but also in the backward transport of solutes.

It is interesting therefore to realize that, previous to the period 1920 to 1922, it was supposed that it was definitely known what tissues were concerned in solute movement, while at that time three distinct hypotheses were advocated; the older one in which there were supposed to be two channels for solute transport, one, the xylem, for upward transport and the other, the phloem, for downward transport; and two more recent hypotheses proposing only one tissue to be chiefly concerned in solute transport in both directions, the one proposing that this transport takes place in both directions through the xylem, and the other that it takes place chiefly through the phloem. A fourth interpretation has more recently been proposed by Münch (1926) and by Crafts (1931) that certain solutes, chiefly organic, are carried either upward or downward through the phloem but not in both directions simultaneously through the same region, while other solutes, chiefly mineral salts, are carried through the xylem in the transpiration stream. Maskell and Mason (1929, 1931) also have suggested that organic materials move in both directions through the phloem but that salts move up through the xylem. It is obvious that the problem as to the tissue or tissues concerned in transport is of major importance because explanations relating to the other problems, such as the mechanism involved, conditions determining the direction of movement, and factors influencing the rate of movement, all will depend upon an understanding of the tissues concerned. It seems therefore desirable that the evidence for the different hypotheses be more closely examined and compared.

SUMMARY

1. Since no cell of a plant that is differentiated into leaf, stem, and root is totally independent but is dependent upon other cells for food, water, or mineral salts, and since the behavior of individual cells, tissues, or organs, as well as the plant itself, is largely determined by the amounts and kinds of these materials present, it becomes obvious that an understanding of the tissues concerned in transport of substances from one part of a plant to another, the mechanism of transport, and the factors influencing the rate and direction of transport, is of major importance to one interested in plant physiology or in interpreting behavior.

2. Until rather recently it has been widely held by botanists that transpiration largely controls both the absorption of inorganic salts from the soil and their transport from the roots to the leaves, as well as the upward transport of organic foods. This conclusion seemed substantiated by the fact that large amounts of water are absorbed from the soil and transported to the leaves and there evaporated; that colored solutions introduced into cut stems or through incisions of one sort or another are quickly carried through the wood to the transpiring leaves; and that cut stems often exude a sap containing various salts and sugars.

3. It has also been widely held that organic materials, moving basally from the leaves are carried through the phloem tissue. This conclusion has been based principally upon ringing experiments that have demonstrated accumulation of foods and increased growth of certain tissues above rings, and a diminished food content and diminished root growth below rings. This conclusion has been further supported by observations showing high carbohydrate contents in the phloem tissues, as well as by the fact that the tissues seem to be so constructed as to favor transport. About 1920 the older accepted theories as to tissues concerned in transport were called in to question. Some investigators proposed that solute transport in both directions takes place through the phloem, others that it takes place chiefly through the xylem. A few years later several distinct theories concerning the mechanism of transport and conditions determining the direction and rate of transport were proposed.

CHAPTER II

EVIDENCE FOR THE UPWARD TRANSPORT OF ORGANIC MATTER THROUGH THE PHLOEM

4. Ringing at Different Distances from the Tip and the Transport of Carbohydrates Previously Stored in the Xylem Region.—In many woody plants carbohydrates are stored in large quantities in the tissues internal to the cambium layer. In the older stems the wood parenchyma and medullary ray cells are rich in stored carbohydrate, while in the younger twigs the pith also is often well filled. Just before bud break in the spring, not only do these living cells in the xylem contain large quantities of soluble and insoluble carbohydrates, but the water-conducting cells themselves also contain soluble sugars, especially sucrose, though in some trees small quantities of maltose and traces or even appreciable quantities of hexose may also be present. At this season the solution in the water-conducting tissues may, in some kinds of trees, reach a concentration of as high as 2 to 4 per cent, or even occasionally somewhat higher. Jones *et al.* (1903) report as high as 8 per cent sugar in the sap from the sugar maple. The presence of this sugar solution at this season of the year and its almost complete absence soon after the shoots have grown have led to the seemingly logical conclusion, that this solution of carbohydrates has been carried through the xylem to the newly developing shoots, allowing for their rapid growth in the spring.

In order to determine whether the carbohydrates stored in the xylem of woody twigs move up to the growing points through the xylem with the water or through the phloem, large numbers of twigs of several different species of woody plants were ringed in the spring a short time before growth started (Curtis, 1920*a*). The rings were made at different distances from the terminal bud so as to vary the amount of stored food available between the ring and the growing point.

TABLE 1.—EFFECT OF RINGING AT DIFFERENT DISTANCES FROM THE TERMINAL BUD UPON SUBSEQUENT GROWTH
Crataegus ringed Apr. 8 before bud break.   Measured May 8

	Number of twigs	Av. shoot elongation, mm.
Check not ringed................................	17	26.8
Ringed in 2d internode from the tip...............	13	6.1
½ xylem and ¾ of phloem cut away in 2d internode..	6	26.2
Ringed in 4th internode from the tip..............	13	8.1
½ of xylem and ¾ of phloem cut away in 4th internode	4	28.0
Ringed at base of 1-year wood....................	8	17.0
Ringed on 3- and 4-year wood....................	11	22.0

The effects of this ringing on the transport of food in *Crataegus*, as indicated by growth of the bud above the ring, are shown in Table 1. From these results it is apparent that something carried by the phloem is necessary for shoot growth. It seems probable that the lessened growth cannot have been due to injury to the xylem resulting from its exposure, because if three-fourths of the xylem is exposed and half of it is completely severed, shoot growth is practically normal. This is evident from the data in Table 1. The two most obvious explanations are that the xylem carries no solutes, or that it carries some but does not carry all the kinds essential for growth. Since the xylem is rich in carbohydrates and low in nitrogen, while the phloem is especially rich in nitrogen, it would seem likely that the cessation of growth above a ring was not due to a deficiency of carbohydrate but to a deficiency of nitrogenous material carried in the phloem. Tests for starch, however, showed that at the time growth practically ceased none was present in any part of the stem above the ring, while starch was abundant in the storage tissues of both xylem and phloem immediately below the ring.   If nitrogen or anything other than sugar were acting as a limiting factor for the growth above the ring, one would not expect the starch to disappear, yet the shorter the piece above the ring, the earlier was the disappearance of starch, and the sooner did growth practically cease.

Similar results were obtained with all the plants experimented with including *Acer saccharum, A. rubrum, Fagus grandifolia, Pyrus communis* (pear) *Pyrus malus* (apple), *Crataegus sp.*, and *Ostrya virginiana.* Detailed data from several of these experiments are given in an earlier paper (Curtis, 1920a). All of these plants store an abundance of starch in the xylem tissues and some of them (*A. saccharum, A. rubrum*, and *Ostrya*) contained an abundance of soluble sugars in the xylem at the beginning of the experiment, and yet the xylem did not seem capable of carrying these solutes longitudinally in sufficient abundance to allow for normal shoot growth.

5. Disappearance of Starch below Rings and Results from Double-Ringing.—Hartig's experiments (1858) are often cited as proving that carbohydrates are carried upward in the transpiration stream. He found that, when a tree was ringed, the starch below the ring disappeared. He therefore assumed that it must have moved up through the xylem, for the phloem connections with the top were severed. Selecting young oak trees of about the diameter of one's arm he ringed them at intervals of eight days from Apr. 1, 1857, until the middle of September of the same year. The rings were 2 in. broad and placed 4 ft. from the ground. Examination the following spring showed that all the starch below the rings in those trees ringed previous to June 3, 1857, had disappeared while those ringed after that date still contained starch; but it disappeared from these also by the autumn of 1858. At the time of ringing he also cut down a few trees. The following year the starch had disappeared from the roots of a number of these felled trees also, but since the roots of some of them still contained starch, he concluded that in the ringed trees the carbohydrates stored in the roots must have been carried up with the water through the xylem. He does not state whether the felled trees that retained starch were cut early in the season or late or at what season they were examined for starch, nor does he state the relative number of stumps that retained or lost their carbohydrate stores.

Since other experiments have given very definite indications that normally the stored carbohydrates do not move through the xylem longitudinally and since in Hartig's experiments the disappearance of the carbohydrates below the ring may have been due to their utilization by the tissues below the ring, a number of experiments were carried out in which two rings were made in the same stem, one to prevent upward movement, and a second at a distance below this first ring to prevent movement back to the roots or other parts.

Hundreds of stems of many sizes and ages were double-ringed in this way and they all showed similar results. It will be sufficient here to present the results from two such experiments. Pairs of stems of *Ostrya virginiana* were selected for experiments in double ringing. The stems formed arms of forks and one arm of each was ringed on Apr. 6, 1919. On May 6 the shoots were beginning growth on all the branches. No differences between ringed and unringed stems were apparent. By May 19 the shoots of the check stems showed considerable additional growth but those of the ringed stems had made no appreciable growth beyond that of May 6. Stems cut at this time showed the following results:

Above the Ring. —No trace of starch was present in any part either in the young twigs or in the older parts of the stem.

Between the Two Rings.—Starch was very abundant in the pith, medullary rays, and cortex.

Below the Lower Ring.—The pith only contained traces of starch, none being present in the medullary rays or cortex.

In the check stem which formed the other arm of the fork traces of starch were present in the pith only in each of the regions corresponding to above, between, and below the rings. No starch was present in the xylem rays or cortex. The period from May 5 to 19 was favorable for rapid growth and utilization of the stored foods as the rainfall preceding and during this period was considerably above the normal; the temperature also was high and the days were cloudy, tending to interfere with the manufacture of carbohydrate by the young leaves. The part above the upper ring was therefore quickly depleted of its stored carbohydrates by the many growing shoots. The part between the rings bore no shoots and seemed to have lost none of its starch, while the part below the lower ring, though it bore no shoots, had become almost depleted of starch. Evidently the sugars from this part had moved back to the fork from where they had been carried either up to the growing shoots of the unringed arm or back to some other part of the tree.

Similar results from experiments on double-ringing were repeatedly obtained with all the plants tested, which, in addition to *Ostrya* included *Acer saccharum, Fagus grandifolia*, pear, apple, and several species of *Crataegus*. A total of several hundred stems were thus double-ringed. In all cases, when the starch had completely or almost completely disappeared from the parts above the upper ring and had largely disappeared below the lower ring, that part between the rings and isolated by them from the food-consuming tissues contained an abundance of starch.

The rapidity and completeness of the starch removal above the upper ring are evidently determined by several conditions. If the upper ring is made close to the terminal bud, the amount of food stored above it is small and the depletion will be more rapid and more complete, while if the ring is made on an older stem, the depletion is less rapid and less complete (see Table 1). The environment also influences the rate and amount of removal. If the water supply is plentiful and the temperature high, growth will be rapid and the carbohydrates more rapidly depleted. If also the light intensity is low, the reformation of car-

bohydrates by the new leaves will be less and the depletion
of the stored supply will be more rapid and more complete.
The spring of 1919, in which most of these experiments
were completed, was especially favorable for the depletion
of stored foods. When the season is dryer and there is
more sunshine, growth is checked and the stored foods are
less rapidly drawn upon and the new leaves may even begin
depositing new stores in the young twigs. In such seasons,
therefore, the starch may never completely disappear
above the rings. These findings as well as those reported
in Secs. 4 and 7 rather clearly indicate that the widespread
idea is wrong that much of the carbohydrate stored in the
trunk and roots of woody plants is transported to the tops
in early spring and there used in shoot growth. (See also
Curtis, 1920*b*.)

**6. The Disappearance of Starch as a Criterion of Car-
bohydrate Transport.**—Since starch disappearance is not
always correlated with the removal of sugar, a few experiments were completed in which sugar analyses also were
used. Such analyses were obtained with both *Acer
saccharum* and *Fagus grandifolia*. Several stems of *Acer
saccharum* were double-ringed on Apr. 6 and 7, 1919.
A number of them were cut between May 6 and 19. In all
cases starch was very abundant between the rings, entirely
absent or present only in traces above the upper ring, and
almost absent or fairly abundant below the lower ring.
The amount present below the lower ring and above the
upper ring depended on the time of cutting, the size of the
stem, and the position on the tree. Analyses were made of
one of the larger stems of the series. This stem showed
15 annual rings at the lower ring where it was 24.5 mm.
in diameter. The lower ring was 16 cm. from the main
trunk and the second ring was 107 cm. above the first where
the stem was 20.2 mm. in diameter. Starch tests and sugar
analyses for this stem are presented in Table 2 together
with similar tests for *Fagus*.

A number of stems of *Fagus grandifolia* were double-
ringed on Apr. 7, 1919, and results very similar to those for

Acer were obtained.   In all cases iodine tests showed little
or no starch above the upper ring and abundant starch

TABLE 2.—EFFECT OF RINGS ON CARBOHYDRATE TRANSPORT AS INDICATED
BY STARCH TESTS AND SUGAR ANALYSES
Acer saccharum

	Mg. invert sugar per 25 g. dry wood	Starch as indicated by iodine tests
Above upper ring.......	53.9	Slight traces in primary xylem only
Between rings..........	155.8	Very abundant in primary xylem and medullary rays throughout
Below lower ring........	124.6	Absent from medullary rays of outer annual ring. Traces present in those of second annual ring. Still larger amounts in third. Abundant in fourth and those internal to it. Also abundant in primary xylem
Check.................	106.8	Fairly abundant in primary xylem and in medullary rays of inner annual rings, small quantities in third annual ring, and absent in outer two*

Fagus grandifolia

	Mg. invert sugar per 75 g. dry wood, extracted by 80% alcohol	Starch as indicated by iodine tests
Above upper ring.......	167.3	Traces in pith cells only
Between rings..........	242.6	Abundant in pith and medullary rays
Below lower ring........	.....	Traces in medullary rays and in pith cells
Check.................	172.1	Traces in smaller rays and in pith†

* This part corresponded to that between the rings of the ringed stems.   Starch in the check stem decreased gradually toward the apex and increased somewhat toward the base where it appeared very much as below the lower ring.
† This part was in a position corresponding to that between rings of the ringed stem.

between the rings.   The stem analyzed for sugar was a
young sapling 3 cm. in diameter at a point 80 cm. from the

ground. The upper ring was made at this point and the lower ring 10 cm. from the ground. This tree, with a check of similar size standing close by, was cut on May 27. At this time the growth in length of the shoots was practically completed and there were no apparent differences between the shoot growth on the two trees. Data are presented in Table 2.

This table shows a direct relation between the sugar contents, as shown analytically, and the starch contents, as indicated by the iodine tests. The relation holds not only where extremes in starch contents are compared, but also where there are four gradations in amounts of starch as shown by the iodine tests, which were made previous to, and independently of, the sugar determinations.

In these few cases where analyses were made, though the amounts above the upper rings were low, a distinct and easily measurable quantity still remained. In both instances the rings were so far from the tip that sufficient food was available above the ring to allow for seemingly normal growth of the shoots.

If analyses had been made of stems which had been double-ringed nearer to the apex, it is probable that there would have been much greater differences between the sugar contents above the upper and between the two rings.

Although in these ringing experiments the evidence is rather clear that there is a direct relation between starch content and soluble carbohydrate content, it is recognized that this relation does not always hold. Evidence is available from many sources (Appleman, 1912; Hopkins, 1924; and others) showing that temperature influences the starch-sugar equilibrium so that, in the potato, for example, at temperatures close to 0°C., starch tends to decrease and sugars increase. These same investigators obtained indications that this change is reversible, the sugar changing back to starch at intermediate temperatures. I have found also that at higher temperatures (25 to 35°C.) the sugar again tends to increase at the expense of the starch. Jones *et al.* (1903) found indications of marked sugar increase in the maple at a temperature of about 0°C. or below, and Sinnott (1918) also observed indications of such a change. Neither, however, has presented analytical data. Rüssow (1884), Fischer (1891), Sinnott (1918), and others have observed also a disappearance of starch and an appearance of fat at low temperatures.

These changes have been observed only at rather extreme temperatures. The temperature at the time that starch tests were made on twigs reported in my first paper (1920*a*) in no instance approached 0°C. but usually varied between 10 and 20°C. The maximum and minimum during the 24 hours previous to the determination for *Acer* in Table 2 was 17 and 7°C., respectively, and that for *Fagus* was 21 and 16°C., respectively. Furthermore all parts of the stem must have been exposed to the same temperature.

The water supply also has been found to influence the starch-sugar equilibrium. Lundegardh (1914), Bruns (1925), and several others have observed that, when water becomes deficient and leaves begin to wilt, starch may be transformed into sugar. In the experiments on ringing, however, water did not become deficient. There was very little sunshine during the month the tests were made and there had been rains amounting to over half an inch or more during the week preceding the time each twig sample was taken. Even if the water supply were a factor, there is no evidence that the supply to the region between the rings would be very different from that to the region above or below. Starch tests on leaf tissues seem more likely to be affected by water changes than in the stem tissues here used.

Light or hydrogen ion concentration may also influence the sugar-starch equilibrium, but the different parts of the stem received similar light exposures and I know of no evidence that would indicate that hydrogen ion differences might be concerned in the experiments reported. It has been repeatedly demonstrated by many investigators that starch removal or deposition is closely correlated with sugar removal or accumulation in many different types of tissue. The disappearance of starch from foliage leaves at night, when the sugar is allowed to be carried away, and its lack of disappearance when sugar removal is checked have been observed innumerable times by students and investigators. The formation of starch when supplied with sugar in the dark has also been repeatedly demonstrated since the early work of Boehm (1883), Schimper (1885), Acton (1889), and Parkin (1899). Hansteen (1894), Puriewitsch (1898), Grünfeld (1926), and others have shown that removal of starch from several types of storage organs is largely determined by the removal of soluble products, the sugars. By so conducting the experiment as to remove the sugar produced, Puriewitsch was successful in causing the loss of starch from endosperms of *Zea, Triticum, Hordeum, Oryza*, the cotyledons of *Phaseolus, Pisum, Vicia*, bulbs of *Hyacinth, Lachenalia, Oxalis*, and the rhizomes of *Ranunculus, Iris*, and *Curcuma*. He was also able to remove the fat from twigs of *Tilia*.

For the starch dissolution it was necessary not only to remove the sugars but also to keep the tissue well aerated. When merely immersed in water, the starch did not disappear. Parkin obtained indications that aeration is necessary also for starch deposition when leaves are supplied with sugar solutions. When standing in the air on porous blocks of gypsum which were immersed in water, the sugar was carried into the water and the starch completely disappeared. Grünfeld was successful in removing starch by using a number of types of porous materials. When the volume of water used was small so that the external sugar solution rose to a high point, about 2.5 per cent, further starch digestion ceased, but when the volume of water was greater the dissolution was more rapid and also became complete. The addition of sugar to the external solution prevented starch digestion. Puriewitsch also found that in many tissues, with the exception of endosperms, he could bring about the redeposition of starch in tissues lacking it by immersing them in sugar solutions. Grünfeld was successful even in refilling endo-

sperms. I have found it a simple matter to cause starch
deposition in twigs lacking starch by injecting sugar
solutions (Curtis, 1918).

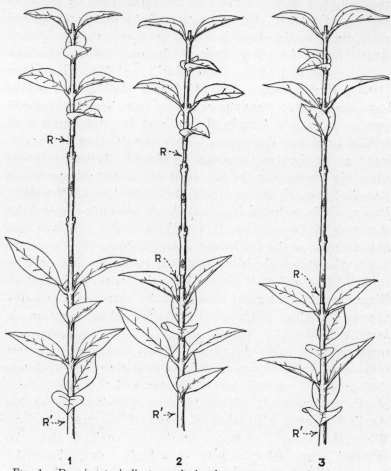

1   2   3

Fig. 1.—Drawing to indicate methods of treatment to study the effects of
rings on upward movement of carbohydrate or of nitrogen when the movement
of water through the stems is similar in all cases. *R* indicates the positions of
rings. In some experiments rings were also placed at *R'*. In all cases ring
wounds were protected with melted paraffin and the stems were of course
attached to the parent plant. For experiments involving use of this method of
ringing see pp. 30, 50, 200, 239.

Not only was it found that starch removal from a piece
of stem is prevented if that part is isolated by double rings
but it was also found that, if the stem lacked starch at the

beginning, its deposition would not occur in any part isolated by rings from a source of supply. This was observed in many experiments of which the type shown in Fig. 1 is a good example. In stems treated as No. 2 of Fig. 1, no starch appeared in any part of the defoliated region isolated by rings, even though it was very abundant in the tissues above the upper ring and below the lower. In stems ringed like Nos. 1 and 3, on the other hand, in which the single ring prevented phloem connection respectively with the leaves above only and below only, there was always abundant starch in the defoliated part. This starch was clearly evident in the pith, xylem parenchyma, phloem parenchyma, and cortex. Stems like No. 3 with the single ring at the base of the defoliated region contained more starch than those like No. 1 with the single ring at the top. The dry weight of the bark (everything external to the cambium) together with the dry weight and volume of the xylem was determined for the defoliated regions. These are presented in Table 3.

TABLE 3.—EFFECT OF NUMBER AND POSITION OF RINGS ON STARCH CONTENT AND DRY WEIGHT OF A DEFOLIATED REGION OF STEM

No.	Position of rings	Starch test	Dry wt. of stem	Dry wt. of wood	Dry wt. of bark	Vol. of wood,* cc.	Dry wt. per cc. of wood including pith
1	Ring at top only of defoliated region..............	Abundant	1.2444	0.7858	0.4586	1.06	0.74
2	Rings at top and bottom of defoliated region.........	Absent	0.9885	0.6077	0.3808	0.91	0.67
3	Ring at bottom only of defoliated region	Very abundant	1.7039	1.0797	0.6242	1.29	0.84

* This was calculated from the diameters at each end of the twig and its length. In the original paper the volumes given were all ten times too high as the decimal point was misplaced. The relative differences, however, were not altered.

These data on dry weights and of the weight per unit volume of these defoliated regions confirm the evidence from the starch tests that the defoliated region, when completely isolated from a source of supply by rings, receives little or no carbohydrate.   However, when isolated from a source above only or from below only, the food moves readily into the defoliated region.   Both the dry weights and the specific gravity calculations vary directly with the starch contents as indicated by the iodine tests and offer evidence, additional to that from the sugar analyses presented in Table 2, that in experiments of this type starch tests give a fair indication of the total amount of carbohydrate present.

Other experiments, in which defoliated and undefoliated regions completely isolated by rings alternated with each other, showed high starch contents in those regions bearing leaves and a low content or complete absence in those defoliated.   The results from some such experiments are reported on page 50.

Knight (1801), though he made no direct tests for carbohydrates, observed the effects of the presence or absence of leaves on the diameter growth of regions of the stem completely isolated by rings.   He observed not only the effects of complete defoliation but also those of partial reduction of leaf area, and found a direct relation between amount of diameter growth and leaf area borne by the isolated region.

Swarbrick (1927) has suggested that these data on the disappearance or appearance of starch between double rings are not to be interpreted as related to the effects of the rings on transport but to something that influences cambial activity.   As mentioned on page 32, however, he fails to distinguish between depletion due to transport and that due to utilization by living cells in the immediate neighborhood.

7. The Effect of Ringing on the Transport of Carbohydrate to Growing Shoots after That Stored in the Xylem Is Depleted.—In order to determine the channel of transport to growing shoots, large numbers of vigorous leafy shoots which had not completed terminal growth were selected and treated as indicated in Fig. 2 (Curtis, 1920*a*). Number 1 was left as a check with no treatment whatever. Number 2 was ringed and leaves left above the ring, in part to test whether the ring interfered with water movement to the leaves and in part to see if leaves could supply

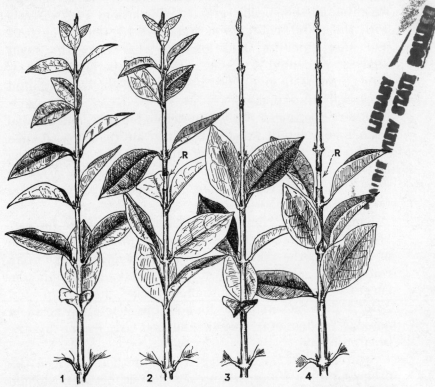

Fig. 2.—Drawing to indicate methods of treatment for studying the effects of rings on the upward transport of solutes into growing shoots. 1, leafy check; 2, leafy ringed; 3, defoliated check; 4, defoliated ringed. Ring wounds were always protected with melted paraffin and the stems were attached to the parent plant.

materials for growth. Number 3 was defoliated for a distance, usually 10 to 20 cm. or to the base of the shoot, to determine the effects of defoliation alone on growth. Number 4 was defoliated to the same extent as No. 3 and the stem was ringed at the base of the defoliated region to see if the material necessary for the growth of the shoot could be carried through the xylem from the manufacturing or storage tissues below. The reason for the defoliation was to eliminate the possibility of the utilization of food manufactured or stored in the leaves of that region. Growth, as measured by increase in length of the shoot, was most commonly taken as a measure of solute movement, though in a few instances the fresh weights, dry weights, sugar contents, and freezing-point depressions were also taken as criteria. Measurements were usually made at a period from one to three days after the beginning of the experiment, though in a number of cases measurements were continued up to periods of six to fifteen or more days. Representative data are summarized in Table 4.

TABLE 4.—THE INFLUENCE OF DEFOLIATION AND RINGING UPON SHOOT GROWTH

Plant	Series	Period of growth, days	No. shoots, av.	Average growth, millimeters			
				Not ringed leaves present	Ringed leaves present	Not ringed leaves removed	Ringed leaves removed
Philadelphus	1	9	5	341	118	270	5
Philadelphus	2	5	14	164	130	80	16
Philadelphus	3	3	8	94	71	36	14
Apple	4	19	6	45	53	34	3
Ligustrum	5	15	7	136	146	74	7
Ligustrum	6	14	6	125	106	58	2

From these data it is evident that growth is very weak in shoots that are both defoliated and ringed. The growth in the other shoots was always distinctly better, but the relative order of their growth depended on the length of shoot and therefore on the number of leaves above the ring, or the length of shoot defoliated, and also in part upon the number of leaves below the ring. For example, if that part of the shoot bearing leaves above the ring is long, the growth of this part is much greater than if the length, and therefore the number of leaves supplying the food, is less. If the defoliated region is short, and a ring separates the region from the leaves below, growth may be

almost nil. The first series of *Philadelphus* in Table 4
had only a few leaves above the ring or only a short distance
defoliated, while the second and third series had more
leaves above the ring or a longer distance defoliated. In
fact, in Series 2 and 3 the rings were made on the older
wood just below the base of the new shoots. Figure 3
shows the appearance of a representative set from Series 2.

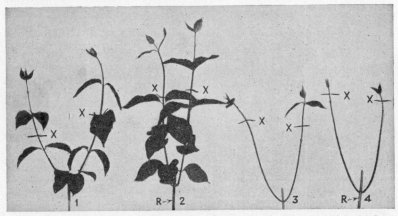

FIG. 3.—Effects of ringing on leafy and defoliated shoots of *Philadelphus*.
1, leafy not ringed; 2, leafy ringed; 3, defoliated not ringed; 4, defoliated ringed.
A black thread tied on each shoot at *x* indicates the position of the bud apex at
the time of ringing.

It would seem that materials necessary for growth are
carried upward through the phloem tissues, that they
cannot be carried through the xylem, but that if the leaves
are present above the ring, they contain or can produce
materials that allow for considerable growth. Since leaves
can produce this material, the evidence seems rather
strong that the check in growth of the ringed defoliated
shoot is due to lack of carbohydrate. The check in growth,
it seems, cannot be due to lack of water resulting from
injury to the xylem for, when leaves are left above the
ring, growth is more nearly normal or may even exceed
that of the check for a short time. Occasionally, however,
ringing is followed by withering of the parts above the
ring, especially if the ring is near the tip, but this occurs
only when this part is defoliated.

After many of these ringing experiments had been completed it was found that Hanstein (1860) had carried out similar experiments and had obtained similar results. He concluded, however, that lack of water cannot be the cause of the withering, for when leaves remain above the ring, certainly more water is necessary than when the leaves are absent but growth continues, while the shorter the part above the ring the less water it will need but the quicker is its death even in a moist chamber.

Hanstein explained this lack of growth or death above a ring when the leaves are removed as due to a lack of "freshly assimilated sap." He seems to have accepted Hartig's idea (1858) that carbohydrates and other products stored in the xylem are carried through the xylem but thought that materials stored in the phloem and "freshly assimilated sap" move in the phloem only. When leaves remain above a ring, they were supposed to supply this special material. Hanstein also observed that ringed willow cuttings placed in dry air showed a withering of the phloem above the ring, while the presence of leaves in this region prevented withering. He concluded that water cannot move readily from xylem to phloem and that leaves aid in this transfer. According to his ideas, therefore, the leaves supply "freshly assimilated sap" which is necessary for growth and can be carried through the phloem only, and they aid also in transmitting the water to the phloem when the latter is separated from the roots by a ring. Hartig (1862) disagreed with Hanstein's interpretation and suggested that the failure of defoliated shoots to grow in a dry atmosphere was due to drying out of the wood at the point of injury, and their failure to grow in a saturated atmosphere was due to failure of the water stream to move.

If, on the other hand, all solutes including sugars are carried through the phloem chiefly and not through the xylem, ringing would check continued growth by withholding the necessary solutes, while the withering might be due not to the lack of any particular solute, but to a deficiency of osmotically active substances. Chandler (1914) has clearly demonstrated that if tissues having different osmotic concentrations are organically connected, the tissue having the higher concentration will withdraw water from the other when water becomes deficient, causing the latter to wither.

To test the effects of the treatments upon the osmotic concentrations of the shoots, the freezing-point depressions of the saps of a few shoots were determined. Instead of extracting the sap, the shoots were crushed and the freezing point of the pulpy mass was determined in each case. Fresh weights, dry weights, and sugars soluble in 80 per cent alcohol were also determined. For these determinations all the older leaves were removed and the stems with terminal buds only were tested.

TABLE 5.—EFFECT OF RINGING AND REMOVAL OF LEAVES ON GROWTH, OSMOTIC CONCENTRATION AND SUGAR CONTENT OF THE SHOOT

	Gain in length in 5 days, mm.	Freezing-point depression, °C.	Mg. hexose sugar per g. fresh wt.	Mg. hexose sugar per g. dry wt.	Percentage of depression due to sugar assuming all to be hexose
Not ringed, leaves present..........	173	0.67	7.81	114.9	12.9
Ringed, leaves present.............	130	0.61	....	.....	....
Not ringed, leaves removed.........	88	0.61	4.5	67.6	8.2
Ringed, leaves removed..........	16	0.49	2.6	52.2	5.8

These data, summarized in Table 5, show that the osmotic concentration of the ringed defoliated shoots is distinctly less than that of the other shoots. It seems highly probable, therefore, that when wilting took place, it was due, not to a direct effect of the ring on water movement through the xylem, but to an effect on solute distribution, and this in turn on the ability of the tissue to compete osmotically for water. Weevers (1923) more recently observed similar wilting of ringed branches bearing leaves which lacked chlorophyll and gives similar explanations for the wilting.

The fresh weights, dry weights, and sugar contents of these ringed defoliated shoots were also lower than those of the other shoots. It is interesting to note that calculations of the molecular concentrations of sugar, assuming it all to be present as hexose, show that in each treatment only a small part of the freezing-point depression is due to sugar, the ringed defoliated shoots showing the least.

The failure of solutes to move past the rings in the defoliated shoots might be ascribed to the failure of a transpiration stream to carry them, since no leaves were present to cause such a stream. Of course, the conditions, so far as transpiration was concerned, must have been similar in the defoliated shoots that were not ringed and in which solutes did move; yet it seemed desirable to determine whether or not a movement of water through the xylem would favor the movement of sugar. To this end a large number of twigs of *Ligustrum ovalifolium* were ringed as in Fig. 1, Nos. 1 and 2, with the exception that an additional ring was made below the lower group of leaves on each twig as at R'. The leaves at the apex of each shoot would insure a transpiration stream through the xylem, while the leaves at the base, with the ring below them, would insure a carbohydrate supply to the xylem. Starting with shoots lacking stored starch in the xylem, it was found that the cortex, medullary rays, wood parenchyma, and pith became densely filled with starch in the defoliated region of those twigs treated as in No. 1, in which the phloem connection with the leaves was intact; but the same tissues were completely lacking in starch in those treated as in twig 2, in which the defoliated region was isolated by rings from the leaves both above and below. In both treatments starch was abundant in the leafy parts of the stem. In those treated as in No. 2 the xylem was richly stored with starch immediately below the ring, but, even though water was moving through the xylem to the leaves above, there was insufficient sugar carried through this tissue to cause any starch deposition in the defoliated part, whereas when the phloem connection to the leaves below was not interrupted by a ring, this region was densely filled with starch.

Similar results were obtained in the experiment cited on page 50. In this instance, however, the ring at the base, R', was omitted. In this series (Curtis, 1923, p. 376) not only were starch tests made with iodine, but the dry weights and volumes of the xylem were determined. These data, as shown in Table 3, are in complete agreement with the starch tests and show that the average dry weights of the xylem of the defoliated regions in treatments 1 and 3 are greater than those of treatment 2 by 29.4 and 77.6 per cent, respectively, and the dry weights per unit volume were 10.5 and 24.0 per cent greater.

Experiments almost exactly like these have subsequently been carried out by Mason and Maskell (1928b, p. 582). Their experimental material was the cotton plant, and though in these experiments they do not give data on dry weights or weight per unit volume, they do give data on the sugar concentration of the sap of the bark and the total carbohydrate contents of the bark and wood in the defoliated region. These are of additional interest because increases or decreases in carbohydrate contents are given over 12-hr. periods. Curves showing such data are given in Fig. 4.

The evidence is clear therefore that, even when a movement of water through the isolated region is insured, carbohydrates are not carried into, and stored in, such a region. Evidence cited in Sec. 5 also shows that if such a region, isolated by double rings, is full of starch to begin with, it is not emptied through the xylem, even when there is active movement of a water stream through this region.

The responses to ringing and double-ringing that have been found to vary with the season of ringing are easily explainable when one takes into consideration the amounts

of materials stored at the time of ringing and the effect
of the rings in isolating the particular region in question

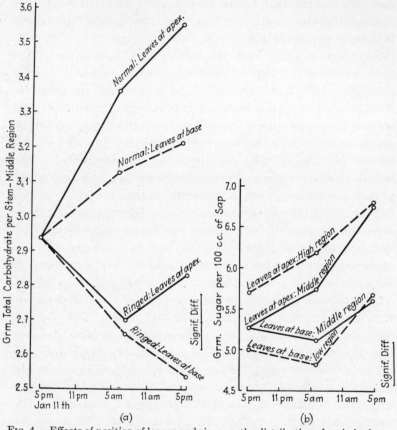

Fᴵɢ. 4.—Effects of position of leaves and rings on the distribution of carbohydrate
in the bark and stem of the cotton plant.   (*From Mason and Maskell.*)
Numbers refer to numbers in Fig. 1.

(*a*) Total carbohydrate in defoliated regions
   "Normal: leaves at apex" similar to No. 3, but leaves below ring removed.
   "Normal: leaves at base" similar to No. 1, but leaves removed above upper ring.
   "Ringed: leaves at apex" similar to No. 2, but leaves below lower ring removed.
   "Ringed: leaves at base" similar to No. 2, but leaves above upper ring removed.
(*b*) Concentration of total sugars in sap of bark
   "Leaves at apex: high region."   The part analyzed was equivalent to the leafy part
   immediately above the defoliated region in No. 3.
   "Leaves at apex: middle region."   The part analyzed was equivalent to that of the
   defoliated region in No. 3.
   "Leaves at base: middle region."   The part analyzed was equivalent to the defoliated
   region in No. 1, but leaves above upper ring were removed.
   "Leaves at base: lower region."   The part analyzed was equivalent to the leafy part
   immediately below the defoliated region of No. 1, but leaves above upper ring were
   removed.

from sources of supply or regions of utilization.   Swarbrick
(1927) seems to have been troubled by these varying

responses and looks to factors other than those mentioned
above for an explanation, but it should be perfectly obvious
that the distribution of foods will vary with the season of
ringing and the position of the ring with respect to regions
of supply or utilization.

Further evidence, that the failure of solutes to move up
past a ring is not due to lack of transpiration above, has
been given by Weevers (1923). By selecting branches of
Acer negundo or *Aesculus*, which bore leaves containing no
chlorophyll and which were therefore dependent on other
parts of the tree for their carbohydrates, he could study the
effects of ringing without resorting to defoliation. He
found that the ringing of such branches stopped their
growth and the leaves eventually withered, whereas the
ringing of similar branches bearing green leaves did not
stop their growth nor cause withering. Analyses for
reducing sugar showed the green leaves to contain 3 per
cent, the yellow leaves 1 per cent, and the yellow leaves on
the ringed branch only traces. The wood and bark of the
ringed branch bearing yellow leaves contained 6 per cent
starch, while that of a similar branch only partly ringed
contained 9 per cent starch. It is surprising, as Weevers
remarks, that the ringed yellow branch contained so much
starch while the leaves of the same branch were withering
and contained only traces of sugar. No mention is made
as to the method of determining starch or whether any
starch was found by the iodine test, except in the leaves
which showed no such test. If acid hydrolysis was used to
make the starch determination, it is highly probable
that the reducing sugars found were not produced from
starch but from the acid hydrolysis of hemicelluloses.
As reported in 1920, I found woody stems containing but
very slight traces of starch, as indicated by the iodine test,
to produce reducing sugars amounting to 17 per cent of the
dry weight of the wood on hydrolysis by boiling with
10 per cent hydrochloric acid for $2\frac{1}{2}$ hr.

8. The Effect of Ringing on Transport to Fruits.—
Although the opinion has been widely held that most

upward moving, organic solutes, and particularly sugars, are carried with the water in the xylem, it has also been recognized that such movement to fruits may take place through the phloem. Hanstein (1860) observed that if phloem connections between fruits and the supplying leaves are cut, fruit growth ceases. Strasburger (1891) made similar observations but (p. 900) claimed the *Umbelliferae* to be an exception. Curtis (1920*a*) demonstrated that apple fruits ceased growth when the phloem connection between the fruit and the leaves was severed, whereas if there were leaves above the ring and these were either below or above the fruit, there was appreciable growth. Münch (1930, pp. 183–208) reported more extensive experiments than others on this phase of translocation. He worked with apples, *Quercus pedunculata*, *Castanea vesca*, *Aesculus pavia*, *Sorbus aucuparia*, *Sambucus racemosa* and *nigra*, and *Heracleum sphondilium*. In all cases he found, as had previous workers, that fruits whose phloem connections with leaves were completely severed failed to continue growth, whereas similar fruits connected by phloem tissues with leaves either above or below the fruit would continue growth.

It is obvious to anyone who has observed the effects of ringing on fruit development that the size of the fruits that develop on ringed branches as compared with control fruits, depends upon whether the rings are so placed as to increase or decrease the total available supply of food from the leaves. That is, if the ring is so placed that there are many leaves on the same side of the ring as the fruit, the latter will be large. If, on the other hand, the ring isolates the fruit so that it is in phloem connection with but few leaves, its growth will be slight. The behavior of the fruit in this respect is very similar to that of the cambium and diameter growth as observed by Knight as early as 1801, and by Hales, in 1727.

Münch also reports experiments on the upward tranfer of foods to fruits situated on defoliated branches. He found little or no reduction in growth of such fruits of

Sorbus, even when they were on defoliated branches at distances of from one to three meters from the nearest leaves, if the phloem connections between fruits and leaves were intact. Haller (1931) reports similar observations with apples. In experiments, in 1931, Dr. MacDaniels and I found that, though fruits on defoliated branches appeared to grow as well as those on leafy branches, the dry weight expressed as percentage of fresh weight was distinctly less, and the fruits were less sweet.

Münch also reports a few results of interesting experiments on the development of fruits when the fruits alone or the fruits and leaves are kept in darkness. Such experiments were carried out with *Sorbus* and *Sambucus* with the parts in darkness, in some cases completely isolated from leaves exposed to light by rings through the phloem, in others the rings were so placed that the supply from leaves must come through the phloem from below, while in others the phloem connection was with leaves above. The completely isolated parts in darkness failed to grow and lost both leaves and fruits. Those connected by phloem to leaves below grew normally or even better than the checks or similar fruits in light, while, in the single experiment reported, those fruits in darkness but receiving food from above fell off. Those above the ring and in the light made but little gain in dry weight. No mention is made as to the number of leaves above the upper ring so one cannot judge whether the poor growth of those fruits in this region exposed to light, and the lack of growth of similar fruits in darkness, as compared with the good growth of fruits in the dark below the lower ring (see his Fig. 29, p. 197), is or is not influenced by the total available carbohydrate. The lessened nitrogen supply to the fruits above the rings may also be a factor in the differences in behavior. The data, however, are inadequate for drawing comparisons between growth of fruits in darkness receiving food from below as compared with those receiving food from above.

He also reinvestigated the question of movement of foods to developing fruits of umbellifers (pp. 200–204). Strasburger (1891, p. 900) claimed that food moved to these fruits through the xylem. Münch found, however, that if precautions were taken to cut all the phloem leading to the fruits, they were unable to receive food from the leaves below. Since the young fruits are green, he also tested the influence of light and darkness on the development of such fruits on ringed stems. The results indicated clearly that most of the food comes to the fruits from other parts of the plant and that this is transported through the phloem.

9. The Effect of Cutting the Xylem on the Transport of Solutes.—Dixon (1922) and others have claimed that the reason why ringing interferes with solute movement is that the ringing results in a plugging of the xylem by tyloses or gums or otherwise interferes with its activity. Though positive evidence has been obtained that such plugging does not always occur, and in fact rarely occurs if the ring is made carefully and the ring wound well protected, yet to settle the question finally it would be desirable to carry out experiments in which not merely the phloem is cut and the xylem left intact, but in which the treatment is reversed and the phloem is left intact and the xylem cut. It is more difficult to carry out the latter type of experiment for obvious reasons. The xylem being on the inside of a hollow cylinder cannot be cut out without some injury to the phloem outside. Its removal also involves the removal of a tissue conducting water to the parts above, which is perhaps the greatest difficulty, and it also removes the support for the parts above.

As previously reported in some detail (Curtis, 1925), various methods were used for supplying the upper part of the shoot with water when the xylem was cut and the phloem was left to bridge the gap. The only uniformly successful method was that in which the operated part of the stem was encased in a tube open at both ends. A water-tight joint was made with the stem at the lower end of the tube by means of a split cork sealed to the stem and to the tube with melted paraffin. This tube, when filled with water, served to supply the shoot above with water

as well as to keep the phloem thoroughly wet. The
method of setting up such an experiment is indicated in
Fig. 5. After first sealing the split cork to the stem with

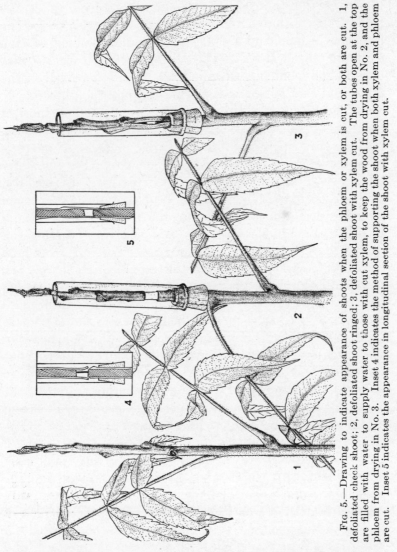

FIG. 5.—Drawing to indicate appearance of shoots when the phloem or xylem is cut, or both are cut. 1, defoliated check shoot; 2, defoliated shoot ringed; 3, defoliated shoot with xylem cut. The tubes open at the top are filled with water to supply water to those with cut xylem, to keep the wood from drying in No. 2, and the phloem from drying in No. 3. Inset 4 indicates the method of supporting the shoot when both xylem and phloem are cut. Inset 5 indicates the appearance in longitudinal section of the shoot with xylem cut.

warm paraffin, it is a simple matter to seal the tube to the
cork if the tube is dipped into hot paraffin to a depth of
about 2 cm. and then quickly slipped over the shoot and

TABLE 6.—COMPARATIVE EFFECTS ON THE GROWTH OF DEFOLIATED SHOOTS OF CUTTING PHLOEM ALONE, XYLEM ALONE, AND BOTH PHLOEM AND XYLEM

Plant and date	Treatment	No. stems	Av. growth, mm.			
			1st period	2d period	3d period	Total period
Philadelphus June 4 to 9, 1925	....	10	1 day	2 days	2 days	5 days
	Check..............	..	4.9	14.0	26.0	45.9
	Phloem cut..........	..	2.7	1.2	2.6	6.5
	Xylem cut...........	..	3.3	6.0	6.8	16.1
	Phloem and xylem cut	..	4.4	2.6	1.4	8.5
Philadelphus June 9 to 11, 1925	....	10	1 day	1 day	1 day	3 days
	Check..............	..	12.9	8.3	10.0	30.2
	Phloem cut..........	..	4.6	1.2	1.1	6.9
	Xylem cut...........	..	9.0	5.5	5.9	20.3
	Phloem and xylem cut	..	5.6	1.4	1.7	8.7
Philadelphus June 10 to 12, 1925	....	10	1 day	1 day	....	2 days
	Check............,.....	..	3.4	9.9	....	13.3
	Phloem cut..........	..	2.0	3.0	....	5.0
	Xylem cut...........	..	4.8	9.9	....	14.7
	Phloem and xylem cut	..	2.6	2.2	....	4.8
Ligustrum June 20 to 25, 1925	....	18	2 days	3 days	....	5 days
	Check..............	..	6.7	9.3	....	16.0
	Phloem cut..........	..	1.6	0.5	....	2.1
	Xylem cut...........	..	3.3	3.0	....	6.3
Rhus Aug. 19 to 27, 1924	...............,....	6	1 day	1 day	1 day 5 days	8 days
	Check*..............	..	3.0	2.8	6.0 39.0	50.8
	Phloem cut..........	..	1.8	0.8	1.3 20.6	24.5
	Xylem cut...........	..	4.2	6.0	6.5 58.0	74.7
	Phloem and xylem cut	..	3.8	4.7	4.7 19.8	33.0
Rhus June 23 to 27, 1925	....	12	1 day	1 day	2 days	4 days
	Check..............	..	3.4	6.8	11.4	21.7
	Phloem cut..........	..	1.0	1.8	1.6	4.3
	Xylem cut...........	..	4.3	4.9	9.3	18.5
Rhus June 30 to July 6, 1925	....	12	1 day	1 day	3 days 1 day	6 days
	Check..............	..	2.2	5.4	47.1 7.6	62.3
	Phloem cut..........	..	1.3	1.3	8.2 2.5	13.3
	Xylem cut...........	..	2.2	5.5	29.3 5.1	42.1

* The checks in this series were undersized.

pressed onto the cork. Data from several sets of experiments are available in the earlier paper (1925). Similar data from experiments not previously reported are presented in Table 6.

Such data have been obtained with many kinds of woody plants and several hundred sets of shoots, in which the effects of cutting the xylem and of cutting the phloem and cutting neither have been compared. The data have

Fig. 6.—Photograph of typical set of shoots of *Rhus*, showing relative amounts of growth about 6 days after beginning of the experiment. 1, check; 2, phloem cut; 3, xylem cut.

uniformly shown that growth is markedly checked when the phloem is cut, whereas, when the xylem is cut and part of the phloem is left intact, growth is very much greater and approaches more nearly that of the check shoots. A photograph of a representative set of *Rhus* shoots is shown in Fig. 6.

To eliminate the possibility of transfer of solutes through the water and across the gap between the cut ends of the xylem, several experiments were set up in which the ends from which the solutes might be expected to issue were sealed with hot paraffin, but this had no influence on the growth of the shoots above. In other instances the tubes were rinsed out frequently with distilled water, but this also had no measurable effects. In still other instances the xylem was cut and the phloem left in place but cut and held in its normal position by a splinter of wood. These, as shown in Table 6, usually showed practically the same behavior as the ringed ones. Occasionally, however, they elongated somewhat more during the first day. This latter was probably due to the fact that completely severed shoots no longer had to compete with the tissues below for their water supply. The ringed shoots were handicapped in their competition through their having a low content of osmotically effective solutes (see Sec. 7).

In a few sets sugar analyses were made, typical examples of which are presented in Table 7.

TABLE 7.—COMPARATIVE EFFECTS OF CUTTING THE XYLEM OR PHLOEM ON GROWTH, WATER CONTENT, AND SUGAR CONTENT OF DEFOLIATED SHOOTS

Plant and Date	Treatment	Av. total growth, mm.	Dry wt., % of fresh growth	Total sugar per stem, mg.	Sugar, %, fresh wt.	Sugar, %, dry wt.
A. *Philadelphus*						
June 13 to 19,	Check.....	63.6	10.8	3.08	0.12	1.12
	Phloem cut.	7.8	9.0	0.08	0.03	0.35
6 stems	Xylem cut.	49.2	10.8	5.32	0.22	2.03
B. *Philadelphus*						
June 25 to July 1,	Check.....	105.3	13.0	2.10	0.094	0.72
7 stems	Phloem cut.	19.7	9.4	1.63	0.087	0.93
	Xylem cut.	47.4	11.8	4.83	0.231	2.08
C. *Rhus*						
June 26 to July 1,	Check.....	63.0	22.3	4.17	0.33	1.48
6 stems	Phloem cut.	15.8	17.2	3.05	0.67	3.89
	Xylem cut.	49.5	20.5	3.90	0.42	2.05

For the *Philadelphus* set, *A*, it is obvious that sugar was deficient in the shoots of the ringed stems and that this lack of sugar probably accounted for the poor growth. This set received very little light before and during the experiment because the bushes were growing close to the north side of a building, the overhanging eaves of which shaded the experimental shoots. The weather also previous to and during the experiment was cloudy. Under such conditions it is to be expected that the carbohydrate supply to the shoots would act as a limiting factor. In set *B*, the plants were growing in the open where they were well illuminated, and the day before commencing the experiment had approximately twice the sunshine. There was fair precipitation during both periods. It is to be noted that, although the total sugar per stem is decreased by ringing, the percentage on the fresh weight basis nearly equalled the check while on the dry weight basis it exceeded it. For the *Rhus* material, although the ringed stems showed less total sugar than the check stems or those with xylem cut, as did the *Philadelphus* shoots, they had a distinctly higher sugar content when expressed as percentage either on the fresh-weight or dry-weight basis. Obviously, therefore, sugar was not a limiting factor and it seems probable that nitrogen or some other soil constituent was lacking. These plants also were grown in the open and had received abundant light.

Since it seemed possible that part at least of the translocation in these shoots with the xylem removed may have taken place through the cambium layer or through the young cells recently cut off from the cambium and not yet differentiated, one experiment was carried out in which, after severing the xylem, the cambial layer of the bark was thoroughly scraped with a knife. For comparison the phloem was cut in matched stems. In these the cambium was not scraped. The data from such an experiment are presented in Table 8.

It is evident from this experiment that the cambium is not essential for translocation, nor is a continuity of the cambium essential for growth as suggested by Swarbrick (1928). At the end of the first two-day period the stems with xylem cut had, in all but shoots 6 and 7, lowered the water in the encasing tubes to a point below the cut end

of the xylem.   Although some of the shoots were slightly
wilted, there seemed to be no permanent ill effects.   It is
to be regretted that only stems having a latex system were
tested by scraping the cambium, for it is possible that the
latex system plays some rôle in transport.   Hanstein
(1864), Schimper (1885), Kniep (1905), and Simon (1917)
give fairly strong evidence, however, that the latex system
is not effective in food transport.   In all the other experi-

TABLE 8.—INFLUENCE OF SCRAPING THE CAMBIUM UPON TRANSPORT WHEN
THE XYLEM IS REMOVED

Measurements in millimeters of increased growth.   Rhus. P = phloem cut,
cambium not scraped. X = xylem cut, cambium surface thoroughly
scraped

No.	July 17 to 19, 2 days		July 19 to 20, 1 day		July 20 to 23, 3 days		Total 6 days	
	P	X	P	X	P	X	P	X
1	1	6	0	11	1	28	2	45
2	2	3	1	12	6	47	9	62
3	1	2	1	4	8	15	10	21
4	1	5	1	12	1	36	3	43
5	1	6	1	9	0	24	2	39
6	1	3	1	10	2	29	4	32
7	1	3	1	10	3	27	5	40
8	1	5	4	8	19*	33	24*	46
9	6	5	0	17	7	38	13	50
Av.	1.7	4.2	1.1	10.3	3.5	30.8	6.0	42.0

* Possibly misread.   Omitted in averages.

ments the behavior of *Rhus* was not different from that of
several other plants having no latex system, so it is likely
that the undifferentiated cambium is ineffective in rapid
transport for appreciable distances.   That the cambium or
similar meristematic cells may take some part in translocation over short distances, however, seems not impossible.   Active streaming which should favor transport in
such cells has been observed by Velten (1872) and Bailey
(1930).   The only certain way of determining whether the
cambium and immature cells developing from it are effective would be to cut all the mature phloem.

It would seem that these data offer convincing proof in favor of the hypothesis already strongly suggested by ringing experiments that upward as well as downward transfer of solutes takes place chiefly through the phloem tissues. It certainly eliminates the criticism that ringing stops solute movement because it causes a plugging of the xylem, for when cut no xylem remains and yet translocation takes place, whereas when the phloem is cut, little or no translocation takes place, even when it is demonstrated that the remaining xylem is not plugged. It also eliminates the criticism that the phloem seems inadequate as a channel, for, although calculations of rates of food movement seem to demonstrate its inadequacy, these experiments definitely prove that the phloem has carried the foods and salts and was therefore adequate in these cases. A comparison of the merits and weaknesses of the various methods used in determining the tissues concerned in translocation is discussed in Chap. IV.

Mason and Maskell (1928*a*, p. 242) suggest that the poor shoot growth of the ringed shoots may have been due to a blocking of the tracheae and that the better growth of those with the xylem cut may have resulted from development of new wood elements. They seem to have overlooked the positive evidence supplied in the original paper that the vessels were not plugged in the ringed stems and that new vessels had not developed in those with the xylem cut. They also remarked on the lack of significant differences between the two treatments in the dry weights of the shoots of *Philadelphus* but note the difference in *Rhus*. They must have overlooked the statement preceding the table on page 580 of the original article which definitely explains that in the *Philadelphus* material, the newly developed leaves and the basal parts of all the shoots except the ringed ones were removed, so that pieces of approximately equal length and weight and having the same proportion of young leaves were selected for analysis. If all the newly developed tissues had been included, the check stems and those with the xylem cut would have had a higher proportion of leaves and older stems and the data would have shown very much higher dry weights for the check shoots and those with the xylem cut.

Others have suggested that measurements of elongation as used in these experiments and in those reported earlier (1920a), are not safe measures of solute movement or growth, for the elongation, it is said, may have been due largely to water absorption. Those making such criticisms, however, have evidently overlooked the fact that in the original publications (1920a, 1925) dry weights and sugar contents were included with the length measurements in several of the tables. Though these data were presented, no great emphasis was placed upon the dry weights in the discussion because the data showed such close agreement between measurements of elongation and those of dry weight, and the differences between the ringed and the others were so great that it was assumed the relationship was obvious to anyone sufficiently interested to question the interpretation. Emphasis was, however, placed upon the fact that the dry weights, expressed as percentages of fresh weights, of the ringed shoots were always lower than those in the checks or in the shoots with the xylem cut. It seemed hardly necessary to point out, what should be an obvious fact that, if the lengths and fresh weights of the ringed shoots were from one-half to one-tenth or less of those of the others and they also had a lower percentage dry weight, the actual dry weights themselves also must have been lower. Therefore the greater shoot elongation of the stems with the xylem cut could not possibly have been due to mere water absorption and extension, for they had a dry weight content often in excess of two to ten times that of ringed shoots.

Schumacher (1931) by first cutting the phloem and then the xylem in the petioles of *Pelargonium* leaves has recently demonstrated a removal of nitrogen from darkened leaves when the xylem alone is cut, and a lack of removal when the phloem is cut.

SUMMARY

4. During the dormant season large quantities of carbohydrate, in both soluble and insoluble forms, are found in the xylem regions, principally in wood rays and xylem parenchyma, of branches, trunks, and roots of woody plants. In early spring the water-conducting vessels also of many woody plants have been found to contain considerable quantities of soluble sugar. It has been assumed that much of this carbohydrate that is stored in the xylem is carried through the wood to the developing shoots, where it is used in their early growth. When rings are made just prior to bud break at varying distances from the apical buds, the closer the ring is to the apex, the less is the growth of these buds above a ring. This points to a relation between the amount of food stored above the ring and the amount of growth. Tests for starch demonstrate an early cessation of growth to be associated with an early depletion of starch above the ring, while the starch in the xylem immediately below the ring may still be abundant. These findings strongly suggest that, when the ring is near the apex, carbohydrate was limiting the growth above the ring and that sugars, even when stored in the xylem region, cannot be transported upward past a ring in appreciable quantities.

5. The disappearance of starch from below a ring made on the trunk of a tree has been interpreted as demonstrating that the sugars from carbohydrate stored below must move up through the xylem. A second ring placed below the first, however, prevents removal from between rings, indicating that the carbohydrate below the first ring had not moved up through the wood but had moved down. Two rings placed a short distance apart will effectually prevent movement of carbohydrate out of or into the region so isolated.

6. Since the disappearance of starch is not always associated with removal of sugar, it has been suggested that many of the experiments do not demonstrate a failure of transport through the xylem, because starch tests were used in many cases as a criterion of the presence of carbohydrate. It is true that a lack of correlation between starch and carbohydrate content has been found to occur in tissues at low temperatures close to 0°C., or high temperatures around 35°C., in tissues that are severely wilted, or at unusual hydrogen ion concentrations; but in the experiments on translocation the parts tested were not exposed to conditions that would be expected to bring about such discrepancies between starch and sugar contents. Furthermore, in every type of experiment where starch disappearance was used as a criterion, a few quantitative sugar tests were also made, and there was a direct relation between sugar amounts as determined by analysis and the amounts of starch as determined by the iodine test. This relation was further established through determination of dry weights, a high dry weight per unit volume and per stem being associated with high starch content. Experiments on feeding of sugars from an external source and on removal by leaching also demonstrate a definite relation between starch content and sugar content.

7. Not only does the carbohydrate that is stored in the xylem tissues fail to be transported upward through the wood when the phloem is ringed, but that made during the current year also fails to be transported through the wood. This was demonstrated by experiments in which the continued growth of the apex of ringed defoliated shoots was found to be greatly reduced when compared with that of similar defoliated shoots not ringed. The amount of growth of ringed leafy shoots is proportional to the leaf area above the ring and, when several leaves are present, is approximately the same as that of normal shoots for the first few days. These results indicate that food necessary for growth moves up through the phloem and not the xylem, and that this food is probably largely carbohydrate because it is produced in leaves. That ringing interferes with upward transport of foods was indicated not only by diminished growth of ringed defoliated stems but by the fact that they also had a low sugar content and low osmotic concentration when compared with similar shoots not ringed. The occasional withering of ringed defoliated shoots is demonstrated to be due, not to any injury to the xylem, but to the low osmotic concentration making the parts unable to compete with other tissues for water. That the failure to carry sugar through the wood is not due to the lack of a transpiration stream is demonstrated by experiments showing no movement into defoliated stems if they are isolated from leaves below by a ring, but ready movement if not so isolated. Leaves were present above in both cases to insure a flow of water through the stem. Other experiments on the ringing of branches with leaves lacking chlorophyll as well as experiments with cotton where the xylem is separated from the wood demonstrate that upward transport of carbohydrates is limited to the phloem.

8. Experiments of several sorts are cited which demonstrate that food moving to fruits is carried exclusively through the phloem. This is true independently of whether the food is coming from the leaves situated above the fruit or below it. If the phloem is intact, food may move distances up to three meters to fruits on defoliated branches.

9. In order to determine more certainly whether xylem or phloem is chiefly concerned in upward transfer, and in order to eliminate the criticism that ringing stops transfer because it results in injury to the xylem, experiments were carried out in which the xylem was removed and the phloem left intact. Such experiments were performed with defoliated shoots and the amounts of growth above the operated regions compared. In experiments of this sort with many kinds of plants it was found that cutting the phloem prevented food transfer, whereas cutting the xylem allowed for approximately normal transfer. That the cambium is not necessary for transport was indicated by experiments in which both xylem and cambium were removed.

CHAPTER III

EVIDENCE FOR THE UPWARD TRANSPORT OF NITROGEN AND SALTS THROUGH THE PHLOEM

10. Effects of Ringing on the Upward Transfer of Nitrogen and Ash Constituents.—Since considerable evidence had accumulated which definitely indicated that carbohydrates, though they are stored in the xylem, are not readily transported longitudinally through these tissues, it seemed desirable to determine the effects of ringing on the upward transfer of salts absorbed from the soil solution, for these have been universally assumed to travel with the transpiration stream. Many experiments were therefore carried out to test the effect of ringing on the upward transfer of solutes absorbed from the soil. The details of several such experiments are presented in my paper of 1923.

It will be sufficient here to summarize briefly some of the evidence presented in that paper. When branches of peach trees were ringed early in the season just before bud break, and sodium nitrate was then added to the soil, these ringed branches made less growth than the check branches, and the leaves also contained less nitrogen and ash. Such results were obtained with all the trees experimented with, but it will be sufficient to describe the results with one tree. One arm of a small peach tree forked in the top was ringed at a point where the stem was 2.5 cm. in diameter, and the ring wound was protected with melted paraffin. In spite of the fact that this ringed branch was the leader and slightly larger than the other, the check branch by the end of the season had made many times the growth of the ringed one. The three largest shoots of the ringed branch were found to have developed no side branches and bore only 50 leaves in all. The three main shoots on the check

47

branch, on the other hand, had developed an average of 24 side shoots each, and these alone had borne over 1,200 leaves. The smaller shoots alone on the check branch bore many times the number of leaves that was found on the entire ringed branch while the three main shoots of the check bore 24 times as many leaves as the corresponding shoots on the ringed branch. Not only were there many more leaves on the check branch, but the leaves averaged about 65 per cent larger in area and 44 per cent heavier dry weight per leaf, 140 per cent more total nitrogen per leaf, 46 per cent more nitrogen per square decimeter, 68 per cent more nitrogen per gram of dry weight, 112 per cent more total ash per leaf, 31 per cent more ash per square decimeter of leaf area, and 50 per cent more ash per gram of dry weight. Since the three main shoots of the check branch bore about 24 times as many leaves as the corresponding shoots of the ringed branch and since these check leaves contained 2.4 and 2.12 times as much nitrogen and ash, respectively, per leaf, the total nitrogen and ash moving through the stem of the check branch must have been over 50 times those of the ringed stem.

Although this evidence indicated rather clearly that the xylem was not effectively carrying nitrogen and ash constituents and that this lack of nutrient salts may have accounted for the poor growth of the ringed stem, it was recognized that the ring may have, for some other reason, influenced growth and other processes of the parts above it, and these in turn may have influenced solute translocation. It was also recognized that the ring had prevented the formation of new xylem at the point ringed, and had also reduced the formation of new stem tissues immediately below the point of ringing. For these reasons other experiments were carried out in which the ringing was done after the leaf formation, shoot elongation, and xylem formation were nearly or quite completed for the season.

Representative data from such an experiment with *Ligustrum* bushes are summarized in Table 9. For this experiment matched stems were selected and one leaf from each pair of opposite leaves was taken at the beginning, Aug. 25, 1920, and its mate was harvested at the end of the experiment. It is noticeable that the leaves of ringed and check stems increased in ash and nitrogen contents, but the increases in the check stems were from 3 to 5 times those in the ringed. Another set of stems, started at the same time but harvested after 75 days instead of 39 and 40 days, respectively, showed changes very similar to those presented in Table 9.

TABLE 9.—EFFECT OF RINGING ON THE GAINS IN NITROGEN AND ASH CONTENT OF LEAVES OF *Ligustrum*

Paired leaves taken one at beginning and the other at end of experiment. Each figure is the amount per stem, an average of 12 separate determinations

	Check			Ringed			Differences, % gain in check in excess of that of ringed
	Aug. 25	Oct. 3 and 4	Av.* gain, %	Aug. 25	Oct. 3 and 4	Av.* gain, %	
Area of leaves............	0.956	1.104	16.6	0.902	1.017	12.9	3.7
Dry wt., g................	1.130	1.376	22.9	1.033	1.696	66.2	−43.3
Total nitrogen, mg........	16.43	34.51	115.9	14.10	17.38	22.7	93.2
Nitrogen, mg. per sq. dec..	17.07	32.36	82.4	16.14	16.88	6.5	75.9
Nitrogen, mg. per gm. dry wt....................	14.41	24.81	67.6	13.90	10.13	−25.5	105.3
Total ash, mg............	85.4	139.9	61.1	79.8	95.2	20.7	40.4
Ash, mg. per sq. dec......	92.0	127.2	38.8	91.9	95.1	3.8	35.0
Ash, mg. per g. dry wt....	77.8	101.4	30.8	79.8	57.1	−27.2	58.0

* The gain for each stem was determined separately and then averaged.

Other experiments with comparable results were carried out with peaches, apple, and lilac. Some of the data are presented in the earlier paper (1923). Additional data are presented by MacDaniels and Curtis (1930). With the lilac, however, the leaves from the ringed branches showed a slight actual loss. This loss may have been due to leaching by rains. A number of workers (LeClerc and Breazeale, 1908; Mann and Wallace, 1925; and others) have observed a removal of potassium by rains. In a few instances, in which the experiments were started late in the summer when no nitrogen was added to the soil, or when there were no rains to wash what was applied into the soil, no distinct increases were evident in either ringed or check leaves. When expressed as a percentage of dry weight, the leaves of the ringed stem showed decreases as one would expect.

Though ringing experiments of the type mentioned have in every case resulted in an interference in upward transfer of solutes, this in itself cannot be considered as conclusive evidence that the xylem is not directly concerned in translocation, for the rate of transpiration from ringed branches seems commonly reduced.

If solutes are carried in the transpiration stream, this reduced transpiration may partly account for the reduction in solutes carried to the ringed branch. To eliminate a possible effect of transpiration, an experiment was carried out with twigs of *Ligustrum* treated as previously described in Sec. 7 and shown in Fig. 1. On all twigs there was a group of four pairs of leaves at the top of the stem to insure a transpiration stream through the stem. In two sets of 12 stems each, rings were made immediately below the upper leaves, and in one of these sets additional rings were also made at the base of the defoliated parts. In all three sets each twig had 4 pairs of leaves at the top, and in each case a ring was present between these leaves and the leaves below. This would tend to make the amounts and rates of water movement through the defoliated parts about equal in all instances. Since the carbohydrate content of the defoliated region would be expected to influence its ability to absorb or retain nitrogen, rings were made at both the top and base of the defoliated region in one set of twigs to insure a low carbohydrate content, and at the base only in the other set to insure a high carbohydrate content. As is clearly shown in Table 10, the ring at the base of the defoliated part has interfered with the movement of nitrogen into this region, both when the carbohydrate content is high and when it is low, and the effect is not due to an effect on transpiration.

Maskell and Mason (1929*a*) suggest that these same data support the hypothesis that the chief path of upward transport of nitrogen is the wood, for, assuming all the twigs at the beginning had a nitrogen content like those in group 2 with two rings, those treated as in group 3 had increased 3.3 mg. per twig and the checks (group 1) increased 4.66 mg. per twig. The increase in group 3 was

TABLE 10.—EFFECTS OF RINGING UPON THE NITROGEN CONTENT OF DEFOLIATED PARTS OF A STEM

Averages mostly of 12 stems	1	2		3	
	Check	Ringed, low carbohydrate	Rel. to check	Ringed, high carbohydrate	Rel. to check
Dry wt. per stem	1.265	0.989	0.78	1.704	1.35
Total nitrogen per stem, mg.	12.11	7.45	0.62	10.75	0.89
Nitrogen, mg. per g. dry wt.	9.62	7.56	0.79	6.08	0.63

70.8 per cent of that in the checks. Their hypothesis assumes that the nitrogen moves up through wood to the leaves, from which it subsequently moves back through the phloem as organic nitrogen and accumulates in the bark and wood. According to this hypothesis they suggest that the defoliated region of the twigs, treated as in group 3, could receive nitrogen only from the eight leaves at the top, those treated as in group 2 could receive no organic nitrogen from leaves, while the checks (group 1) could receive nitrogen from the entire plant except the eight leaves at the top. The increase in nitrogen of twigs in group 3, receiving organic nitrogen from only eight leaves, since it was nearly 71 per cent of the increase of those twigs receiving nitrogen from the entire plant, suggested to them that this experiment adds support to the hypothesis that nitrogen moves to the leaves through the xylem and is transported from them through the phloem. They seem to overlook the fact that the amount of nitrogen found in

the stems with no ring below the defoliated part may give
no indication of the total amount that has moved into this
region. This part is in complete connection with the rest
of the plant and one would not expect it to accumulate
materials in excess of amounts found in other parts. Perhaps the amount finally found is only one-half or even
one-tenth of the amount that may have moved in and out
again. Above the ring, however, in group 3, there was no
opportunity (except by leaching which should be similar
in all treatments) for the nitrogen to leave the tissues after
it had once entered. Even after the long period of 39
days, only about 71 per cent as much total nitrogen had
entered this tissue as had been *retained* by the other stems,
which may have received and reexported many times the
amount finally found.

Furthermore, though the twigs with the single ring at
the base had more nitrogen than those with two rings, this
does not mean that all these twigs at the beginning had a
low nitrogen content similar to the double-ringed stems
at the end of the experiment. Respiration must have
appreciably reduced the carbohydrate content between the
two rings. This would tend to result in a decomposition
of the proteins and the production of more soluble forms of
nitrogen. This would very likely result in some release
and leaching of nitrogen into the transpiration stream and
thus tend to reduce the amount present. Some nitrogen
might similarly enter with the transpiration stream from
below, but the low carbohydrate between the two rings
would reduce the tendency to retain any passing through.
Maskell and Mason (1929a) found an appreciable loss of
nitrogen from between rings on the stem of cotton, which
can probably be accounted for on the same basis, that is,
release of nitrogen from starved tissues. In a later paper,
however (1930a), they observed a slight increase in defoliated parts between rings. Since the amount originally
present in the stem was not determined and since there
are no data showing the amounts passing into, and out of,
the bark when phloem connections are not broken, no

definite conclusions can be drawn with reference to increases or decreases in these *Ligustrum* twigs.

Several have suggested that most of my data, showing that ringing causes a retardation of upward transport both of carbohydrates and of nitrogen and ash constituents, can be explained on the grounds that the rings have caused plugging or other morbid changes in the xylem, and that they are not to be interpreted as demonstrating that upward transport takes place through the phloem. As is pointed out in Sec. 25, however, there is abundant evidence that in many of the experiments there was no sign of any interference to flow through the xylem. When the ring wounds are thoroughly protected by melted paraffin, as was the practice in all of these experiments, the xylem does not become plugged. Since with these woody plants ringing has consistently interfered with upward transport of nitrogen and ash constituents, even when no plugging has taken place, the interference cannot be ascribed to blocking the xylem.

Although the xylem has not become blocked, it is true that, in many cases at least, the amount of transpiration has been less from the leaves of the ringed stems. No extensive data are available showing how much transpiration is lessened by ringing. A few measurements with standardized cobalt chloride paper have shown that the leaves of ringed branches of *Ailanthus* were losing about one-half to one-third as much water at midday as similar leaves of check branches. These measurements were made about three weeks after the rings were made, and yet at this time the xylem of the ringed stems was not plugged but carried dyes past the ring as readily as did that of unringed stems.

This reduction in transpiration from ringed shoots seems to be due largely to the effects of the ringing on the leaves and perhaps chiefly to the effect of the high carbohydrate and low nitrogen on the stomates. To test this point Miss Pleasants has made a number of observations and found that the stomates on the leaves of ringed branches of a number of woody plants will open only for a short time each day, or may show almost no opening at all, while those on normal branches will open more widely and remain open longer.   There is also a possible effect of high carbohydrate on leaf structure, thickness of cuticle, thickness of wall, etc., and also perhaps a slight effect of the high concentration on vapor pressure, though the latter effect is probably very slight.

That a reduction in transpiration should result in a reduced solute transport through the xylem does not necessarily follow.   I know of no experimental evidence showing that the normal upward transport of nutrient salts is in any way interfered with when transpiration is reduced to a minimum by high humidity.   It has been suggested that the minimum transpiration necessary for transport has not been reached in experiments at high humidity.   The amount of transpiration from the leaves of the ringed stems, however, has almost certainly exceeded this minimum, yet in some instances the increase in nitrogen or ash of these leaves has been exceedingly small as compared with the increase in the check leaves.   Since in most cases the ringed branches were in competition for water with check branches on the same plant, one might postulate that a slight reduction in transpiration from the ringed stem might greatly favor flow to the check stem.   In other experiments, however, in which single main stems were ringed in some cases while one of a forked pair was ringed in others, no differences in response were evident between the branches having competition and those having none. When one realizes that any solutes passing the ring must be trapped in the tissues above, whereas much of the material passing into the check leaves may be transported out again, it is surprising that the tissues above a ring do not accumulate more than they do, even if most of the solutes are carried in the phloem and only small amounts leak into the xylem.   If, on the other hand, the transport is chiefly through the xylem, I see no satisfactory explanation for the failure to accumulate above a ring, even assuming that the rate of transpiration is greatly reduced.

There are no extensive data showing the extent of transport into and export from leaf tissues, but Chibnall (1923), basing his calculations chiefly on the fresh weight basis, claimed a diurnal transport of from 2 to 4 per cent, or more, of nitrogen. He also cites data from others who claim a diurnal transport. Maskell and Mason (1929a), expressing the fluctuations as percentages of the mean content, found about 10 per cent fluctuation of nitrogen on the fresh-weight basis and about 4.17 per cent fluctuation on the residual dry-weight basis. (Subtracting the standard deviations due to sampling there would be respectively 8 and 2.75 per cent.) In a second series they found diurnal variations amounting to about 16 per cent on the fresh-weight basis and 14 per cent on the residual dry-weight basis. Even accepting one of the lower figures, that an amount equal to 4 per cent of the total nitrogen of the leaf is transported from the leaf each night, then, if the final amount has not changed, at the end of 25 days, an amount equal to the total amount present at the end has been transported from the leaf. This would greatly increase the differences between the analyses of the ringed and check stems, for little or none would be lost from the leaves of the ringed stems. If nitrogen is removed from the leaves during the day also—and Maskell and Mason (1929a) claim a greater transport by day than at night— then the total amount removed under the conditions here assumed would be at least twice the amount actually found. *This would mean that the real difference between the amounts moving through the check stems and the ringed stems is much greater than the actual difference found by analysis.* Under such conditions it would seem that the differences in transpiration rates could not account for the great differences in transport.

At the time of performing the ringing experiments reported in this section, I had assumed that, in order to solve the problem as to what tissue is concerned in the upward transport of nitrogen and ash constituents, all that was necessary was to demonstrate an upward movement through the phloem, for it was claimed that the phloem was inadequate to carry solutes at normal rates. That the phloem can carry these solutes upward has been conclusively demonstrated in the experiments on the behavior of defoliated shoots where first one tissue, the phloem, and then the other, the xylem, have been cut. The experiment on equalizing the transpiration stream also clearly indicates that nitrogen moving into a defoliated region of the stem enters chiefly by way of the phloem and not the xylem. At that time it also seemed to me that the only adequate mechanism that might account for transport was the rotational streaming of the phloem cell contents. If then the phloem was demonstrated as capable of carrying materials both upward and downward, it seemed obvious that the movement in both directions was and could be simultaneous. With the mechanism for unidirectional flow proposed by Münch (1927) and Crafts (1931), however, it is clear that the proof of movement in both directions through the phloem is not proof of simultaneous movement in both directions. Although evidence presented in Chap. V seems clearly to show that hypotheses proposed by Münch and by Crafts are untenable, the upward movement of sugars and of inorganic constituents through the phloem into defoliated regions, and the downward movement from the leaves to the roots do not offer conclusive proof of simultaneous movement in both directions. The experiment devised to equalize the transpiration stream through defoliated regions, therefore, does not conclusively prove that transpiration does not control upward movement of nitrogen into leaves. It is possible, as far as these particular experiments show, that nitrogen and nutrient salts are carried into the leaves with the transpiration stream and are retransported from the leaves through the phloem into growing shoots or defoliated regions.

In spite of the fact that the data from these experiments with defoliated shoots seem less conclusive than when first proposed there still remains the extensive and clear-cut evidence, from the experiments in which larger stems were ringed and leaves were left above the ring, that ringing does interfere with upward transport of salts, even when there is no injury to the xylem. It is true that all of these experiments are open to the criticism that transpiration from the leaves above the ring is likely to be lessened, but, as pointed out earlier in this section, this difference in transpiration would seem inadequate to account for the great differences observed, *especially in view of the trapping effect of the ring in preventing reëxport from the parts above it.*

If transport through the phloem is unidirectional at any one time and place (see Chap. V), as assumed by Münch (1930) and by Crafts (1931), then it is obvious that, while carbohydrates are moving down from the leaves to the roots, any upward transport of salts from the soil must take place exclusively through the xylem. Under such conditions it would not be possible for organic or inorganic material of any sort to move up through the phloem. If, on the other hand, simultaneous movement in both directions through the phloem of the main stem is demonstrated, then, although small amounts of any solutes that may leak into the xylem may be carried in the transpiration stream, still the major part of the upward transport may take place through the phloem at the same time that a downward movement is taking place through the same tissues.

If carbohydrates are carried almost exclusively through the phloem—and even those that may be stored in abundance in the xylem regions are not transported through the xylem (see Secs. 4 and 5), and the evidence points very strongly to such a conclusion—it seems unlikely that the plant can have developed a mechanism that would carry one type of solute exclusively through the xylem and another through the phloem.

The findings of Auchter (1923), although not so clear-cut in their indications as to the tissues concerned in transport as are these ringing experiments, yet at the same time may be considered to support the contention that the movement of water is independent of the movement of nitrogen. He found that in straight-grained trees, where roots and branches are well distributed around the circumference of the trunk, the sugars from the leaves on one side move chiefly to the roots directly below them, and that nitrogen absorbed by the roots on one side of a tree moves principally to the branches directly above. Since cutting the roots on one side diminished the growth of shoots on the opposite side as well as directly above, probably because of decreased water supply, and defoliation of one side increased shoot growth on the opposite side, probably because of increased water supply, it seems that water moves rather freely from one side of the tree to the other. This evidence, though not very conclusive, tends to support the suggestion that water and mineral salts move independently from the roots to the leaves. Other evidence of a somewhat similar nature is presented by MacDaniels and Curtis (1930). In this work spiral rings passing twice around the trunk were made on a large number of apple trees. Sodium nitrate was added to the soil and it was found that the nitrogen had followed the spiral and then moved up vertically after it passed the end of the spiral ring. The branches on the side that was obstructed by the end of the spiral received very little nitrogen, and behaved like branches that had been completely ringed. That the nitrogen was moving through the phloem, and not the xylem, was indicated by the fact that the response was the same whether the phloem only was removed in a spiral, or the phloem and the xylem to a depth of two annual rings were removed. Of course, by the end of the season new spiral layers of both phloem and xylem were formed, and the nitrogen may have followed these, but since the vertical xylem under the spiral phloem ring was intact for a part of the season at least, the nitrogen, if it is carried in the xylem, should have followed these vertical xylem tubes instead of moving in a spiral.

11. Evidence Tending to Contradict That Presented in Sec. 10.—Clements (1930) has recently published data which he thinks demonstrate that nutrient salts are carried chiefly through the xylem. He has ringed stems of grapes, plum, and three varieties of raspberry. This was done early in the spring before the new shoots had formed. At the end of the growing season he has compared the total nitrogen and total ash contents of the ringed stems, including the new shoots and leaves that had developed from their buds, with those of similar stems taken at the beginning of the experiment before new shoots had formed. Averages of his findings are presented in Table 11.

TABLE 11.—DATA FROM CLEMENTS SHOWING INCREASE OF NITROGEN AND ASH OF RINGED SHOOTS

Plant	No. of stems averaged	Total nitrogen relative to sample at beginning*	No. of stems averaged	Total ash relative to sample at beginning*
Grape....................	22	43.5	5	43.3
Plum....................	6	2.7		
Black raspberry...........	1	3.8	1	4.3
Cuthbert raspberry........	9	5.8	3	7.0
Columbian raspberry......	5	4.8	2	8.9

* Clements calls this "increase" over the sample at the beginning. The increase, however, is less by one in each case.

Since the final contents average from nearly 3 to nearly 44 times the amounts originally present, he concludes that the xylem is chiefly concerned in transport. With the exception of the grape, which he says is very well suited for ringing experiments, the final amounts were from three to nine times the amounts originally present.

He criticizes my experiments partly on the grounds that I had no checks at the beginning, but he had no checks at the end. Actually in many of the experiments I reported, I did have check samples taken both at the beginning and again at the conclusion of the experiments. It is true that in none did I include the entire twigs, stems, and leaves, at both periods, but in several cases check leaf samples were taken both at the beginning and at the end of the experiments. When such samples were taken, in most cases there was a clear increase in nitrogen and ash in both ringed and unringed stems, but there was a much greater increase in the unringed stems. Since Clements had no sample from unringed stems at the end of the season, he has no evidence concerning the relative amounts of movement through ringed and normal stems. The increases he obtained over the original amounts were great, it is true, but I am sure the increases in total nitrogen and ash in the peach trees ringed before shoot growth started (see p. 48) were equally great, yet in the check branches the increases were still greater by at least 50 times.

Clements also states that the ring will prevent formation of new xylem, which is true if the rings are made only in the early spring. In most of the experiments reported in my 1923 paper, however, rings were made, partly for this very reason, much later in the season, when much or all of the new xylem had been laid down.

Evidence directly contradictory to that of my own with woody plants has been reported by Maskell and Mason for cotton plants (1929*a*, 1930*b*, and Mason and Maskell, 1931). They have found accumulation of nitrogen above rings in excess of the amounts found in unringed stems, and amounts below rings less than in similar regions of unringed stems. This evidence clearly supports their contention that nitrogen, perhaps in the form of nitrate, or even as organic nitrogen if analyses of tracheal sap are a criterion, is carried upward to the leaves through the xylem, is perhaps there synthesized into organic nitrogen, and retransported through the phloem to other parts. Whether this contradictory evidence is due to a difference in kind of plant used, or to some other factors cannot be settled without further experimental evidence. Most of the data of Maskell and Mason were obtained within 12 to 52 hours after ringing, whereas in my earlier experiments with woody plants, the time interval was much longer, ranging mostly from 22 days to two months or more. In later experiments with apple and *Ailanthus*, however, samples were taken at daily intervals up to a week. Though the data do not show differences that are statistically significant, and therefore are not presented, they indicate a gradual day-to-day increase in nitrogen of the leaves of the check plants above that in the ringed. They show no hint of excess in the ringed over that in the check at any period during the experiment.

The data of Maskell and Mason indicate a diurnal variation in nitrogen and ash contents of leaves. If the diurnal variation is real, it is conceivable that the ring, by preventing the removal from the leaves, makes it appear as if these leaves had actually imported more than the check leaves, whereas it is possible that they had merely exported less, either because the ring had prevented export, or because the higher carbohydrate content had enabled the leaves to retain more nitrogen as well as other mineral elements. In interpreting the data of Maskell and Mason (1929*a*) it should also be remembered that only three days before the experiment started the basal part of each stem was cleared of all leaves and branches for a distance of two feet. This would tend to result in a distinct decrease in the carbohydrate content of the plant as a whole and thus would favor a more rapid transport of carbohydrate and nitrogen from the remaining leaves of the check plant. The ring would prevent such transport from the leaves of the ringed plant. Saposchnikoff (1890) observed that the leaves of *Helianthus* plants, from which all but two leaves were removed, lost dry weight at the rate of 0.653 g. per square meter per hour, while leaves of plants with fourteen leaves lost at the rate of only 0.198 g. per hour. The plant with leaves reduced to one-seventh the number lost 3.3 times as fast. With *Cucurbita*, a plant with two leaves remaining lost dry weight at the rate of 0.449 g. per square meter per hour, while a plant with six leaves lost at the rate of 0.269 g. per hour. No mention is made as to the proportion of leaf surface removed in the work of Maskell and Mason, but the effect would tend to accentuate removal from the

remaining leaves. Furthermore, the deficiency in carbohydrate, particularly in the lower part of the stem and the
roots, would tend to starve these tissues and increase the
leakage of nitrogen from them into the transpiration stream.
Schumacher (1930) has demonstrated a marked transport
of nitrogen from leaves which have been starved by dark-
ening. Thus when a single leaf of an otherwise normally
treated plant was darkened, from 70 to 80 per cent of the
original nitrogen was transported from the leaf in a week
through the phloem. This evidence points toward the
inability of a starved tissue to retain its nitrogen when
the carbohydrate content is lowered.

Steward in correspondence has suggested another somewhat similar explanation for the disagreement between my
findings and those of Maskell and Mason. He points out
that these workers used only three of the upper leaves
of the cotton plant and that the increase of nitrogen in
these younger leaves of the ringed stems over that in the
checks may have been due to a redistribution within the
parts above the ring. Thus it is possible that the ring, by
preventing movement of nitrogen basally from the older
leaves, has tended to increase its movement into these
younger leaves. Or, as was suggested in the foregoing, if
carbohydrates were deficient in the upper leaves, the
increased supply due to diversion by the ring might favor
an increased accumulation of nitrogen in these same leaves.
Mason and Maskell state that the leaves used were three
mature leaves taken from near the top of the main axis
of each plant. I have failed to find any statement as to
what proportion of the total number of leaves these
formed. It is also not clear as to whether these "mature"
leaves had or had not reached their maximum growth.
In some plants even what might be considered as mature
leaves, under favorable conditions, will seem to continue
growth or withdraw materials from still older leaves.
Although it is possible that the changes in composition of
these leaves may be largely due to redistribution within
the upper part of the plant, it cannot be assumed to be a

probability. This is another of the many translocation problems that await further investigation.

In experiments with stems of *Ailanthus*, I have found clear indications of a redistribution between the leaves of a single branch. The nitrogen of the older leaves decreased, while that of the younger leaves increased. A method similar to that previously used (Curtis, 1923) and recently extended and described by Denny (1930) as the "twin leaf" method was used. *Ailanthus* with its large compound leaves, bearing ten to twenty pairs of well-matured leaflets, was found highly suitable for determining absolute changes in dry weight, fresh weight, and nitrogen content, as well as for determining percentage changes of the various components.

The finding of a high nitrogen content in both bark and wood above a ring, and its decrease below, would somewhat offset the suggestion that the differences may be due chiefly to a redistribution within the upper part. Even if all parts above showed an increase in nitrogen, however, and those below decreased, the criticism still stands that roots and stems below the ring were abnormally starved and would therefore lose much of their nitrogen to the transpiration stream.

In later papers (Maskell and Mason, 1930*b*; and Mason and Maskell, 1931) they have confirmed their findings of an increase of nitrogen above rings and have found that the total ash, as well as potassium and phosphorus, behave in much the same way. In these experiments they may not have heavily pruned or defoliated the lower part of the stem just previous to ringing as reported in the earlier paper, but no leaves were left below the rings so the stems and roots were certainly deprived of carbo-hydrates which would favor loss to the xylem. The increase in nitrogen of the stems immediately above the ring may have been partly due to stoppage of nitrogen moving down, and partly to an effect of the increased carbohydrate in causing a redistribution within the upper part. Mason and Phillis (1934) found, in nitrogen-starved plants which contained high carbohydrate, that nitrogen diminished in the older more basal leaves, increased in the upper younger leaves and stems, and increased also in the older part of the stem at the base. Abnormal starvation and release from the parts below the ring and redistribution above the ring may largely account for the findings observed but does not prove that most of the nitrogen and ash constituents are normally carried chiefly through the xylem.

12. Diurnal Fluctuations in Nitrogen and Ash of Leaves, Indicating Transport with the Transpiration Stream.—It has been tacitly assumed by many that during the day, when transpiration is taking place at high rates, salts are rapidly carried to the leaves in the transpiration stream, that in the leaves the inorganic ions are combined with organic substances, and the resulting compounds are retransported from the leaves to regions of utilization or storage. A diurnal fluctuation in nitrogen and ash contents of leaves showing high contents during the day and diminished amounts at night would tend to support this assumption.

Although Chibnall (1923) and Maskell and Mason (1929a) give data which they claim prove an appreciable diurnal variation, and although their data clearly show statistically significant increases during the day and decreases during the night, they do not positively demonstrate an absolute diurnal variation, for the data are expressed as variations in percentages of fresh weight or of residual dry weight, and these themselves may be variables. A gain in fresh weight at night, and a loss in fresh weight during the day, would make a seeming loss and gain, respectively, in nitrogen. It is also possible that much or all of the diurnal variation expressed even on the residual dry-weight basis may be merely apparent. With a steady gain in total nitrogen an increase in residual dry weight at night might appear as a loss in nitrogen while a failure to gain in residual dry weight during the day would appear as a gain in nitrogen. Though the labile dry weight of the tissues studied certainly increases during the day, it is very possible that the gain in residual dry weight, the more permanent tissue, takes place chiefly at night. Direct experimental data on this point are lacking, yet there are clear indications that permanent cell enlargement and perhaps nuclear divisions, occur largely at night. Furthermore since the residual dry weight makes up such a small part of the total weight of the plant, slight fluctuations in its amount will make a relatively large fluctuation of the nitrogen content when expressed as a percentage of the residual dry weight.

Considerable care should be taken before drawing conclusions from the data based on percentage. Chibnall is justified in pointing out the fallacy of interpreting changes in nitrogen, when expressed as percentages of dry weight, as real changes in nitrogen, for the altered percentages may be due largely to changes in dry matter and not to changes in actual nitrogen content. He is also right in suggesting that changes in percentages of water content between morning and night, or night and morning, may be due, at least partly, to changes in dry matter content resulting from photosynthesis or translocation. He seems to imply, however, as have also others, that differences in water content of from 0.1 to 1 per cent or thereabout, if they are due to changes in actual water content, introduce but slight errors when expressing nitrogen or any other constituent on a fresh-weight basis.

In comparing methods of expressing nitrogen, A as weight of nitrogen per unit number of leaves, B as nitrogen per gram dry weight, and C as nitrogen per unit fresh weight, he gives the following data obtained with plants of *Vicia faba* (Table 12). All the leaves from 12 plants were picked.

Using these same data, from which it is obvious that the leaves contained 86.82 per cent water and 13.18 per cent dry matter, let us assume two samples are taken, one in the morning with the composition indicated above, and the other the evening before with the same actual total dry weight and nitrogen contents; that during the night enough water had been absorbed by the leaves to alter the percentage water content from 85.82 to 86.82.   This is a one per cent difference which is seemingly slight.   Actually, however, to bring about such a one per cent difference in water content by absorption of water alone, 100 g. of fresh leaves must have absorbed 7.59 g. of water.   With no actual change in dry matter or nitrogen content, there-

TABLE 12.—SAMPLING ERRORS AND METHODS OF EXPRESSING NITROGEN IN LEAVES OF *Vicia Faba*
(From Chibnall)

	Wt. of nitrogen per 100 leaves, method A	Nitrogen percentage of total dry wt., method B	Nitrogen percentage of total fresh wt., method C
Mean.....................	0.432	5.71	0.753
Probable error..............	±0.0195	±0.036	±0.0068
Percentage error.............	4.50	0.63	0.91

fore, the nitrogen, which formed 0.753 per cent of fresh weight in the morning, would have formed 0.815 per cent of the fresh weight the evening before.   Expressed on this fresh-weight basis, therefore, 7.6 per cent of the original nitrogen would seemingly have disappeared over night, and this apparent change is all due to the slight change of only 1 per cent of fresh weight, a seemingly insignificant figure.   Diurnal differences in water or dry-matter contents, when expressed as percentages of fresh weight, are often much greater than 1 per cent.

Chibnall suggests that expressing nitrogen as a percentage of dry weight is misleading, with which I agree; but if the change in percentage water content was due solely to a loss of dry matter, as he claims, then to change the water content from 85.82 to 86.82 per cent there must have been a loss of 1.15 g. of dry matter, or 8.75 per cent of the original dry matter.   (In actual experiments he estimated a loss of 10 per cent of the dry matter over night.) Expressing nitrogen as a percentage of dry matter this change in dry matter would cause a seeming gain of nitrogen from a content of 5.25 per cent to one of 5.71 per cent, an apparent gain of 8.75 per cent. The order of error, therefore, under the assumptions here made, seems about the same whether expressed as percentage of dry weight or of fresh weight, if, on the one hand, the change is due to dry matter loss and on the other to water absorption. If expressed as a percentage of fresh weight, and the percentage change is due solely to loss of dry matter, which is the condition assumed by Chibnall, then with no real change in nitrogen the loss of 1.15 g. of dry matter would make a seeming change of nitrogen from 0.753 to 0.763 per cent, a seeming gain of 1.46 per cent over the original nitrogen. If the change in the dry-matter content expressed as percentage of fresh weight is partly due to water absorption and partly to dry-matter loss, as is more likely, the change in nitrogen content, which is apparent and not real, would be between the extremes here given, that is between 1.46 and 7.6 per cent.

Although his figures show a high percentage error by method A, and low percentage errors by methods B and C, there would be no systematic error due to lapse of time by method A, whereas changes in either dry weight or fresh weight with time would introduce errors into both methods B and C.

Data obtained from carefully matched leaves, which Denny has called the "twin leaf" method, are much more dependable for determining real diurnal variations. By the use of this method Denny (1930) found no indication of a significant diurnal variation in the nitrogen content of *Salvia* leaves. Gouwentak (1929) by the half-leaf method found no consistent diurnal variation in *Helianthus*. Although the method is superior to others for determining changes in absolute amounts of water, nitrogen, ash, etc., in specific organs such as leaves and fruits, it is obvious that the changes may not be strictly normal. Removing every other leaf, for example, will alter the sugar water, and nitrogen content of the remaining leaves.

In the summer of 1930 I carried out a rather extensive series of tests to determine if there were diurnal variations in the water, nitrogen, and dry-matter contents of leaves of *Ailanthus*. Eighteen matched pairs of vigorous shoots of *Ailanthus* were selected for the experiments. On each shoot six leaves were tagged and numbered in order, No. 1 being a young leaf near the terminal bud which was still growing. This younger leaf had not reached its maximum size nor had leaf 2. Number 4 had probably completely ceased growing. Leaf 6, though the oldest leaf used in the experiment, was not the oldest on the shoot, but was still well colored and apparently functional. Still older leaves were in some cases becoming yellow, and in a few instances abscised during the experiment. Shoots 1 and 2, 3 and 4, 5 and 6, etc., were matched one with the other. In some cases they were forks on the same saplings, in others two separate stems, although these probably arose as sprouts from the same root system. Each leaf bore from 15 to 20 pairs of well-matched leaflets. One half of the leaflets were taken at the beginning, and the second half at the end of each 12-hour period. Collections were made night and morning; those for the day period were harvested at 7 A.M. and 7 P.M., while those for the night period were harvested at 7:30 P.M. and 7:30 A.M. One hundred and forty-four samples were taken in all, so that there were 72 sets, 36 showing the change in composition during the 12-hour period during the day, and 36 for the 12-hr. night period. After analyzing 72 samples it became evident that, though there were distinct diurnal variations in absolute dry-matter content of the leaflets, there were no consistent changes in either total water or total nitrogen content, except in the younger leaflets which were not mature. It is to be noted that these younger leaflets which were still growing showed a gain in fresh weight and nitrogen content both during the day and during the night. There is an indication

TABLE 13.—DIURNAL CHANGES IN ACTUAL FRESH WEIGHT, DRY WEIGHT, AND NITROGEN CONTENT OF MATCHED LEAFLETS of *Ailanthus*

	Day period						Night period						Av. of original total weights per leaf		
				Difference evening minus previous morning						Difference morning minus previous evening					
Date	Shoot No.	Leaf No.	Fresh wt., mg.	Dry wt., mg.	Total N., mg.	Date	Shoot No.	Leaf No.	Fresh wt., mg.	Dry wt., mg.	Total N., mg.	Fresh wt., g.	Dry wt., g.	Total N., mg.
July 31 A.M. to July 31 P.M.	1	2	+177.1	+241.7	+3.2	July 31 P.M. to Aug. 1 A.M.	2	2	+285.5	− 17.9	+0.2	Day period		
	7	2	+149.5	+125.6	+1.2		8	2	+ 62.0	− 92.4	+0.1	7.5716	2.0877	82.4
	13	2	+239.5	+175.6	+1.7		14	2	+140.0	−103.0				
Aug. 1 A.M. to Aug. 1 P.M.	3	2	+ 55.5	+ 91.2	+1.2	Aug. 1 P.M. to Aug. 2 A.M.	4	2	+230.5	− 90.0	+0.5	Night period		
	9	2	+102.3	+122.0	+1.9		10	2	+369.5	− 83.4	+1.7	7.4550	2.1953	83.2
	15	2	+170.3	+139.1	+2.3		16	2	+413.5	+ 0.4	+1.2			
Av......... Odds.........			+149.03 / 768	+149.2 / 1,666	+1.9 / 1,110				+253.5 / 332	− 64.4 / 124	+0.74 / 34.5			
July 31 A.M. to July 31 P.M.	1	4	+ 20.9	+ 72.4	−0.3	July 31 P.M. to Aug. 1 A.M.	2	4	+170.0	− 65.0	+0.4	Day period		
	7	4	+105.4	+133.8	+2.0		8	4	+255.0	− 51.4	+1.6	9.4698	2.6766	91.6
	13	4	+242.2	+158.7	+1.1		14	4	+111.5	−113.4	−0.2			
Aug. 1 A.M. to Aug. 1 P.M.	3	4	+ 66.4	+ 73.4	−0.7	Aug. 1 P.M. to Aug. 2 A.M.	4	4	+150.0	−121.6	−1.5	Night period		
	9	4	+ 11.8	+ 80.8	−2.0		10	4	+ 73.0	−154.3	−0.6	9.1300	2.6845	87.2
	15	4	+ 73.3	+109.2	−0.9		16	4	+ 34.5	−111.1	−1.0			
Av......... Odds.........			+ 82.7 / 27	+ 77.8 / 25.5	−0.13 / 1.4				+132.3 / 216	−102.8 / 1,428	−0.22 / 2.3			
July 31 A.M. to July 31 P.M.	1	6	+ 94.5	+ 70.5	−0.1	July 31 P.M. to Aug. 1 A.M.	2	6	+141.0	− 47.6	+0.3	Day period		
	7	6	+142.0	+ 91.2	+1.4		8	6	+144.6	− 68.7	−0.9	9.2577	2.4922	74.2
	13	6	− 76.5	+ 31.4	−2.6		14	6	−186.6	−142.1	−1.1			
Aug. 1 A.M. to Aug. 1 P.M.	3	6	− 24.9	+ 26.8	−3.4	Aug. 1 P.M. to Aug. 2 A.M.	4	6	+195.2	− 69.6	−0.7	Night period		
	9	6	+104.7	+104.7	+0.5		10	6	−170.0	−109.0	−1.4	9.0401	2.4896	68.5
	15	6	+ 14.7	+ 77.8	−0.3		16	6	+ 46.0	− 74.7	+1.2			
Av......... Odds.........			+ 42.4 / 6.1	+ 67.1 / 570	−0.75 / 4.3				+ 45.0 / 3.0	− 85.3 / 1,110.0	−0.43 / 5.0			

of a loss from the older leaves, but the changes are not statistically significant.   The data are presented in Table 13.   Since these samples were taken during a hot dry period when conditions were favorable for rapid transpiration, it was rather surprising to find so little variation in water content.   This lack of variation is probably due to the fact that the samples were taken just before direct sunlight struck the leaves in the morning, and shortly after they became shaded in the evening.   If samples had been taken at midday and midnight it is probable the water content would have varied more.*   Working with bean plants supplied with nitrates at high concentration, Chang (1932) has found diurnal increases in the leaves.   His findings are discussed in Sec. 14.

Even if a diurnal variation were clearly demonstrated, with an increase of nitrogen or ash during the day and a decrease at night, it would not necessarily follow that the increase during the day is brought about by increased transpiration hastening the transport of nitrogen into the leaf.   A formation of protein during the day would tend to steepen the diffusion gradient of soluble nitrogen into the leaf, and thus cause a movement bearing no relation to the transpiration stream.   The increased protein formation would be expected to result from an increased supply of carbohydrate due to photosynthesis, and need bear no relation to any assumed or real influence of light on protein synthesis.   The striking influence of light on the ability of *Nitella* cells to concentrate halogens in the vacuolar sap, as reported by Hoagland, Hibbard, and Davis (1926), points to light effects entirely independent of transpiration, for these cells were submerged.   Brooks (1926) has reported a similar effect of light in causing cells of *Valonia*, a submerged marine organism, to concentrate dibromophenol indophenol.

13. Relation of Transpiration to Solute Absorption and Movement in Intact Plants.—As has already been men-

---

* I am indebted to Dr. H. L. Chance for making the tedious nitrogen determinations.

tioned in the introduction, when it was recognized that plants required certain inorganic salts, that these were necessarily absorbed from the soil, that the soil solution was very dilute, that most land plants absorbed large quantities of water from the soil, and that most of this water evaporated from the leaves; it seemed perfectly logical to conclude that the amount of water lost from the leaves would determine both the amount of solution and therefore salts absorbed, as well as the distribution after absorption. In more recent years, however, it has been recognized that passage through membranes reduces or precludes the possibility of mass flow, and diffusion therefore predominates over mass flow. Under such conditions each substance, solvent and solute alike, diffuses independently, and the movement of one through the membranes may have no effect on the diffusion of the other.

A number of investigators have experimentally demonstrated that there is no direct relation between water absorption and salt absorption. Among these are Hasselbring (1914), Muenscher (1922), Prát (1923), and Hoagland (1923). Experimental evidence is therefore accumulating which shows that there is no direct relation between water absorption and salt absorption. Prát (1923) claims a slight positive effect, but it is interesting to note that in those cultures having high transpiration rates and a slightly increased salt absorption, his data show the external salt solution to have been distinctly increased because of the decreased volume of solution which resulted from the high rate of transpiration. It is highly probable that the observed increase in salt absorption was due to this increased external salt concentration and not due to any effect of transpiration toward directly absorbing the external solution, nor is it necessarily due to an increased transport from the roots to the leaves. If he had kept the external concentration constant this effect would probably have been eliminated. Muenscher (1922) and a number of other investigators have found that an increased external salt contraction will increase salt absorption.

That transpiration is likely to influence salt absorption indirectly through its effect on metabolism and growth is without doubt, but the ultimate effect is determined less by transpiration and more by the effect on the plant and one cannot predict whether an increase in transpiration will increase or decrease salt absorption. The data given by Muenscher clearly indicate that the methods used to alter transpiration, rather than differences in transpiration themselves, are chiefly responsible for differences in ash contents.

Most of the investigators who have studied the effects of transpiration on ash absorption have studied the effect on total ash and not that on the individual constituents. It is highly probable that different constituents will be influenced differently, not, however, because transpiration directly influences the absorption of different ions, but because it is likely to alter metabolism and thus alter the proportion of ash constituents. The differential absorption of ions would probably be more influenced by the factors used to alter transpiration than by the total transpiration as such. For example, an increase in transpiration brought about by raising the temperature would probably have a different effect than an increase brought about by low humidity or by increased light intensity. Schloesing (1869) claimed that high transpiration of tobacco plants in the open increased the absorption of inessential elements, while relatively greater amounts of essential elements were absorbed by the plants in the humid chamber with low transpiration. His data, however, show a greater quantity of four of the essential elements in the dry chamber and only three in the humid chamber. Though considerable emphasis is laid upon this early work of Schloesing, especially in a number of textbooks on plant physiology, notably in Palladin's "Plant Physiology" (1926), it should be remembered that the leaves of only one plant were analyzed from the humid chamber. This one plant was grown in the humid chamber for a period of 30 days, while the three check plants were grown in the open for a period of 42 days. The plant in the humid chamber, with a volume of 200 liters, was supplied with a constant flow of 500 liters in 24 hours of air containing some hundredths ("quelques centièmes") of carbon dioxide, while those in the open had only the amount normally present in the air, probably not over 0.03 per cent. He suggests that the high starch content in the humid chamber was due to its accumulation, because metabolism was checked due to a lack of nutrients, and the nutrients were low because transpiration was low. It seems more probable that it was due to the excess carbon dioxide, and had nothing to do with transpiration. Furthermore the high silicon, and perhaps also the high chlorine, of the plants in the open may have been due to the dust accumulating on the plants in the open. The high chlorine might also be due to higher light intensity, independent of transpiration for, as previously mentioned, Hoagland, Hibbard, and Davis (1926) observed that increased light intensity greatly increased the ability of *Nitella* cells to accumulate chlorine and other halogens.

The available evidence indicates rather clearly that nutrient absorption is neither determined nor directly influenced by water absorption, and this seems to be at present rather generally accepted by botanists. That movement after absorption is influenced and determined by transpiration is, however, considered as an established fact by many botanists. The studies on the influence of transpiration on solute absorption, on the other hand, give fairly strong evidence that translocation after absorption does not take place in the transpiration stream. If translocation does take place with the water in the water-conducting tissues and the rate of transport were determined by the rate of transpiration, then the rate of removal from the absorbing organs should be determined in part by the rate of movement of the transpiration stream. MacDougal (1925, p. 28), disagreeing with me on this point, states that "The rate at which ions enter the root and cross the endodermal membrane is determined by their own ionic mobility and by the colloidal condition of the membrane as altered by the action of other ions present in inter-ferences or antagonisms," and goes on to say that the "transpirational pull" might vary widely without influenc-ing mineral nutrient absorption. He is partly correct in stating that the rate of ionic movement is determined by their own ionic mobility and by the condition of the mem-brane, but he seems to overlook the fact that, if the solutes move across membranes abutting on the water-conducting vessels—and they must so move if these solutes are carried through the water-conducting tissues as he assumes—then their concentration on the vessel side of the membrane must have an important effect on the rate at which they move across. The rate of water movement through these vessels, as determined by the rate of transpiration, should therefore directly influence the rate of solute movement away from the absorbing regions and thus, in turn, the rate of absorption. The fact that the rate of absorption is not determined by the rate of transpiration is therefore clear evidence that the translocation is not dependent upon water movement.

Instead of finding that high transpiration decreases the ash content of the roots and increases that of the tops, as might be expected on the assumption that nutrients are translocated in the transpiration stream, Muenscher (1922) found that, when transpiration was altered by light and shade, the plants with high transpiration had a much higher ash content of the roots and less in the tops, while those with low transpiration had less in the roots and more in the tops. This difference was very marked whether the ash contents were expressed as percentages of dry weight or fresh weight or as ratios of total ash. Differ-ences in the same direction but less marked were evident when differences in transpiration were brought about by differences in humidity. It is highly probable, as previ-ously mentioned, *that the differences in ash distribution are not directly determined by transpiration influencing absorp-tion or translocation, but indirectly through the influence of transpiration, or the means used to alter it, on some other phase of metabolism and growth.*

Mason and Maskell (1931, p. 150) have suggested that one reason there is little relation between transpiration and total ash content is that the salts are retransported from the leaves to the roots where they have a damping effect on further absorption. According to this suggestion, therefore, transpiration would merely hasten circulation within the plant and have little effect on total absorption. Though not an impossible suggestion, it seems rather forced and it has little supporting evidence. If it were correct one could expect large quantities of salts to be trapped above a ring (see Sec. 10, p. 57).

Some have considered that a certain minimum amount of transpiration is sufficient (this is implied in Livingston's editorial footnote, Palladin, 1926, p. 150) and that, since transpiration has not been completely eliminated in any experiment, this minimum may always have been exceeded, and, for this reason, the experiments on the influence of transpiration on salt absorption have shown no direct relation between water absorption and nutrient absorption. A very striking and direct relation has been observed, however, between the rate of absorption and conduction of dyes and inorganic salts introduced by injection or through cut stems and the rate of transpiration. Furthermore, Birch-Hirschfeld (1919) found such conduction in cut stems practically to cease when transpiration was greatly reduced. The suggestion that a certain minimum is always exceeded therefore seems to have no support.

Though these studies of the influence of transpiration on salt absorption and movement in intact plants could hardly be considered as offering conclusive proof that salts are not carried in the transpiration stream, they do distinctly support the evidence obtained from ringing and xylem-cutting experiments and cannot be criticized on the grounds that the conducting tissues are interfered with.

Haas and Reed (1927), on the other hand, have published data which they think demonstrate a distinct influence of transpiration on the movement of ash into leaves of an intact plant. They found, for instance, that immediately following a period of hot desiccating winds, the ash content of the uninjured leaves of citrus was higher than that of the leaves which had been killed by the desiccation and therefore supposedly unaltered with respect to ash. The data they offer, however, seem far from conclusive. In the first place it is possible that different leaves had a different composition to begin with, and the desiccating winds tended to kill those of one composition, those which had low total ash, low calcium, high potassium, high sulphate and high phosphate, while the others which were not killed, instead of changing in composition may have originally had a different composition. In the second place, though their data seem to show a clear increase in the calcium content of the ash and a very slight increase in the content of magnesium and chlorine, they at the same time show a decrease in the potassium, sulphate, and phosphate content of the ash, and though the differences were not great they are of the same order as the calcium change if expressed in percentage of the original contents.

Though the wilted leaves 10 days after regaining turgor tend to have an ash composition more nearly like that of the killed leaves, some of the constituents show an ash content even less than before the wilting. Furthermore, since the ash contents are expressed in terms of dry weight only, some of the differences, especially the gain of total ash during the hot dry period and the apparent loss of ash after recovery of turgor, may have been due, respectively, to an effect of desiccation and heat on the loss of dry matter, and an effect of regained turgor and lower temperature upon reformation of carbohydrates in the leaves, and not to any effect of changed transpiration on absolute ash content. It seems very possible that high temperature and low water supply might reduce the carbohydrate content by decreasing photosynthesis and increasing respiration, thus causing an apparent temporary increase in ash. Maximov (1929, p. 241) reports an instance where there was a loss of 40 per cent of the dry weight of leaves of *Impatiens* during a five-day period of intense wilting. He also states that Iljin observed a decrease of 15 to 30 per cent in absolute dry weight of wheat plants during an excessively dry period. If a plant contained 3 per cent nitrogen or ash and the dry weight decreased 40 per cent, the percentage of nitrogen or ash would change from 3 to 5 per cent, an apparent increase of 66.6 per cent in spite of the fact that there was no real change in total nitrogen or ash.

14. Absorption and Transport under Special Conditions. Although much of the evidence points strongly toward little or no direct effect of transpiration upon absorption and transport of mineral salts, it can be easily demonstrated that under special conditions the rate of transpiration may greatly influence both absorption and transport. When roots are supplied with toxic solutions, such as eosin for example, the solute is absorbed and transported in the transpiration stream. In fact it seems probable that experiments with toxic dyes of this sort are partly responsible for the widespread notion that transpiration determines absorption and transport of solutes.

A high concentration of salts which are not usually considered as toxic may result in injury to the absorbing tissues and thus be carried with the transpiration stream. Thus the addition of excess sodium chloride to the soil will sometimes cause distinct "burning" of the leaf edges, or death of entire leaves without apparent injury to the stems or the lateral or terminal buds. It seems that in these cases the salt has been carried with the transpiration stream to the leaves, with much less injury to other tissues.

Mr. Maguire has brought to my attention the fact that plants of *Galium* may continue to grow for a considerable period, developing flowers and fruits long after the lower part of the stem as well as the roots seemed dead. When behaving in this manner, the plants were growing in a soil with plenty of moisture. When severed from the root system the tops promptly wilted. It would seem that these plants were making considerable growth after the roots were dead and were absorbing the soil solution directly through nonliving tissues.

I have found that bean plants are able to develop fairly well and remain fresh for several weeks, and even mature pods, after the main stem had been scalded when only the first pair of leaves had formed. Although the roots were not examined, they, in all probability, were dead while the tops were still fresh. Chang (1932) found that leaves of bean plants with killed roots absorbed more nitrogen during the day than did those of check plants. Kramer (1933) has found that roots killed by heat may continue to be effective in absorbing water, for the plants so treated remained alive and unwilted for several days.

It would be of interest to determine the influence of transpiration upon salt absorption of such plants with dead roots. One could expect in this case some direct relation between the amount of salts absorbed and the amount of transpiration, because living cells with high semipermeability would be absent. Any treatment tending to injure the roots or increase their permeability can be expected to favor more direct absorption of unaltered soil solution, or bring about contamination of the transpiration stream with the leachings from weakened cells. Such injury may result from toxic agents, pathogens, poor aëration, or starvation of the roots resulting from heavy defoliation or pruning of the tops. Strasburger (1891, p. 865) recognized that salts which do not readily enter living roots will enter when the latter are killed.

Even in plants with living healthy roots, the concentration of salts in the soil solution could be expected to have an influence on the relative amounts transported through the xylem and phloem. For example, with a low amount of available nitrogen in the soil, one would expect the living cells of the root to retain that absorbed, and perhaps synthesize organic nitrogen compounds, which in all likelihood would be retained by the living cells and transported chiefly through the phloem. The work of Osterhout (1922), Hoagland (1923), and others indicates that living cells can absorb nitrate and other ions and concentrate them within the cells, even without change to organic forms. One would expect, therefore, that if nitrogen were deficient, the living cells would have greater ability to retain the nitrate and prevent it passing through them into the xylem. In fact, any reaching the xylem would, in all probability, be quickly absorbed by the neighboring living cells. If, on the other hand, nitrates or other nutrients are in excess in the soil, the living cells of the root might soon have their accumulation capacity satisfied, in which case they could not prevent the excess from passing into the xylem and the transpiration stream. There seems little doubt that, if solutes get into the transpiration stream, they will be carried with it unless removed. If certain nutrients, as for example nitrogen or potassium, are present in such amounts that the living cells of the roots are in a sense saturated, there seems no reason why they may not pass into the transpiration stream. Here they may be carried to the leaves or may be removed by the living cells along the path if the concentration within the cells is not in equilibrium with the xylem solution.*

* Professor Hoagland has kindly shown me some of his findings that have not yet been published. These suggest a very different interpretation. His findings indicate that when roots are most rapidly accumulating bromine or potassium against a diffusion gradient, they are at the same time secreting these same elements into the xylem. At least they appear in the guttation water or in that which exudes from a cut stump and seems to come from the xylem. Whether this is an active secretion from healthy cells or a release of solutes, chiefly inorganic, from maturing cells is not clear. The latter explanation is in line with the suggestion of Priestley (1920, 1929) that maturing xylem cells release their contents, although Priestley suggests that the solutes are chiefly organic. The large amounts obtained, however, and the speed of release to the xylem would seem to preclude the possibility of their all having been released from maturing or dying cells. If active secretion is established the suggestion that the living cells of the root would be likely to remove certain ions from the xylem and thus tend to prevent their transport with the water is unsound. It is still likely, however, that living cells along the path above the absorbing roots will remove some of these ions from the xylem water. The polar secretion of ions, however, is not indicated in experiments with *Nitella* (Hoagland, 1923; Hoag-

Often under natural conditions these elements, nitrogen and potassium, are deficient in the soil. Under such conditions one might expect most of their transport to take place through the phloem. Even ions, such as Ca^{++} or SO_4^{--}, that seem not to be concentrated in living cells, would probably not be carried in the transpiration stream because protoplasm is so highly impermeable to them that they would not get through the living layers into the xylem, unless the concentration of salts is so high as to destroy the semipermeability of the cells or they are injured in some other manner. Ions or compounds to which cell membranes are highy permeable and which are not retained by the living cells might then be rather readily carried by the transpiration stream. This may account for the rapid transport of lithium with the transpiration stream. This possibility, that under one set of conditions the transport of a given element, like nitrogen, may take place chiefly through the phloem and under another chiefly through the xylem, complicates the problem greatly and may easily lead to misinterpretations and contradictions.

The cotton plants used by Maskell and Mason may have been growing in a highly fertile soil with excess nitrogen. The heavy pruning of the plants, by the removal of all the

---

land, Hibbard, and Davis, 1926) nor with potato and other storage tissues (Steward, 1932).

If salts are secreted only from actively growing cells or come from maturing cells, it would seem that most actively growing roots would at the same time release the greatest amount of salt to the xylem water. This is in agreement with observations that greater root pressures are associated with conditions favoring more active growth of roots. One could therefore expect that those plants which show most active guttation or bleeding would also carry relatively larger amounts of salts through the xylem. In this connection it is worth noting that Clements (1930, see Table 11) found a very much greater salt movement past the ring on grape stems than on those of plum or raspberry. The copious and long-continued exudation from the xylem of grape is well known. This interpretation would also indicate greater salt transport through the xylem of rapidly growing herbaceous plants, such as *Cucurbita*, which exhibit vigorous exudation, while in more slowly growing woody plants, which show less frequent and less active root exudation, more of the salts may be transported through the phloem.

lower branches and leaves three days before the experiment began, would certainly tend toward severe starvation of the roots and would thus favor leaching of nitrogen into the transpiration stream. This would be especially marked in plants with ringed stems. This special set of conditions might, therefore, account for the data they obtained. Such a condition might also account for their failure to find a clear-cut diffusion gradient for any particular form of nitrogen. Much of the nitrogen may have been moving through the xylem for the reasons stated above. Some may have been moving to the leaves through the phloem or xylem before being converted into organic forms. Some may have been absorbed by the living cells along the path and there converted into organic nitrogen. Their assumption that all synthesis must have taken place in the leaves and that upward transport is exclusively through the xylem has but little supporting evidence.

It is possible that herbaceous or annual plants carry relatively more of their mineral nutrients through the xylem than do woody perennials. I have found strong tests for nitrates in the sap bleeding from stumps of Iresine plants, yet Thomas (1927) has obtained evidence that in apples little or no nitrate is present in the xylem. Wormall (1924) also found but little in the sap of the vine. Eckerson (1924) found the roots or stems of tomato to be capable of reducing nitrates to organic forms which might be expected to be carried more readily in the phloem. Mason and Maskell (1931, p. 149), however, found organic nitrogen in tracheal sap of cotton in about the same concentration as inorganic nitrogen, and Anderssen (1929) found all the nitrogen in the sap of pear stems to be organic. From this, one might even contend that nitrogen is transported upward chiefly as organic nitrogen which possibly leaches into the transpiration stream more readily than nitrate.

In all of my experiments on the effect of ringing on nitrogen and ash transport I have worked with woody plants, the roots of which are perennial and at all times are likely to contain a fair supply of carbohydrates.

Furthermore, with but few exceptions I always took precautions to have branches and leaves below rings in such positions as to keep the roots well supplied with carbohydrates. Root starvation, therefore, did not complicate matters.

Chang (1932) has carried out an extensive series of experiments with bean plants, and his findings point to transport of nitrogen through the xylem with the transpiration stream. He worked with large numbers of plants carefully selected for uniformity and, by selecting carefully matched plants or by use of a stamp method, was able to follow changes in nitrogen contents on an absolute basis, which was independent of changes in leaf area, water content, and dry-matter content.

In order to obtain appreciable changes in composition over 12-hour periods he watered the plants, which were growing in a sandy soil, with Knop's solution of four times normal strength. Since herbaceous stems could not easily be ringed, possible transport through the phloem was stopped by scalding the stems for a distance of about 5 mm. The results of such an experiment, showing diurnal changes in normal plants as well as those in plants with scalded stems, are presented in Table 14. He found that normal plants, as a whole, absorbed more nitrogen during the day than at night; the growing shoot gained during both the day and night, but slightly more in the day; the leaves gained markedly during the day and lost nitrogen at night, while the roots gained most at night and much less or not at all during the day. His data clearly demonstrate a diurnal fluctuation in the nitrogen content of leaves.

It is clear that the plants with scalded stems behave practically the same as normal plants, with the exception that at night the leaves did not lose nitrogen and the shoots gained slightly more. Though the difference was not statistically significant, it was apparent in all four sets of experiments. This difference is probably due to the fact that scalding has prevented removal from leaves to the roots and that starvation of the roots has resulted in par-

TABLE 14.—CHANGES IN TOTAL NITROGEN OF PLANTS WITH STEMS SCALDED COMPARED WITH NORMAL PLANTS
Expressed as milligrams of nitrogen per plant

Treatment	Period	Shoots	Odds	Leaves	Odds	Tops	Odds	Roots	Odds	Whole plant	Odds
Normal..........	Day	2.14 ± 0.20		1.50 ± 0.42		3.63 ± 0.48		0.08 ± 0.25		3.71 ± 0.65	
Stem scalded..........	Day	2.12 ± 0.20		1.67 ± 0.46		3.78 ± 0.54		0.04 ± 0.24		3.82 ± 0.68	
Difference..........		-0.02 ± 0.21	1:9	0.17 ± 0.48	3:7	0.15 ± 0.55	2:8	0.04 ± 0.27	1:9	0.11 ± 0.74	1:9
Normal..........	Night	1.60 ± 0.24		-1.27 ± 0.50		0.34 ± 0.53		1.62 ± 0.34		1.95 ± 0.82	
Stem scalded..........	Night	1.86 ± 0.22		0.21 ± 0.37		2.07 ± 0.44		1.24 ± 0.25		3.32 ± 0.60	
Difference..........		0.26 ± 0.25	1.5:1	-1.47 ± 0.44	32:1	1.75 ± 0.49	76:1	0.38 ± 0.29	2.3:1	1.37 ± 0.72	6:1

tial release of their stored nitrogen. In another series, where the stamp method was used to determine true changes and where the growing shoots were cut off, scalding the stem resulted in a slightly greater gain of nitrogen in the leaves during the day and less loss during the night. These slight differences again were probably due to the prevention of transport to the roots, and to the greater release from starved roots.

Chang also determined the influence of killing the roots on nitrogen absorption and distribution. The roots were killed by placing the pots in scalding water for ten minutes. Data from this experiment are presented in Table 15. During the day the leaves of such plants absorbed significantly more nitrogen than did those of check plants. The shoots absorbed slightly more, but the difference was not statistically significant. Taking the leaves and shoots together the differences were not significant. At night the leaves of the root-killed plants lost slightly less than the normal leaves, but the difference was not significant. It would seem then that killing the roots has not appreciably altered the absorption or movement of nitrogen to the tops.

These findings of Chang's tend to support those of Maskell and Mason, but I am not convinced that they represent normal behavior. In the first place, in order to show measurable and significant changes over 12-hour periods, nitrate was added at concentrations much in excess of those normally found in soils. As pointed out earlier in this section, high concentrations can be expected to lead to unusual leakage into the xylem, where transpiration would carry it to the leaves. In the second place, starvation of the roots would tend to result in still less retention and more seepage into the xylem. As seen in Table 14, the roots of the stem-scalded plants retained less nitrogen, although the tops of those same plants actually absorbed significantly more nitrogen than the check plants and the plant as a whole, including the roots, actually had

UPWARD TRANSPORT OF NITROGEN 85

Table 15.—Changes in Total Nitrogen of Plants with Roots Killed Compared with Normal Plants

Expressed as milligrams of nitrogen per plant

Treatment	Period	In shoot	Odds	In leaves	Odds	Roots	In top	Odds	Whole plant
Normal.........	Day	1.56 ± 0.5		2.89 ± 0.45		0.02 ± 0.23	4.45 ± 0.49		4.47 ± 0.68
Root killed.....	Day	1.38 ± 0.12		4.69 ± 0.51			6.07 ± 0.56		
Difference......		−0.18 ± 0.16	1.5:1	1.80 ± 0.54	45:1		1.63 ± 0.60	18.1	
Normal.........	Night	1.22 ± 0.18		−1.03 ± 0.44		0.98 ± 0.23	0.20 ± 0.5		1.18 ± 0.65
Root killed.....	Night	1.58 ± 0.17		−0.52 ± 0.41			1.00 ± 0.45		
Difference......		0.36 ± 0.17	9:1	0.52 ± 0.41	1.5:1		0.80 ± 0.4	5:1	

more total nitrogen, although the difference was not statistically significant.

In contrast with these findings of Chang's, ringing experiments with woody plants have consistently shown less nitrogen in the leaves above rings than in normal stems. This was evident in both short-time and long-time experiments. If nitrogen had been carried in the transpiration stream, one would expect more nitrogen in the leaves of ringed stems, because the ring would have a trapping effect, preventing export from the leaves above. The fact that there was consistently less nitrogen in these leaves would indicate but slight normal transport through the xylem. With these woody plants, although nitrate was in some cases added to the soil about the plant, undoubtedly the amount was much less than that in the solution about the bean roots. Furthermore, in no cases were the woody plants heavily pruned or defoliated and in no cases were the rings so placed as to prevent an adequate supply of carbohydrate to the roots, so root starvation did not complicate matters.

SUMMARY

10. Ringing experiments with several species of woody plants have consistently shown a reduced absorption of nitrogen by the leaves above the ring, as compared with those of normal stems. This has been true both if the ring is made early in the season before shoot growth has occurred when the ring would prevent formation of new xylem in the region of ringing, and when the ring is made after leaves had developed and the current year's xylem is mostly formed. When the experiment is so arranged as to equalize the transpiration streams passing through defoliated regions isolated by rings and those not so isolated, less nitrogen was found in the wood and bark of those stems that were ringed at the base than in those not ringed. This occurred independently of whether the carbohydrate content was high or low. In practically all cases some nitrogen and minerals were found to pass rings but much less than in normal stems.

11. Mason and Maskell, working with cotton have consistently found accumulation of nitrogen and ash in leaves and bark above rings and diminished amounts below rings. This contradictory evidence may be due to the fact that all of their experiments were so conducted as to bring about starvation of roots and release of nitrogen to the transpiration stream by all parts below the ring.

12. Increase of nitrogen in leaves during the day and decrease at night has been claimed to indicate transport to the leaves in the transpiration stream. It is pointed out, however, that diurnal fluctuations may not in all cases be real but merely apparent and due to the method of expressing composition. Expressing composition changes on a per leaf or per organ basis seems usually preferable for determining absolute changes, but this method has its disadvantages in tending to alter to a greater or less degree the normal changes. Even when demonstrated to be real, an increase of nitrogen in leaves during the day as compared with that at night may be due to the increased carbohydrate or to light causing greater retention and accumulation, and may thus be entirely independent of transpiration.

13. Evidence of recent years has clearly demonstrated no predictable relation between transpiration and salt absorption. It is commonly assumed, however, that after absorption, salts are transported in the transpiration stream. It is pointed out that a failure to obtain increased absorption with increased transpiration is an indication that salts are not carried in the transpiration stream as commonly supposed. Furthermore, a greater accumulation of salts in roots with less in the tops in plants under higher transpiration does not point toward transport with the water. It is probable that observed differences in mineral absorption and distribution are not directly influenced by transpiration, but indirectly, through the influence of transpiration, or the means used in altering it, on some other phases of metabolism. The suggestion that salts carried down to the roots through the phloem tend to have a damping effect on further absorption, and that this accounts for failure of transpiration to increase absorption, points toward a rapid circulation of salts in the plant. The failure of rings to trap large quantities of salts above the cut phloem, however, strongly negatives this suggestion. Certain cases of reported accumulation of salts in leaves under conditions of hot winds are discredited on the grounds that the changes were expressed as percentages of dry weight, and the conditions were such as to cause a marked change in dry weight.

14. When toxic solutes are supplied to the roots, they are carried with the transpiration stream, probably because they have injured the protoplasmic membranes and are therefore carried more directly with the water. Living cells are known to be able to accumulate certain ions against a concentration gradient if the external concentration is weak. It would seem, therefore, that such ions would tend to be absorbed by the living cells of the root and stem, would be transported in them, and not be liberated into the transpiration stream. This would seem especially to apply to nitrogen which may be quickly transformed into organic compounds in these tissues. On the other hand, if these salts are in excess so that the accumulation capacity of the living cells is exceeded, large amounts can be expected to leach into the water-conducting tissues and be there transported. Ringing in such a fashion as to starve the roots will tend to reduce their capacity to accumulate or retain the nitrogen and ash they originally held, and the effect will be to increase leakage into, and transport through, the xylem. The fact that under conditions of root starvation or excess supply in the soil, nitrogen and ash constituents may be carried chiefly in the transpiration stream, while under more normal conditions they may be carried chiefly through the phloem, may account for much of the contradictory evidence. Recent experiments with herbaceous plants indicate a secretion into the xylem by actively absorbing roots. This is contrary to the suggestion that living root cells would prevent entrance into the xylem.

CHAPTER IV

EVIDENCE INDICATING DOWNWARD TRANSPORT THROUGH THE XYLEM

15. Findings and Interpretations of Birch-Hirschfeld.— Anatomical studies and experiments on ringing since the time of Malpighi (1679) and Knight (1801) and especially since those of Hartig (1858, 1861, 1862) and Hanstein (1860) have led botanists to agree that downward translocation of solutes occurs almost exclusively in the phloem tissues. Luise Birch-Hirschfeld (1919) seems to have been the first seriously to question the validity of this conclusion. Her skepticism with regard to a movement through phloem resulted chiefly from experiments, principally with lithium salts, which indicated that introduced solutes moved with extreme slowness through these tissues.

Strips of phloem tissues from both woody and herbaceous plants were dipped into solutions of lithium nitrate, mostly of 0.13 M concentration, and it was found by spectroscopic tests that the lithium had moved along the strips a distance of only 1.5 to 2.5 cm. in 24 hr. This rate of movement was approximately the same as that through unspecialized parenchyma tissue as found in potato, kohlrabi, rutabaga, and the living pith from *Sambucus* and *Sylphium*. Since it had been suggested that living cells were concerned in hastening translocation, she studied the effect of killing the tissue but found that the distance lithium moved in a given time, instead of being decreased, was increased about a third when the tissues were killed by boiling. This increased movement was probably due in part to decreased resistance to diffusion in dead tissues and in part, as demonstrated by the experiments of Steward (1930), to driving out gases from the intercellular spaces and thus increasing the area for diffusion. Since it had been suggested by Pfeffer (1900, Vol. 1, p. 589) that the bending movements of stems might aid in translocation, she studied the effects of bending and twisting and otherwise manipulating strips of phloem from *Cornus alba* and *Liguster amurense*. The treatments, however, had no tendency to hasten movement. Further attempts were made to increase the movement by causing evaporation from the exposed ends of the strips of phloem or parenchyma, the lower ends of which were dipping into the salt solution, but here also there was no increase in rate of movement over that in completely turgid tissues which were kept well moistened.

Experiments were also tried in which the phloem was separated from the xylem for a distance of from 6 to 25 cm. but with one or both ends left attached to the xylem. "Plastilina" was placed between the xylem and the separated phloem tissue so that cross transfer could not take place. The phloem thus isolated was kept from drying by encasing the entire stem in glass cylinders with moist filter paper. Both cut branches and rooted plants were used, but in all instances the lithium solution was introduced through the cut end of the stem or a cut side branch. Leaves were present both above and below the region where the phloem was separated from the xylem. Though within from three quarters of an hour to an hour, lithium had moved through the xylem to the farthest tips of the plant and quickly passed over into the phloem from the xylem, the longitudinal movement through the phloem, where it was separated from the xylem, was extremely slow. After from 20 to 26 hr. the lithium had spread longitudinally through the phloem either from above or below a distance of only 1.5 to 5.0 cm. In one instance it seemed to have moved 15 cm., but this she considered an exception and marked it with a question mark. In comparable experiments with several twigs in which the phloem was connected at one end only, the lithium was found to have moved through the phloem for distances of only 2.0 to 3.8 cm. in 40 to 50 hr. In rooted plants of *Cornus alba* and *Prunus padus*, in which lithium nitrate was introduced through a small side twig which was cut off, or through a cut petiole, it was found that, though lithium had penetrated throughout the transpiring shoots within a few hours where the phloem had not been separated from the wood, it had, even after 3 days, moved a distance of only 3 to 4 cm. into the phloem where this was separated from the xylem.

Other attempts were made to force solution through the phloem tissues by dipping strips of phloem attached to the base of leafy shoots into solutions of lithium nitrate, but in from 25 to 30 hr. the lithium had moved a distance of only 2 to 3 cm. There was little difference in movement between those from which there was rapid transpiration and those with slow transpiration, in fact the latter showed slightly greater movement. When pieces of xylem were cut out and the exposed phloem was protected from drying by enclosing in a glass tube closed with "plastilina," lithium did not pass the operated region if the length of xylem removed exceeded about 2 cm. With 2 cm. of xylem removed some diffused through the phloem and was carried above for 8 to 15 cm. after 20 to 32 hr. The leaves in these cases became wilted. The movement here seemed, however, to take place through the xylem for in other experiments in which crystals of the salt or a strong lithium nitrate solution (1 M) were not introduced into cut xylem but were placed on a leaf or on the cortex of the stem, from which the epidermis and periderm were removed, the inward moving lithium traveled only 1 to 2 cm. if transpiration was prevented but extended 10 to 40 cm. when transpiration was not prevented.

Experiments were also carried out to determine the ability of phloem tissues to absorb water and solutions. These showed that the amount of water absorbed through the phloem was only one two-thousandths to one one-thousandth that absorbed through the xylem.

All of these experiments led her to conclude that translocation through the phloem is extremely slow, whereas movement through the xylem tissues is immensely more rapid. That water and solutions can be rapidly carried not only upward through the xylem but also backward through these same water conducting tissues has been recognized for a long time and was reported by Hales (1727), Strasburger (1891, pp. 582 and 936), and others. That this backward movement may be considerable was clearly indicated in the experiments of Yendo (1917). Birch-Hirschfeld, however, seems to have been the first among modern botanists* to suggest that there may be a normal backward flow through the xylem and that it may account in part at least for the backward translocation of dissolved materials.

To test the frequency, extent, and speed of the backward movement and the factors influencing it, she carried out various experiments using principally lithium nitrate which was introduced through cut side twigs, or even in a few instances through uncut tissues, by dipping leaves into lithium solutions, or placing drops of strong solutions on the surfaces of leaves with thin cuticle, or by placing small crystals of the salt between the bark and the wood.

The experiments were carried out under a variety of conditions. In some the leaves were present both below and above the point of introduction. In these, even when cut branches were used and the base immersed in water, the lithium reaction was apparent in 2½ to 8 hr. at a distance of 10 to 16 cm. below the point of introduction, and chiefly on the side where the solution was introduced through a cut side twig. For this experiment a rather strong solution $(0.5M)$ was supplied. In one experiment with two leafy shoots of *Liguster amurense*, drops of $0.75M$ lithium nitrate solution were placed on the surface of a leaf near the middle of a side twig. The cut shoots were standing in water, one free in a room and the other in a moist chamber. For the twig in the moist chamber in which the side twig was 8 cm. long, the lithium reaction

---

* At the time of Hales and other early investigators there was speculation concerning the flow and ebb of sap through the wood.

was evident after 8 hr. at a distance of 13 cm. above the side twig and 15 cm. below it.   In the same time the shoot free in the room whose side twig was 11 cm. long showed lithium had moved up into the tip of the main shoot and backward a distance of 8 cm.   A similar backward spread took place when solutions were injected through cuts into the stems of rooted plants.   If transpiration was vigorous, the spread was at times more extensive in these rooted plants.

If leaves were absent below the point of injection, the backward movement of lithium was very slight, only a centimeter or two in 20 hr. if the base of the cut twig stood in water, but if it did not dip in water, lithium was found to have moved backward to the cut surface, a distance of 15 to 27 cm. in 20 hr.

Many experiments were described in detail in which the backward spread of lithium nitrate and eosin solutions were studied in relation to the effects of factors influencing the rate and extent of the backward flow, the extent of tangential spread, the relation of movement to method of introduction, etc.

In order to determine whether the phloem tissues were adequate in carrying foods, she compared the observed rates of movement of lithium and eosin through phloem tissues with the probable rates at which products of assimilation must be carried from the leaves.   Assuming that carbohydrate is manufactured by photosynthesis at the rate of 0.5 g. per square meter per hour for 10 hr. during the day, and that the whole of this is transported within 24 hr. she estimated that carbohydrate might be expected to be removed from the leaf at the rate of 0.28 g. per hour (actually this figure should have been 0.208, but this mistake is not important for she might as well have assumed a higher rate of photosynthesis).   The area of a bean leaf was determined as was also the area of the cross section of a petiole and that of the sieve tubes of the petiole. Using the above figures, she calculated that, from the particular leaf in question, carbohydrates would be removed at the rate of 0.003 g. per hour, or a movement of 0.0007 g. per hour per square millimeter of cross section of entire petiole, 0.0008 g. per square millimeter of cross section of the vessels, or 0.006 g. per square millimeter of cross section of sieve tube. She calculated the rate at which lithium moved into parenchyma or phloem tissues from a 1 per cent solution and found after 20 hr. that this was only about 0.000005 g. per square millimeter per hour, or only about one-hundred-sixtieth as fast as the sugars actually seem to move, assuming the movement through the entire living part of the petiole, or only one-thousandth as fast as it should move if the movement is restricted to movement through the sieve tubes. She points out that sugars could hardly be expected to diffuse even as rapidly or penetrate the cells as easily as lithium nitrate, therefore it seems impossible that these phloem tissues could carry solutes fast enough. Measurements of water movement through phloem tissues also showed extremely low rates and if solutions as strong as 10 to 20 per cent sugar, or even if sugar moved as fast as water alone, gram for gram, the mass movement of sugar would be too slow by more than a hundred times.

All the experiments on the transfer of introduced dyes or salts indicated without exception that the transfer of these solutes through the phloem or other living tissues is extremely slow, whereas the transfer through the xylem vessels is immensely more rapid and very easily demonstrated. Rapid transfer of solutions within the xylem tissues takes place readily not only from the base toward the transpiring leaves, but a backward flow is also easily demonstrated if solutions are introduced through cut side branches or incisions. (See also Yendo, 1917; Rumbold, 1920; and others who observed flow in both directions.) Such a backward movement occurs even when leaves are entirely absent below the point of injection. Since injected dyes move vertically through the xylem and transverse movement is very slight, as pointed out by Strasburger and as shown by her own experiments, it seemed to Birch-

Hirschfeld that solutions may be moving up through certain channels of the xylem and down through adjacent ones, and she suggested that backward movement of solutions might thus carry sugar from the leaves. The fact that injected dyes were carried back in transpiring shoots, even when the plant was well supplied with water, seemed to favor this interpretation. She suggests that under natural conditions the wetting of the leaves with dew or rain might allow for an extensive backward flow, or that unequal insolation of neighboring parts might also bring about considerable back flow.

Though Madam Birch-Hirschfeld's experiments led her to doubt the effectiveness of the phloem or other living cells in the transport of solutes, and though she definitely suggested the possibility and gave experimental evidence supporting the hypothesis of a backward flow through the xylem, still she felt that the problem was far from settled and suggested that living cells might transport the normally moving substances in a manner different from that in which lithium nitrate is transported.

16. Findings and Interpretations of Dixon and His Co-workers.—Dixon, in 1922, and Dixon and Ball (1922) more boldly supported the hypothesis that the xylem is the channel through which most of the backward movement of solutes takes place. All evidence based on ringing experiments is summarily dismissed on the grounds that ringing always results in some sort of plugging of the xylem. The strongest plea against a consideration of the phloem as a channel for backward transfer is that the phloem must be inadequate for carrying the amount that is carried, because the narrowness of the tubes, their high colloid content, and frequent cross walls seem to preclude the possibility of rapid transfer through them. In order to estimate the probable rate of normal transfer, Dixon selected a potato tuber weighing 210 g. connected by a stolon with a diameter of 0.16 cm., in which the "bast" had a maximum cross-sectional area of 0.0042 sq. cm. The tuber contained at least 50 g. of organic matter and this must have been transported through the stolon in less than 100 days. Assuming that the solution moving through the phloem had a concentration of 10 per cent sugar, the volume moving into the tuber must have been 500 cc. to carry the 50 g. of sugar. Therefore the rate of flow must have been at an average of about 50 cm. per hour if the entire cross-sectional area were available for transfer or twice this amount if allowance is made for a returning stream. This, however, seems impossible because one can hardly conceive of this amount of solution being forced through the narrow sieve tubes with their frequent cross walls and high colloid content. Dixon assumed a solution of 10 per cent but says this is excessive because the sap bleeding from cut stems seems never to reach 4 per cent (see also Dixon 1924). As high as 8 per cent has been reported in the sap from the maple by Jones *et al.* (1903), and, of course, one is not justified in assuming that the solution bleeding from the xylem has the same concentration as that in the sieve tubes. The figures assumed for the amount of organic matter transported and the time allowed for transportation, as well as the assumed concentrations are sufficiently liberal, however, to indicate that minor corrections could not appreciably change the conclusion.

Dixon (1922) claims to have been the first to have made such calculations on the rates of transport and this point is again mentioned by Mason and Maskell (1928a), but Dixon evidently failed to read all of Birch-Hirschfeld's paper, even though he cites her experimental evidence as strongly supporting his hypothesis, for she made very similar calculations based on the relation between the amount of photosynthate made in a given leaf area and the cross-sectional area of the phloem of the petiole through which such carbohydrate must be transported.

Dixon also estimates the probable amount of daily removal of photosynthate from the leaf of *Tropaeolum majus* making calculations very similar to those of Birch-Hirschfeld, and concludes that if two-thirds of the photo-

synthate made within a leaf during the day is moved from
the leaf each 24 hr., a 10 per cent solution would have to
move at the rate of 140 cm. per hour if restricted to a tube
the size of the cross-sectional area of the phloem.   (He made
an error in his calculations so that the figure should be 14 cm.
not 140 cm., but even this lower figure seems impossible.)

Still more accurate calculations were made by Mason
and Lewin (1926). They made accurate determinations
of the rate of increase in dry weight of the greater yam
and found that between the thirty-first and thirty-fifth
weeks the average weekly increase of dry weight of tuber
per stem was over 45 g.   Since 95 per cent of the material
was combustible, 42.7 g. of organic material must have
been transported each week through the stem.   The
average total cross-sectional area of sieve tubes and vessels
per stem was 0.05747 ± 0.0019 sq. cm.   Of this the sieve
tubes occupied less than 20 per cent, or 0.0115 sq. cm.
Then making the very liberal assumption that a 25 per cent
sugar solution was being carried through the sieve tubes,
this would have to move at an average velocity of 88 cm.
per hour in order to carry the solutes at the rate they were
carried.   A movement at this rate seems of course impossible.   The writers are not justified, however, in assuming
that translocation is limited to sieve tubes only, for it is
possible that all of the elongated living cells when in continuous series act as conducting cells.   It is possible that
by sieve tubes they mean entire phloem.   In some plants
the phloem consists largely of sieve tubes with companion
cells, whereas in other plants the proportion of sieve tubes
is very low.   What the condition is in the yam used by
Mason and Lewin I do not know, and they give no indication as to how much of the phloem consists of sieve tubes.
Yet even if the entire cross section of the living part of the
stem is assumed to carry sugar, it seems difficult to see
how materials are carried so rapidly (see Sec. 34 for other
calculations of rates).

The seeming inadequacy of the phloem as a conducting
tissue and the ease and rapidity with which solutions can

be forced through the xylem led Dixon and his co-workers to conclude that Birch-Hirschfeld's suggestion of backward flow through the xylem was more satisfactory than the commonly accepted one that the phloem is the channel of backward movement.

Dixon and Ball (1922) give additional experimental evidence that the xylem may carry solutes backward. They carefully dug a large potato plant, and before any wilting became visible cut off the apex of a leaf under an eosin solution. Within an hour the veins of all leaves as well as the stems and roots were stained, while the tuber also, when sectioned the next day, showed staining. The dye was carried exclusively through the vessels of the xylem. The following quotation from Dixon (1922) gives added evidence for a possible backward flow.

Another very striking experiment may be carried out with the imparipinnate leaf of *Sambucus nigra.* Its petiole is split longitudinally for a few centimeters and half removed. The remaining half is set in a solution of eosin. The solution is rapidly drawn up the wood capillaries of the intact half-petiole and soon appears in the veins of the pinnae on the same side of the leaf, beginning with the lowest, and gradually working up into the upper ones. Finally it appears in the terminal pinna. All this while the veins of the pinnae on the other side remain uncoloured. Now, however, the eosin begins to debouch into the base of the uppermost of these pinnae and spreads through its veins; finally it makes its way down the offside of the rachis to the bases of the lower pinnae, and from thence spreads into their veins. In this case we see very clearly how transpiration actuates an upward current on one side and a downward current on the other. It is interesting to note that if the terminal pinna and its stalk are removed, the eosin does not appear in the pinna of the second side, or only after a considerable time when the small anastomosing conducting tracts are utilised.

For evidence that normally occurring solutes may be carried backward in uncut stems, Dixon appeals to the backward conduction of a stimulus, such as that in *Mimosa* causing the folding of pinnules. Evidence has been given that the transference of the stimulus is due to the transport of something of the nature of a hormone which is carried in the transpiration stream. That this substance is carried in the transpiration stream is indicated by the fact that it moves most rapidly toward those leaves that transpire most rapidly, and that it can pass a ringed or dead part of the stem or even through a connecting tube or through a block of gelatin. The fact that the stimulus may be carried in a basal direction is cited as proof that the water current also is often carried backward. Snow (1924, 1925), however, has given evidence that the response to a stimulus is not always due to the transport of a dissolved substance and it is possible that the backward transfer is transmissive and is not due to the movement of a substance. Even if the transfer of a stimulus were demonstrated to be due invariably to the movement of something in the transpiration stream, this is not satisfactory evidence that normal solutes, sugars, proteins, and salts from the soil solution are carried in the transpiration stream either upward or downward. Furthermore, Dixon claims that ringing or killing the stem does not interfere with the transport of this hormone, whereas there is abundant evidence that ringing or killing does most decidedly interfere with the movement of these normal solutes.

For conditions that may be considered normally to bring about a backward flow through the vessels, he mentioned the same ones that Birch-Hirschfeld suggested, that is, rain, dew, and unequal insolation.* He also suggested that the changes in volume that have been observed in leaves might account for a backward flow. So far as I am aware, however, such contractions in volume as he calls upon to account for backward flow occur only when water loss exceeds absorption, and under such conditions water would tend to be drawn from the vessels not pumped back into them, unless one considered the water as drawn back by other competing leaves, but even in that case any solution thus drawn back would tend to be carried to the other leaves and not toward the trunk or roots away from the transpiring top.

* The same causes were suggested by Hales, in 1727, to account for the ebb of sap through the wood.

Fischer (1888), Atkins (1916), and Dixon and Atkins (1915, 1916) have observed sugars to be present in the vessels of woody plants not only in the spring, as have a large number of other investigators, but also in midsummer. Fischer did not, however, find any sugar in the herbaceous stems he tested nor even in woody shrubs. Fischer's conclusions were based on the reduction of Fehling's solution when pieces of woody stem were heated directly in it. Linsbauer (1920) has questioned Fischer's interpretation and gives evidence to show that the reduction of Fehling's solution was due not to sugar but to nonsoluble constituents of the cell wall. Atkins and Dixon by centrifuging pieces of woody stem supposedly threw out sap normally present in the vessels which, in their experiments, contained anywhere from little or no traces of sugar up to solutions of 0.5 to 1 per cent sugar. In later experiments, however (Dixon and Ball, 1923), sap contained in the vessels was forced out by placing the leafy branch under high air pressure, and this sap contained no traces of sugar unless the tissues were first killed or made permeable by toluene vapor. Therefore he postulated that there must be some mechanism regulating changes in permeability so as to synchronize increases in permeability of cells neighboring vessels with a time when water is flowing backward through the vessels.

17. Findings and Interpretations of Kastens.—Emma Kastens (1924) has accepted Birch-Hirschfeld's and Dixon's hypothesis and considers that solutes move in both directions chiefly through the xylem. She offers an ingenious explanation of the effects of ringing which, though they probably will not receive wide acceptance, are at least worth mentioning for some of the ideas expressed are hinted at by others though less definitely stated. Haberlandt had suggested that in the potato the phloem produces hormones which are essential for regeneration. Kastens, however, suggests that instead of producing the hormones the phloem merely carries hormones of various types especially "cell-division hormones" and "metabolism hormones." For example, the accumulation of food above a ring, she suggested, is due not to a check in backward movement of food through the phloem but to wound tissue development, callus formation, or root formation which cause food to accumulate in that region. The explanation is therefore the reverse of that normally given. Furthermore, the low content of food below the ring is suggested as due to the failure of these tissues to grow, not that the failure to grow is due to lack of food. The normal distribution of "cell-division hormones" and the "metabolism hormones" is upset by cutting the phloem which carries them, and the abnormal distribution of foods is a result of this change in hormone distribution. The blocking of the xylem she also considered as partly responsible for the failure of food to move down past a ring. Experiments of her own and those of Hanstein with plants having internal phloem, she considers as proof of this interpretation. For example, if the outer phloem of a potato stem is cut and the upper part of the shoot is darkened, the shoot continues to grow above the ring, or regeneration of buds occurs in this darkened part if the buds are removed. Since it seemed to her that the amount of internal phloem left could not carry sufficient food, this must have been carried by the xylem while the necessary hormones are carried in the phloem. If "cell-division hormones" are produced by dividing cells and are carried to new regions through the phloem, it is difficult to see why, if the growing tips are not removed, growth does not continue in ringed defoliated shoots where there is no internal phloem. Perhaps in this case she would suggest that "metabolism hormones" are necessary and that these are produced only in leaves exposed to light. If this latter is the case, the term "metabolism hormones" is merely substituted for Hanstein's "newly assimilated sap" and for which I would substitute carbohydrate. It is interesting that Dixon calls upon hormones carried exclusively in the xylem to support his hypothesis whereas Kastens appeals to hormones carried exclusively in the phloem to support the same hypothesis.

18. Findings and Interpretations of MacDougal and of Arndt.—MacDougal (1925), though not so positive in his acceptance of the hypothesis that the xylem is concerned in backward transfer of solutes, nevertheless seems to think it a feasible hypothesis and offers data which, to him, tend to give it support. By anatomical studies and the injection of dye solutions he is led to the conclusion that in conifers water with contained solutes rises in the inner layers of the wood and that the backward transfer of solution from the leaves takes place through the outer layer. Though he specifically states that the transpiration stream does not rise in the outer layer of wood and bases his conclusions on movements of dyes in cut and injected stems, his own data seem not to bear out his conclusion. In a few instances (pp. 13 to 17, 22 to 23) he found the dye to move upward (in cut stems) somewhat farther in the inner than in the outer layers, but in several other instances (pp. 17, 18, 19, 24, and 31) he found movement to a greater height in the outermost layer.

In introducing dyes through holes or slits to determine the direction of movement, he sometimes found greater upward than downward movement in the outer layer. For example, in an experiment with a Monterey pine (p. 31) the dye moved up 10 cm. in the outer layer and down only 4 cm. Again (p. 15) he found the greatest downward movement not in the outer layer but in the internal layers.

Different quantities of sugars found in the different layers were cited as evidence that these may be moving down in the outer layer. For example, in July (p. 27) the outer layer of wood in the Monterey pine was found to contain sugar to the extent of 0.204 per cent of the dry weight, whereas the next inner layer contained only 0.007 per cent. By September, however, the second layer had nearly as much as the outer (p. 31). When the layers were separated at this time, the outer had 0.146 per cent sugar and the next inner layer 0.128 per cent. The two layers were said to have 0.05 per cent sugar, but this must be a misprint.

To obtain the sap for analysis the layer of wood was cut into thin shavings and extracted, but no mention is made of the method of extraction. Presumably the tissues were killed in this extraction, so sugars from the living cells were included. Only reducing sugars were determined. In a later paper (1926, p. 79) he reported other analyses of sap which in these cases was evidently obtained by suction from the various layers of the wood. On June 24 the sap from the outer layer of wood contained 0.027 per cent sugar, while that from the second and third layers contained 0.016 per cent. Another section of the same trunk examined two days later yielded a sap of 0.02 per cent sugar in the outer layer, and 0.005 per cent from the second layer, 0.007 per cent from the third, and 0.006 per cent from the fourth. On July 2, a sample from the outermost layer of a small tree showed 0.0049 per cent sugar. On July 13 and 14, samples from the outer layer of a small tree showed a concentration of only 0.017 per cent sugar, while those from the second and third layers contained 0.028 per cent to 0.030 per cent, respectively. He explains the low concentration of the outer layer in this instance as due to the fact that this was the outer layer of recently formed internodes in which dyes move up more readily than in inner layers. Five days after this, the tree was cut and extractions were taken from the outer layer of the lower part of the trunk. The outer layer in this case contained 0.014 per cent sugar and the inner layers had 0.012 per cent. In mid-August a sample from the second and third layer of a small trunk showed 0.14 per cent sugar and one taken from a similar trunk on Oct. 24 contained 0.02 per cent sugar. Though the sugar contents were usually somewhat higher in the outer layers than in the inner layers of wood, there were striking exceptions. The differences were not great and the concentrations showed such great fluctuations that it is difficult to see how this can be considered as evidence for downward transfer in the outer layers. The actual concentrations found were extremely low, in all but one instance less than 0.03 per cent, so that a backward flow much in excess of that found would be necessary to carry the necessary amounts of sugar. Even if the sap obtained from the outer layers invariably contained more sugar than the inner layers, this would not offer very strong support for the hypothesis of downward transfer through these tissues. One might expect a higher concentration in vessels which have recently matured, which are closer to active cambium cells containing a high sugar content, and which are also closer than the inner tissues to the sugar-conducting cells of the phloem. MacDougal does not explain how he collects the sap from the separate layers by suction. Presumably the layers are blocked off at the point where suction is applied. Even though suction is applied on the cut end of a given layer, the possibility remains that within the tissues there may be flow from one layer to another. That such flow may occur is indicated by his own observations, as well as those of others, that introduced dyes may pass from one layer to another and even back again.

Though he is not positive as to the tissues concerned in downward movement of foods and states that the prevalent view that foods move down through the phloem is based on very imperfect evidence, he has no hesitation in saying, "Positive identifications of the route of upwardly moving solution is much more easily obtained." Apparently he takes no stock in the evidence that I have published, but it is rather disappointing that he offers no explanations of the data obtained. Dixon (1924, p. 54) is equally positive in his statement: "Taking all the evidence into account we may conclude with certainty that the rising water current conveys upward not only dissolved inorganic substances but that it is of importance in transferring organic substances also from the lower parts of the plant to its upper extremities." He also disappoints one in that the only answer he gives to the extensive data on ringing experiments is that ringing may result in plugging of the xylem vessels. It would be interesting to know how he would explain continued transfer when the xylem is completely removed (Curtis, 1925). Furthermore, as is explained in Sec. 25, ringing is not necessarily followed by plugging and yet solute translocation is seriously interfered with. Dixon and some of those supporting his hypothesis claim the ringing interferes with upward translocation because it results in plugging the outer layers of the xylem, but according to MacDougal's suggestions the upward translocation, in the pine at least, is chiefly in the inner layers and little or none occurs in the outer layers which are supposed to be concerned largely in downward movement.

Arndt (1929), on observing the movement of eosin solutions introduced into cut stems or roots of the coffee tree, concluded that solutions move both downwards and upwards through the xylem vessels and that the downward movement would be adequate for transporting foods. He found that the presence of leaves was not necessary for such movements, for they occurred even after he had supposedly eliminated influences of negative gas pressure, capillarity and saturation deficits of the xylem. He found greatest movement—and this occurred simultaneously in both directions—in the outer layer of wood and suggests that this layer may be "composed of closely associated conduits which are hydrostatically isolated from each other" and that "a more complicated vascular mechanism exists in plants than has usually been postulated." In common with many other investigators Arndt seems to fail to recognize that movement in conduits after they are cut open may have no bearing on normal water or solute movements.

19. Comments on Evidence Supposed to Prove Backward Flow through the Xylem.—The hypothesis that the xylem is the principal channel for the backward transport of solutes seems to have been proposed because injected solutions failed to be carried through the phloem in appreciable quantities, and because the narrowness of the phloem tubes together with their high content of seemingly viscous, colloidal material, and the frequency of their cross walls seemed to preclude the possibility of an adequate transport through the phloem. The xylem tubes, on the other hand, are large, have relatively infrequent cross walls, a content of low viscosity, and injected solutions are easily and rapidly carried in either direction or can be readily forced through the tissue in either direction. The seemingly frequent presence of sugars occurring naturally in these xylem tubes also tends to favor this hypothesis.

The evidence discussed in Chap. II, however, especially that which demonstrates that translocation takes place when the xylem is completely removed, seems to show conclusively that the phloem can and does carry solutes at a rate at which they seem normally to be carried. In the light of this evidence, therefore, negative evidence, such as the seeming inability to force solutions through the phloem, or that it is difficult to conceive of a highly efficient mechanism, is not very convincing.

Though it is possible that occasionally there may be a small amount of backward flow of water through the xylem, it seems probable that the frequency and extent of such movement are normally much less than those indicated by injection experiments. As is discussed in more detail in Sec. 20, the backward flow of an injected solution could be expected to occur whenever a conducting system under tension or reduced pressure is opened and solutions at higher pressure are introduced. That backward flow is frequent or normal has not been demonstrated. Even if backward flow were as frequent and extensive as might be assumed to be indicated by injection experiments, the commonly low sugar content, or almost complete lack of sugar found in the water-conducting tubes of the xylem at the season when extensive backward translocation must be taking place, reduces the likelihood of appreciable amounts of sugar being carried through this channel.

Even if backward flow were frequent and extensive, and even though there is considerable resistance to transverse flow of water through the xylem, there is no indication of a mechanism that would bring a backward flow through certain of the channels while water is being lost from the leaves and absorbed from the roots. Even if such a mechanism exists and were demonstrated, it would have to be so coordinated with permeability or other changes that sugars would be secreted only into the downward moving streams and these would have to flow continuously or, if some accident should start the stream running in the wrong direction, some regulatory system would have to come into action immediately to unload the sugars from the reversed stream. With such a system one would be almost forced to call upon hormones or something even more subtle than these to aid in the regulation (see Sec. 17).

As stated in the preface, it is possible that many of the advocates of this hypothesis no longer favor it, yet in view of the fact that many investigators, including Dixon, MacDougal, Mason and Lewin, and Arndt, advocated it even after the publication of my paper which demonstrated continued transport after the complete severance of the xylem, and in view of the fact that evidence of the sort used to support this hypothesis is still used to support the contention that the xylem is the channel chiefly concerned in upward transport, it has seemed advisable to discuss this evidence in the detail here presented.

SUMMARY

15. Attempts of many sorts were made by Birch-Hirschfeld to bring about a rapid movement of lithium nitrate or eosin through phloem and parenchyma tissues. The materials were introduced through incisions of various sorts or by applying strong solutions or crystals to the surface, and attempts to bring about movement involved physical manipulation and high rates of transpiration. These materials, however, could be caused to move through phloem or parenchyma at only very slow rates, rarely over 5 cm. in 24 hr. The movement in killed tissues was slightly faster than in living tissues. The cross-sectional area of the sieve tubes of the petiole of a bean leaf was measured, and, assuming a moderate rate of photosynthesis, calculations as to rates at which pure sugar or sugar solutions must move to empty the leaf in 24 hr. gave figures over a hundred to several thousand times the rates at which she was able to force water through the phloem. On the other hand, when lithium salts or eosin were introduced into the xylem, they were quickly carried throughout the plant, not only toward the transpiring leaves but also backward to leafless parts. Since the phloem seems incapable of carrying solutes at the necessary rates, whereas the xylem carries introduced solutions with great rapidity in both directions, she suggested that it is possible that the xylem is the normal path of backward transport.

16. Dixon and his associates summarily dismiss all evidence based on ringing experiments on the grounds that ringing always results in plugging of the xylem. Calculations are presented showing the rates at which sugar solutions must move if the transport of sugar from photosynthesis is restricted to the phloem of leaf petioles, or that moving to the storage tuber of potato or yam is carried through the phloem. These calculations indicate, for example, that if restricted to flow through the sieve tubes, a 25 per cent solution of sugar must move at a rate of 88 cm. an hour to carry the requisite amount of sugar to the storage tuber of the yam. Since such rates of movement appear impossible, because of the narrowness of the sieve tubes, their frequent cross walls, and their content of colloidal material, it is definitely proposed that solutions must move back through the xylem where solutions flow easily. This suggestion is supported by observations of rapid backward flow of colored solutions throughout an entire potato plant, roots, tubers, and tops, when the dye is introduced through a cut leaf. To support the suggestion that a backward transport through the xylem is normal, the evidence of backward transport of a hormone causing movements in pinnae of *Mimosa* is cited. The finding of sugar in the sap obtained by centrifuging pieces of stem is cited as proof of sugar being normally present in the transpiration stream during midsummer.

17. Kastens considers that foods are carried in both directions through the xylem and not the phloem, and that the disturbed growth responses following ringing are to be explained on the grounds that special hormones controlling behavior are transported through the phloem. The change in food distribution above and below rings, therefore, is partly due to the influence of the hormones on growth and that growth in turn controls food distribution, and partly to the effect of the ring in plugging the xylem through which the foods move.

18. MacDougal, as a result of anatomical and injection studies, concludes that in conifers water with its contained solutes rises in the inner layers of the wood, and that possibly sugars are carried downward in the outermost layers of wood, which are not directly connected anatomically with the leaves. Injection experiments are claimed to indicate a greater downward flow through the outer layers of wood. These same layers also were often found to have a higher sugar content than the inner layers. This, it is suggested may indicate that sugars are being carried down through these outer layers. Arndt, as a result of injection experiments with the coffee tree, found rapid movement of eosin both upward and downward through the outer xylem layers, even when all effects due to unequal gas pressure, capillarity, and saturation deficits were supposedly eliminated. This led him to suggest that the xylem is normally concerned in transport in both directions, but that the mechanism involved is unknown.

19. The principal reason why it has been proposed that the xylem is chiefly concerned in backward movement is that it has not been possible to force solutions through the phloem in appreciable quantities and because the narrowness of the sieve tubes, their frequent cross walls, and their high content of viscous material seem to preclude the possibility of movement through them at adequate rates. On the other hand, solutions can be easily caused to flow with great rapidity in either direction through the xylem. These tissues have also apparently been found to contain appreciable quantities of sugar. Although the phloem seems inadequate as a path for transport of appreciable amounts of sugar, evidence cited in Chap. II, where it was conclusively demonstrated that it can carry materials at adequate rates, even though the mechanism may not be understood, removes the major objection to transport through the phloem. Although it has been claimed that sugar is present in xylem vessels during midsummer, this claim is not well substantiated. There is no evidence that solutions or water normally move backward through the xylem, and even if such flow should occur, no mechanism has been proposed whereby the backward flowing solution can be directed to the tissues using the foods.

CHAPTER V

A COMPARISON OF CRITERIA AND METHODS USED TO DETERMINE THE TISSUES OF TRANSPORT

Different investigators have arrived at very divergent conclusions concerning the tissues concerned in solute translocation. This divergence and contradiction seem to be due very largely to the criteria and the methods depended upon to determine the channels of transport. For example, from a comparison of the results obtained from many experiments it is obvious that, when colored solutions or solutions of almost any sort of substance are introduced into cut stems or injected into various tissues, these solutions are carried rapidly, extensively, and almost exclusively in the xylem tissues and it is also obvious that transpiration, directly or indirectly, determines both the direction and the rate of movement of the solutions introduced. On the other hand, if the channel for the movement of naturally occurring solutes, those manufactured by the leaves or absorbed by intact and uninjured roots, is sought for, not by artificially introducing materials but by cutting or blocking first one possible channel for transport and then another, it is found that these naturally occurring solutes seem unable to move in normal quantities either apically or basally through the water-conducting tissues of the xylem, whereas they seem capable of being carried in approximately normal quantities and at normal rates through the phloem tissues. A critical consideration of these criteria and methods, therefore, seems desirable.

20. The Movement of Solutes Introduced through Cut Tissues.—Studies of solute movement based upon observations of the movements of solutions artificially introduced into possible conducting tissues are open to serious criticism. Thus for the xylem it is practically certain that the pressures or tensions in the water and air columns will be altered as a result of the cutting incident to injection. For example, where a column of water may have actually been moving upward under reduced pressure or under tension, the opening of the column accompanied by the introduction of a solution at a different pressure may result in an actual reversal of the flow over part at least of the system. On the other hand, the injected solution may flow into a channel in which there was originally only gas at reduced pressure. An interpretation based on the movement of the introduced solution may therefore be completely erroneous. The reversals observed by Birch-Hirschfeld (1920), Dixon and Ball (1922) and others and the erratic behavior of injected solutions reported by MacDougal (1926) can probably be explained as resulting from cutting into such a closed system with different parts at varying pressures or showing varying resistances to flow.

I am not convinced that the conclusions arrived at by MacDougal, Overton, and Smith (1929) are based on indisputable evidence, that is, that specific regions of annual rings of woody plants are concerned in water transport and others are normally filled with gases. The seasonal fluctuations in gas and water contents also, as reported by these investigators (pp. 50 to 52) as well as by many others previously, may not really exist or may be greatly exaggerated because of the method of investigation. If, during a season of high transpiration or deficient water, one carefully exposes the wood without cutting into it, the presence of water in the conducting vessels is made evident by the somewhat translucent appearance which is almost instantaneously lost when the vessels are cut across.* The abrupt change in appearance is obviously due to the displacement of water by air or a partial vacuum when the columns under tension are ruptured. Little or no evidence is available as to the extent of this displacement. In all probability when such ruptures take place,

* This behavior was brought to my attention by Dr. Crafts.

the finer capillary tubes or those with smaller openings through pits or pit membranes will withdraw water from the coarser ones or from those with larger pit openings, thus giving the appearance that the latter has been gas-filled previous to cutting. Bailey (1916) reports observations on sizes of pores in pit membranes and calculations of pressures necessary to rupture membranes at air-water surfaces. Data on the approximate pressures at 20°C. necessary to force air through water-filled, or water through

TABLE 16.—APPROXIMATE PRESSURES NECESSARY TO FORCE AIR INTO WATER-FILLED CIRCULAR PORES, OR WATER INTO AIR-FILLED PORES OF VARYING DIAMETERS AT 20°C.

Diameter of pores, microns	Pressures, g. per sq. cm.	Atmospheres
0.5	6,000	5.80
1.0	3,000	2.90
2.0	1,500	1.45
5.0	600	0.58
10.0	300	0.29
25.0	120	0.116
50.0	60	0.058
100.0	30	0.029
200.0	15	0.0145
500.0	6	0.0058

These were calculated from the formula $p = \dfrac{2T}{r}$ where p = pressure in grams per square centimeter, T = surface tension of water which is 73.5 dynes per square centimeter or 0.7496 g. per square centimeter at 20°C., r = radius.

air-filled circular openings of various sizes are given in Table 16. These data also indicate relative powers of tubes of differing diameter to compete for water when the system is cut and exposed to air. Pores through pit membranes range from 0.5 to 5μ in diameter, and tracheids and vessels in various woody plants range from 10 to 200μ in diameter. It is obvious from these data that differences in capillary forces alone up to one or more atmospheres may be concerned in influencing the redistribution of water after cutting.

Attempts to inject solutions into the phloem may, and usually do, result in complete failure, not necessarily because materials do not normally move there but because of the nature of the cells and the probable nature of the movement in them. Because the phloem cells are so small, because of their high colloid content and high internal pressures, and because their walls are not rigid, it is practically impossible, by ordinary injection methods, to introduce a solution into the cell. An attempt to cut into the tissue is almost certain to rupture the system, and mass injection can never be expected to be successful as a means of introducing solutes into such tissues. If translocation through the sieve-tube system is brought about by protoplasmic streaming, as seems to be probable, the only methods that at present seem feasible would be to introduce some dye that is taken up by the protoplasm or other substance that can be detected in small quantities. These may be absorbed through intact cells or it may be necessary to introduce them by micro-injection. Even here there is danger of upsetting the mechanism by the introduction of a foreign substance or by the puncture of the cell, and it is improbable that materials could be thus injected in sufficient quantities to be of great aid in studying translocation. Schumacher (1933), however, has found it possible to introduce fluorescein (see Sec. 37) but the amounts carried must be small as compared with the amount of sugar carried. The injection, natural or artificial, of a virus, also, may be of use in translocation studies because of the possibility of its self-multiplication. But it would seem to be of doubtful value for testing normal movements (see Sec. 38).

Furthermore, even if a given solution could be introduced into one or the other tissue without disrupting the normal pressures or movements, and the introduced substance was found to be carried after injection, this would merely establish the fact that the material when introduced might be carried in that tissue, but it would not establish as fact that it is normally so carried.

21. The Movement of Solutes Introduced through Uncut Roots.—When eosin is added to the medium around a rooted plant, this is found to be actually carried in the xylem vessels. This would seem to indicate translocation in the xylem when the solute is not artificially introduced through cuts. Eosin, however, is toxic and it seems probable that when it comes into contact with the living cells of the root it kills them or makes them become abnormally permeable, and then, of course, with no effective semi-permeable membranes the solute would tend to be carried directly with the water. The evidence that normal salts are not absorbed with the water, as discussed in Sec. 7, would indicate that this eosin movement is abnormal. The absorption of lithium through uncut tissues might be explained in a similar way. Birch-Hirschfeld (1920), for example, found that, if a strong solution of lithium nitrate (0.75 M) was placed on the surface of a leaf, or if crystals of the salt were placed under the bark and in contact with thin-walled cells, the lithium was evidently carried in the xylem. Such strong solutions would tend to kill or at least increase the permeability of the living cells so that the tissues, though seemingly intact, are not uninjured.

That lithium or comparable solutes can be used as tests for normal solute movement may be open to serious criticism. Certainly the results obtained through its use seem to contradict those obtained by other experiments. For example, when a lithium salt is added to the soil, it seems readily to pass a ring (Curtis, 1923). This might be explained in various ways. Possibly the lithium is toxic and increases the permeability of cells and therefore is carried with the water. But the concentration used in this experiment gave no clear indication of toxicity. That lithium is fairly quickly absorbed by intact tissues from seemingly nontoxic solutions and that it is then carried rapidly through the water-conducting tissues appears to be fairly well established. Possibly certain ions are carried in greater quantity in the xylem while others are carried chiefly in the phloem. It is conceivable that different tissues might thus absorb ions differentially. Attempts are being made to determine if certain of the normally occurring elements are more readily carried in the xylem than others.

On the other hand, the lithium test has been used as a qualitative test only. If minute quantities of solutes are carried rapidly in the xylem, whereas much larger quantities are carried more slowly in the phloem, then qualitative tests might indicate greater translocation through the xylem. The quantitative data on ash as well as on nitrogen indicate that small quantities of these solutes are unquestionably carried through the xylem. Merely qualitative tests like those with lithium are therefore open to criticism and may lead to false conclusions. Furthermore, as pointed out in Sec. 14, lithium and other elements to which membranes are relatively permeable and which may not be accumulated in cells, may be more readily carried in the transpiration stream.

This criticism against using qualitative tests only would seem not to hold for experiments reported by Bodenberg (1927), for he found that, when lithium or caesium nitrates were supplied to rooted woody plants, these would not pass either upward or downward through a part of stem where the xylem was cut out. In these experiments he found no lithium or caesium to pass through the phloem bridge even in as long a period as 21 days. The suggestion that larger quantities are moving more slowly in the phloem is not supported by this evidence. In this same paper Bodenberg reports finding that cutting the phloem delayed but did not prevent the transfer of these salts, while cutting the xylem completely stopped their movement in either direction. Though he states that he enclosed the stems in glass tubes for keeping the phloem wet he does not describe the method sufficiently to give one confidence that this was not the cause of the lack of transfer. In earlier experiments (Curtis, 1925) I found that failure to keep the phloem thoroughly wet resulted in no translocation through it. It is also possible that in cutting out the xylem, the phloem also was destroyed. The one instance mentioned of regeneration of new xylem would, however, tend to refute both of these objections. In view of the objections to the use of lithium and caesium salts as discussed in this section as well as the points discussed in Sec. 14, it seems that experiments with these salts cannot give any clear idea as to the normal behavior of nutrient salts.

In a more recent paper Bodenberg (1929) has stated that the objection that lithium salts are not satisfactory for use in experiments on transfer appears to be groundless, because he found that they were not rapidly carried across woody stems of willow varying in diameter from 1 to 5 cm. However, one would hardly expect woody tissues, either alive or dead, to offer no resistance whatever to the cross transfer of salts like those of lithium, and since Bodenberg gives no data comparing the rate of transfer of the lithium ion with that of others, his data are far from convincing. Even if it were found that lithium moved across a woody cylinder less rapidly than potassium, for example, which is not unlikely, the major criticisms of its use to demonstrate translocation remain. Furthermore, Bodenberg did not even demonstrate that water moved across the stem for he had to supply the shoot with water through a wick. In the illustration he gives (Fig. 1, p. 34) he shows a willow stem 10.5 cm. long and 2.5 cm. thick. The root is on the underside of the horizontally placed stem and the shoot is on the upper side, offset 5 cm. from directly above the root. Since water would not move fast enough from the root to the shoot to keep the latter turgid, a wick was led from a separate vessel of water to the upper side next to the shoot to supply it with water. Under such conditions one would hardly expect even water to move to the shoot from the root, to say nothing of the lithium or any other dissolved substance.

22. Tests for the Deposition of Solutes Introduced through Cut or Uncut Roots.—The method of adding some substance to the soil solution and subsequently testing for its location in the plant has been occasionally used as a test to indicate the tissues taking part in translocation. This method escapes the criticism that some tissue has been cut open for the plant is, or at least may seem, intact.

The method has been recently used by Overton (1925) who found that after plants were watered with solutions of selenium or tellurium, these elements were found in abundance in the xylem, while they were almost absent from the phloem and other tissues. In the discussion that followed the talks on translocation before the British Association Meeting in Toronto, in 1922, Prof. Overton cited similar experiments with potassium salts as definitely establishing the xylem as the channel for transport. There are, however, very serious criticisms to this method. The region of deposition or accumulation of a substance may give little or no indication as to what tissues carry the material. For a time it was thought that carbohydrates were carried in the starch sheath or endodermis, for it formed a continuous chain of cells which was well filled with starch. But this notion was abandoned when Heine (1885) demonstrated by modified ringing experiments that this tissue was not concerned in transport. Bokorny (1890) thought the deposition of iron in the walls of thick-walled cells of both xylem and the sclerenchyma cells of the phloem, and its absence in other cells, proved that water and solutes were carried in the walls of these cells and not through the lumen. Scott and Priestley (1928), and Scott (1928) have more recently considered that the microchemical detection of dyes or inorganic ions in the walls is evidence that the materials move along the walls and not through other parts of the cell. The finding of deposits of iron or dyes or any other substance in a cell or on its walls may be proof that these elements had reached that point, but it does not prove that those walls or cells were the channels through or along which the material was being carried. In fact, the very accumulation in the walls or in the cells might be considered to indicate that they are not effective channels of transport, for the fixation on or in a nonmoving body would tend to interfere with further movement.

23. The Occurrence of a Substance in a Tissue as a Criterion of Its Movement through That Tissue.—The complete absence of a substance from a possible conducting channel is obviously conclusive proof that that substance is not at the time being carried through that tissue. On the other hand, the presence of a substance in a possible conducting channel, though it is often cited as proof of its transport, is not conclusive proof that it is being carried in that channel, or that the channel concerned plays a significant part in the transport. In the first place, as mentioned in the preceding section, the presence of a substance in the walls of the supposed channel, or in a form that would be blocked at constrictions cannot be considered as good evidence for transport. In the second place, a substance, even when present in the lumen in easily transportable form, may not be transported in sufficient amounts *if at the time of its presence the vehicle or solvent is not moving or is moving at an inadequate rate.* In the third place, if the substance is present in a moving vehicle but is present in small amounts, the channel in consideration may play merely a minor or insignificant rôle in the transport.

One of the most serious obstacles to an acceptance of the hypothesis that the phloem is the chief channel for upward transport of solutes is that, in a number of plants, solutions at appreciable concentrations have been found in the xylem vessels. For example, the sugar in the vessels of certain trees, notably the sugar maple (Jones *et al.*, 1903), has during certain seasons been found at concentrations as high as 2 to 8 per cent (2,000 to 8,000 p.p.m.). Many investigators have given data on the composition of the liquid bleeding from cut stems of many woody plants. Among such reports are those of Schroeder (1871), Jones, Edson, and Morse (1903), Morcau and Vinct (1923), and many others.

Wormall (1924) and Priestley and Wormall (1925) collected about 110 liters of sap that exuded from the stumps of 12 grape vines, and, on the analysis of over 90 liters, found a total solid content of 0.156 per cent. The ash content was 0.056 per cent, the total sugar 0.0338 per cent, and the organic acid content 0.056 per cent. It was assumed by these writers that this solution was moving to the apical meristems and that the composition of the solution was indicative of the composition of the material supplying the growing point. Though these particular investigators may no longer hold to the hypothesis that an analysis of this solution will throw light on what substances are essential for maintaining growth of the shoots, it seems desirable that the point be considered somewhat further since the notion is widespread that these solutions, bleeding from stumps, are solutions naturally moving to and nourishing the growing shoots.

It should be pointed out that the time of most vigorous bleeding and highest sap composition coincides with a period when there is little or no loss of water from the tops, when there is little or no growth, and therefore at a time when there is probably little or no natural flow even of water. The concentration of bleeding sap rapidly falls at about the time of the opening of the buds. This rapid disappearance at this season has been noted by a number of investigators among them Schroeder (1871), Jones *et al.* (1903), and Moreau and Vinet (1923). It has not been clearly established, however, whether the disappearance precedes, accompanies, or follows the establishment of a moving stream through the xylem. The commonly accepted hypothesis is that the solution moves up to the developing shoots which use the sugar and other solutes in their growth, but it is not clear whether the disappearance precedes or is a result of the flow. The evidence is fairly clear, however (Curtis, 1920*b*), that the developing shoots are not dependent on food stored in the trunk, and the ringing experiments also indicate that the food is not carried longitudinally through the xylem. It would seem more likely that the food stored in the xylem is moved out radially to the phloem or cambium, and that it largely disappears from the xylem vessels before the transpiration stream is actively moving.

The available evidence points rather clearly to the suggestion that the occasional high sugar content of the xylem is less related to transport, and is more related to conditions influencing the ability of the storage cells to retain their carbohydrates. The investigators mentioned in the preceding paragraph found the xylem sap of woody plants to fluctuate inversely with the temperature, especially increasing to a marked degree at air temperature slightly below the freezing point of water. As was mentioned in Sec. 6, many investigators have found that accumulated starch and other carbohydrates tend to be changed to soluble sugars at these low temperatures. With this formation of excess sugar, possibly also associated with an increase in permeability, the cells evidently lose carbohydrates which pass into the water-conducting vessels. As the temperature rises again, starch seems to be redeposited and sugar may be reabsorbed into the living cells. The disappearance of sugar from the xylem vessels as the temperature rises may therefore be entirely unrelated to any transport through the xylem.

The finding of appreciable amounts of solutes during the limited season of bleeding is not very strong evidence of transport during the growing season when bleeding usually ceases. It is true that Fischer (1888) and Dixon and Atkins (1915 and 1916) claimed that there was sugar present in the xylem vessels in midsummer at concentrations ranging up to 1 per cent. The evidence presented, however, is far from conclusive that such amounts of sugar are actually present in the vessels carrying water. Linsbauer (1920) has demonstrated that the reduction of Fehling's solution observed by Fischer was probably not due to sugar in the cells but to a reducing effect of the cell walls. Dixon and Ball (1923), when they determined the sugar content of the sap in the vessels by forcing the sap out by high gas pressures on the leaves, were unable to find sugars present. It seems possible that the rather violent treatment of centrifuging may have extracted sap from living cells or from tissues not carrying water. Dixon and Atkins (1916) stated that the question is open as to how far the pigments and oxidases that they found in the sap obtained by centrifuging are normally present in the transpiration stream of uninjured stems, and how far they may come from cells injured by the treatment. If the pigments result from injury to the cells, it is highly probable that the sugars and other solutes also may get into the sap for the same reason, and in still greater quantities because the living cells are so rich in them.

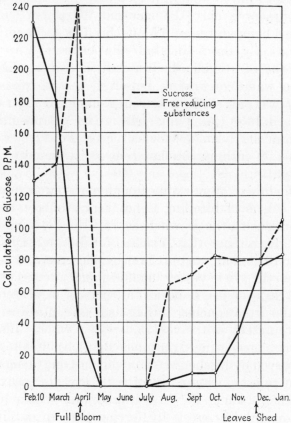

Fɪɢ. 7.—Free reducing substances and sucrose in tracheal sap from pear branches. (*From Anderssen.*)

Anderssen (1929) has determined the concentrations of various constituents of the tracheal sap which had been obtained by gas displacement from the main branches of three-year-old Bartlett pear and Royal apricot trees at various seasons during the year. As can be seen from Fig. 7 (adapted from Fig. 6 of the paper cited), the maximum total sugar content was found in February, and the concentration rapidly decreased and became so depleted shortly after blooming that its presence was not detected. Sugar was not again found in measurable amounts until August, from which time it gradually increased until leaf fall. It is noteworthy that even at the maximum the total sugar content was only 0.036 per cent (360 p.p.m.), and this was found before there could have been an actively flowing transpiration stream. It is true that he found a somewhat higher concentration in the outer layers when radial distribution was investigated, but even the maximum here observed was only 0.05 per cent (500 p.p.m.) and was found early in April before any great leaf surface or transpirational area could have been developed. From February to May, the period of maximum sugar content in the outer layers, the concentration averaged only 0.04 per cent. Anderssen's suggestion, therefore, that the starch in the inner ring, when hydrolyzed, is transferred along the medullary rays and delivered into the outer tracheae, and the implication that the xylem is an important channel for upward transport of sugar find but little support in the evidence given. Mason and Maskell (1931, p. 149; 1928a, p. 235) found that the tracheal sap obtained from the cotton stem by water displacement contained sugars at a concentration of 0.0155 to 0.0443 per cent (155 to 443 p.p.m.). This is of the same order of concentration as found by Anderssen, yet their experimental data rather conclusively demonstrate that the xylem is not an effective channel for sugar transport in the cotton plant. They also found the tracheal sap of cotton to contain 0.01216 per cent total nitrogen, 0.01164 per cent calcium, and 0.00386 per cent phosphorus.

The presence of solutes in the exudation from plants at periods when guttation is taking place is also evidence that the vessels contain materials in solution. The concentration of this exudate is approximately the same as that of the tracheal sap. Wilson (1923) found the exudate from maize seedlings to contain as high as 0.1 per cent (1030 p.p.m.) total solute, and timothy to contain from 0.022 to

0.0573 per cent (220 to 573 p.p.m.). In two out of three sets of data given, the organic matter greatly exceeded the inorganic. Enzymes, sugars, nitrates, and nitrites were identified and it seems that the concentration and composition of this exudate are similar to those obtained from bleeding vines.

The finding of inorganic constituents and nitrogen in tracheal sap seems a more serious difficulty to the accept-

TABLE 17.—INORGANIC CONSTITUENTS IN TRACHEAL SAP OF PEAR AND IN THE SOIL EXTRACT

(From Anderssen Table I)

	Soil extract, Nov. 10		Tracheal sap	
	18 in. depth, p.p.m.	36 in. depth, p.p.m.	Nov. 10, p.p.m.	May 10, p.p.m.
Ca..............	18.0	7.5	16.6	84.7
Mg..............	7.2	5.4	0.8	23.5
K...............	140.9	230.0	23.6	59.6
Fe..............	1.8	1.0	1.0	2.1
SO$_4$..............	37.2	30.0	8.3	31.8
Cl..............	14.0	9.5	3.2	4.5
PO$_4$.............	1.0	trace	10.6	25.2
Totals...........	220.1	283.4	64.1	231.4

ance of the phloem hypothesis than is that of finding sugar. This is because, relative to the probable amounts used, the inorganic content of tracheal sap seems higher than that of sugar, except possibly during the periods when the sugar contents are extremely high. Wormall (1924), for example, found about a third of the solids of the sap from bleeding grape vines to be inorganic material. Anderssen (1929), as shown in Table 17, found appreciable quantities of inorganic ions while some, in fact, were present at concentrations in excess of those found in a soil extract. In Fig. 8 is presented a curve from Anderssen showing changes with the season in conductivity of tracheal sap from pears.

From the curve it is fairly clear that the maximum conductivity of the sap is found shortly after full bloom, and
probably at the time of minimum carbohydrate content of
adjacent parenchyma. As Anderssen states, this is a time
of high respiratory activity in these tissues. It is likely,
therefore, that carbohydrate starvation at this period
makes the cells incapable of retaining their solutes which

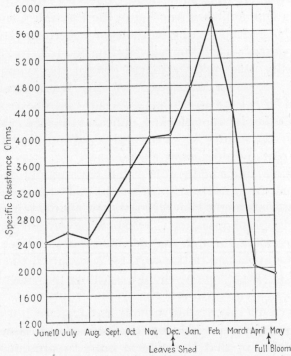

FIG. 8.—The specific resistance of tracheal sap from pear branches. (*From
Anderssen.*)

therefore leach into the xylem. Transpiration can hardly
be taking place at a very high rate at this time, so it is possible there is no great amount of transport. In fact,
Anderssen states that leaves begin to develop at or shortly
after the period of full bloom. Evidence from ringing
experiments clearly demonstrates some transport of such
solutes in the transpiration stream. This positive evidence
of the presence of solutes in the tracheae and transport

through the xylem has not demonstrated, however, that the xylem is the chief channel for transport. One can expect that any living cell will lose some of its contents to a bathing water solution, whether the latter is or is not in a conducting channel. That the transport of such leachings in the transpiration stream is normally of great consequence has not been demonstrated.

24. Evidence from Movement Observed after Cutting or Blocking One and then Another of the Possible Conducting Channels.—Although the methods of experimentation and criteria described in Chap. IV and in Secs. 20 to 23, when uncritically used, point strongly toward the xylem as the effective tissue for transport, evidence from experiments reported in Secs. 4 to 9, that is, when first one tissue and then the other is cut or blocked, indicates that the xylem does not carry the solutes under natural conditions, but that the phloem can and does carry them.

Of course, one could contend that cutting first one tissue and then the other might upset normal translocation so that materials might be forced into new channels in order to pass the point of operation. It should be obvious, however, that movement through the phloem when the xylem is cut cannot be explained in this way, for certainly if the normal channel is the xylem, it should continue movement when the phloem alone is cut and the xylem is uninjured. I have heard it frequently stated verbally and have seen it at least once in a publication (Mason, 1922) that both tissues must be necessary or that the phloem must be present to help the movement through the xylem. The continued movement when the xylem is completely removed, however, seems definitely to refute such an explanation.

Although it has been conclusively demonstrated, by experiments where the xylem has been completely severed or the phloem has been isolated from the xylem, that the phloem is capable and adequate, for carrying both inorganic and organic solutes in either direction, these same experiments do not conclusively demonstrate a simultaneous transport in both directions. Until this point is cleared up and the mechanism of transport through the phloem is clearly established, one is not justified in saying that the xylem is or is not necessary for upward transport of solutes of one sort or another.

25. Possible Injury to the Xylem When the Phloem Is Cut.—A number of botanists have hesitated to accept data obtained from ringing experiments because they have felt that ringing has had an effect other than the mere severance of a possible conducting channel. Dixon (1922, 1924), for example, lightly passes over all of the evidence based on ringing experiments on the assumption that ringing always results in some sort of plugging of the xylem. However, he depends for his evidence solely upon the observations that others have made when ring wounds were not protected. In the earliest experiments that I carried out to determine the channel of upward transfer (Curtis, 1920a) it became evident that conduction of water through the xylem was interfered with by drying or plugging near the ring if this wound were not thoroughly protected by a layer of melted paraffin wax. In all subsequent series the xylem was always protected.

When the xylem was well protected, no indication of even partial plugging was evident. Various methods have been used to test for plugging. Ringed parts have been sectioned and examined under the microscope and these showed no sign of plugging, whereas unprotected wounds showed visible plugging of the underlying xylem. After the effects of ringing on solute transfer have become evident, as measured by growth responses, carbohydrate analyses, and ash and nitrogen analyses, it was found that introduced dyes readily passed the region of the ring. After the completion of ringing experiments of this sort, the comparative rates of flow of a dye solution through ringed and check stems, when both led from the same main stems forming a Y, have been tested. The dye (acid fuchsin) was found to pass just as rapidly into and through the ringed stem as through the other. If there was any increased resistance in the ringed stem, this should have become evident, for both stems were in competition one with the other. When a defoliated shoot is isolated by a ring, its higher water content, when compared with a similar defoliated shoot not isolated by a ring, is also an indication that the xylem has not been plugged and that water has moved readily. A dye injected into the xylem below such a ring is readily carried past the ring (Curtis, 1925).

Gardner (1925) states that the xylem is unavoidably injured when a ring is made. In order to escape the injury attendant on ordinary ringing, he scraped away the cortex and applied a 7 per cent solution of potassium hydroxide, which was supposed to kill all the tissues external to and including the cambium, but no others. Though he considers this method superior to other methods of ringing, the reasons for its supposed superiority are not evident. It may be true that he found less injury than when a ring was carelessly made by a knife and left entirely unprotected, but there is certainly no necessity for causing the knife edge to penetrate the xylem at all, and a coating of warm paraffin wax would have prevented other injury. It is rather difficult to conceive of the possibility of applying strong potassium hydroxide or any other soluble material to the outside of a tissue and insure its penetration in sufficient quantities to kill the cambium without penetrating any farther. Furthermore, after the outer tissues are killed, though they may act as a partly protecting layer, they probably do not protect the xylem from loss of water as effectively as does paraffin. The fact that the cambium will become active and regenerate new tissues when the phloem and bark are removed over an area several centimeters in diameter, if it had been immediately coated with warm paraffin, is proof that loss of water has not been excessive and that the heat of the paraffin was not too great.

Swarbrick (1927) also claims that ringing inevitably injures the outer layers of xylem. The injury, however, is undoubtedly due to carelessness and can be entirely avoided. He reduced the injury from drying by covering the wound with adhesive tape, but in comparing the two I have found that the adhesive tape is less efficient than paraffin. Since it seems probable that the loss of water may be effectively checked by the tape, it may be the abnormal aeration or the presence of microorganisms in the space below the tape that makes this method of protection inferior. Drinkard and Ingham (1917) found that waxed paper or adhesive tape were fairly effective in preventing the drying out of ring wounds and in promoting their healing. Various paints, tar, and even grafting wax that was softened with linseed oil all proved injurious. Healing beneath the waxed paper was still further promoted if the ring wound was first sterilized with a saturated solution of salicylic acid or 10 per cent creolin. Other disinfectants used were less effective. The fact that healing was better when evaporation was prevented and fungus growth eliminated by disinfection, would indicate that growth of microorganisms may have injurious effects. No tests were made in which warm paraffin was directly applied to the wound. Weevers (1928) assumed that cocoa butter was better than paraffin because it could be applied at a lower temperature, but he made no experimental comparison. Since its melting point is so low, it may be preferable to paraffin in certain cases. Mason and Maskell used vaselin to protect ring wounds. Though I have made no comparative tests with ring wounds, I did find that twigs coated with vaselin were killed, while similar twigs coated with melted paraffin were uninjured (Curtis, 1918). Anderssen (1929) states that "Even though the ring of bark is removed without directly injuring the tracheae, the wounding and exposure to the air is sufficient to cause injury resulting in the clogging of such tracheae with air and gums." But he overlooks the possibility of protecting the exposed tissues and thus preventing such clogging.

Summers (1924) has made measurements of water loss from ring wounds and partly explains the effects of ringing, both in his own experiments and mine, as due to this drying. He failed to recognize, however, that as all the ring wounds were protected from such loss in the experiments I reported, the water loss was not a factor, and yet the behavior under similar types of ringing was similar.

It is surprising how frequently possible injury to the xylem is called upon to explain the effects of ringing on transport. Yet one-fourth to one-half or even three-fourths of the xylem may be completely severed without any appreciable alteration in the behavior or composition of the tissues above, if a small part of the phloem also remains. When proper precautions are used, I have found that the resistance to flow of water past a ring is not measurably altered. Gardner (1925) says, "Ringing evidently decreases the conducting capacity of stems in some cases as much as 45 per cent," while "The bent section shows no tendency to obstruct the passage of water." But such effects are not evident from his data. As a measure of the resistance he determined the time necessary to force 2 cc. of water through the stem under a head of 4½ ft. of water. He gives such measurements for flow through pieces of equal length (usually 12 cm.) from upper, middle, and lower parts of the stems of the pear. This was done for normal stems, ringed stems, and bent stems. For ringed and bent stems, the rings or bends were located in the middle portion. The average time of five stems for flow in the middle section of normal shoots was 9.95 min. and for the lower portion 8.74, a ratio of 1.14 to 1. For the eight bent shoots the times were, respectively, 6.8 and 5.1, a ratio of 1.34 to 1. In the ten ringed stems the times were, respectively, 11.25 and 7.19, a ratio of 1.57 to 1. He says half of the ringed stems had healed over completely. Leaving the five stems out and averaging only the five that did not heal over, the average times were 10.9 and 7.8, a ratio of 1.40 to 1, a figure very like those of the normal or bent stems. Gardner evidently compared the resistance of the middle portion to that of the part above the ring but this is not a safe comparison for, as he says, the part above the ring had increased considerably in diameter with a corresponding increase in conductive capacity. This even exceeded that of the lower part of the stem which, in the normal stems, has the highest conductance of the three parts. One would hardly be justified in explaining the change in relative rates of flow between upper and middle parts as due to the plugging of the middle part by a ring, when it is obvious that the change is due to increased conductance of the upper part and not to a decreased conductance of the middle part. Although the wounds presumably were not protected, the increased resistance was very slight at best.

Maskell and Mason (1929a) also mention an increased resistance to water flow resulting from ringing and they state that it becomes evident about 14 hr. after ringing, but they imply that a failure of the leaves of ringed plants to maintain a normal moisture content is due to an interference in water transport; whereas a change in moisture content is certain to result from a failure to transport solids from the leaf and there may be not the slightest interference in water flow. Furthermore they used vaselin as a protective agent which I have found to be injurious to twigs, and it has not been demonstrated to be harmless as a ring wound dressing.

Even if further investigations demonstrate conclusively that partial plugging invariably results from ringing, the effect is at most slight when the ring wound is protected, and especially so when compared to deep notching or the cutting of one-half to three-fourths of the xylem, and yet when the xylem is injured by such cutting, there seems to be a relatively slight effect on transport. When, on the other hand, the phloem is completely cut, the transport is significantly reduced. Evidence from most of the types of ringing experiments here reported clearly demonstrates that a narrow bridge of phloem is adequate for almost normal food transport. And since with complete ringing but a part of the xylem at most can be plugged, because the parts above show no signs of water deficit, it seems more reasonable to interpret the experiment as proving that the narrow bridge of phloem is carrying the sugar, nitrogen, or ash, rather than that it is preventing a stoppage in the xylem and thus allowing it to be carried in the narrow bridge of xylem.

It is interesting that a large number of writers unhesitatingly accept the evidence from ringing experiments to the effect that organic matter is carried in the phloem but balk at the same type of evidence when it is interpreted as demonstrating transport of salts through the phloem.

Although I am convinced that the hindrance to transport past a ring is not due to increased resistance to flow, the criticism still remains that, possibly through an indirect effect of accumulated carbohydrates on transpiration, the actual rate of flow through ringed stems may be lessened. This point is discussed in Sec. 13.

Some have hesitated to accept the evidence obtained from ringing experiments because they felt that ringing has altered growth, and the altered growth has been the cause of the changed solute distribution, not the result. Such is evidently the contention of Kastens (1924), Hooker (1924), and Swarbrick (1927), while others in conversation have expressed similar doubts. It seems that these doubts are really due to the fact that their previous assumptions were wrong. For example, Kastens, assuming that solutes must move through the xylem, because the phloem seems inadequate, explained behavior as due to lack of specific hormones. Hooker (1924) and others, assuming that salts and nitrogen must be carried through the xylem, explain the deficiency of nutrients above the ring as a result of the poor growth, not the cause. Hooker evidently overlooked the fact that ringing interferes with salt and nitrogen movement not only in the cases where the ringing was done before shoot growth was completed, but in a large number of cases when the ringing was done after terminal growth and enlargement of leaves had ceased. Some seem to have in mind that this altered growth is due to an interference in the movement of "hormones," or "inhibitors" or "stimulators," or to an interference in the transmission of "stimuli." But a much simpler and more straight-forward explanation that fits the facts and does not require special assumptions is, that solute movement, in both directions, takes place chiefly through the phloem tissues. Therefore, when these tissues are cut, the normal movement of these solutes is interfered with, and growth changes result. I do not deny the possibility that some stimulus may be transmitted through the phloem or other tissues, or that hormones may be transported through them, or that some such stimulus or hormone may influence growth and solute distribution. The evidence seems clear, how-ever, that certain solutes are carried chiefly through the phloem and that the distribution of these solutes may be the factor determining the nature and extent of the growth. That growth may in turn influence the distribution of solutes is also clear, and the possible interrelation of the two is discussed in Secs. 41 and 42.

SUMMARY

20. It is not safe to interpret movements of solutions that are introduced into cut tissues as indicative of normal movements. Any one or more of the following phenomena: the direction of movement, rate of movement, type of substance moving (liquid, gas, or solute), and method of movement (that is, the forces concerned) may be different from what was naturally taking place before the substance was injected. Movements of solutions and gases that have been observed in the xylem of cut or injected stems, therefore, may be highly misleading and cannot safely be interpreted as indicating normal movements. For similar reasons, a failure to obtain flow through the phloem tissue, by methods that are successful in causing flow through the xylem, need not preclude the possibility of rapid movement through these tissues.

21. When intact plants are placed in certain solutions, especially solu-tions of eosin and of lithium salts, it has been found that these solutes are rapidly carried through the xylem. The eosin probably travels through the xylem because it is toxic and injures the living cells which might other-wise prevent its entrance into the transpiration stream. The use of lithium is criticized on the grounds that it may alter the permeability of the cells, that it has been used as a qualitative test not as a quantitative test, and that its behavior may be different from that of most of the normally occur-ring solutes.

22. Tests for deposits of dyes or specific elements in cells or on walls of certain tissues have been taken as proof of transport through that region. Some have cited this as proof of transport through the lumen of the cells stained and others that the transport has been along the wall itself. Such deposits clearly demonstrate the arrival of the material, but they do not demonstrate that those cells or tissues are concerned in transport. In fact, deposits in nonmoving parts of the cell seem more strongly to point to ineffectiveness of that tissue as a path of transport.

23. Sugars, organic acids, organic forms of nitrogen, and many inorganic elements have been found in the sap exuding from cut stems, or in that forced out of the xylem by various means. This has been cited as proof that the xylem is the channel through which these materials are naturally carried. These materials, however, seem especially abundant at seasons when the plants are leafless and may largely disappear through absorption by living cells before there is an active transpiration stream. The finding of these small amounts in the xylem sap probably accounts for the transport that has been demonstrated to take place through the xylem, but it does not prove that the wood is the major path of transport.

24. Experiments, in which first one possible channel and then the other is cut, result in little or no transport of naturally occurring solutes when the phloem is cut, and transport at approximately normal rates when the xylem is cut. This method of experimentation is not open to the criticisms that apply to methods where attempts are made to force solutions through the tissues that might be supposed to carry the materials and which have been cut open to admit the material used in testing. Although it has been clearly demonstrated that the phloem can carry both organic and inorganic solutes in either direction, it has not been conclusively demonstrated that movement in both directions is simultaneous.

25. Many have doubted the evidence for transport through the phloem that is based on ringing experiments because they have felt that ringing has resulted in a plugging of the xylem. Although plugging may result from ringing, it has been found that careful protection of the ring wound with melted paraffin may entirely prevent such stoppage. Although definitely sought for, no evidence was obtained indicating that plugging might have been responsible for the responses obtained. Several have claimed that injury to the xylem is unavoidable but the evidence supporting such claim is weak and in several cases is shown to be definitely unsound. Even if partial stoppage were demonstrated always to occur, this can hardly account for the marked reduction in solute transport following ringing, for the stoppage cannot be complete if the parts above continue to receive adequate water. It is rather surprising to find that many individuals unhesitatingly accept the evidence from ringing experiments when it shows a reduced sugar movement, but when similar evidence from similar ringing experiments points to a check in movement of nitrogen or ash, it is assumed to be false and due to plugging of the xylem.

CHAPTER VI

THE METHOD OF MOVEMENT THROUGH THE PHLOEM

26. Peculiarities of the System.—Although it has long been recognized that solute translocation, at least the backward translocation from the leaves, takes place through the phloem, until recently very little attention has been given to a consideration of the possible mechanism of this transfer. Since the structures of the xylem and the phloem tissues are so very different, it is obvious that the methods by which materials are moved through the tissues are also probably different. Any hypothesis explaining the mechanism of solute movement must therefore be adapted to the tissue concerned.

Because of the rigid walls of the xylem conduits, water and solutions are readily moved through it by differences in tension or pressure initiated at either end of the system, but it appears impossible by similar methods to force solutions, or even pure water, through the phloem at adequate rates, even though the cells form a continuous longitudinal series. This is probably due to the fact that the phloem cells have small lumina with nonrigid, perhaps somewhat elastic side walls; are connected, one cell to the next, by rather minute pores which may be completely filled with protoplasm; contain living protoplasm; and probably have a high content of rather viscous, colloidal material. A pressure or suction applied externally at one or the other end can be expected, therefore, to be ineffective in forcing solution through the system.

Birch-Hirschfeld (1920), whose findings have already been discussed in some detail in Sec. 16, has demonstrated that it is impossible to force water or solutions through phloem tissues by methods that are easily successful in forcing solutions through the xylem. This experimental

133

evidence and the fact that the sieve tubes have a high content of colloidal material, part of which may be very viscous, seemed to preclude the possibility of a unilateral mass flow of sieve-tube contents.

It is possible, however, that the conditions necessary for such a flow have not been met experimentally. Birch-Hirschfeld attempted to draw solutions through phloem strips by causing rapid evaporation from the leaves. This, however, would tend to place the water columns under tension, and although water would tend to be drawn from the phloem and thus put its contents also under reduced pressure or even tension, it would not insure a pressure gradient through the phloem. In experiments with stems of *Philadelphus*, from which the xylem was cut out and the phloem left intact, I was not successful in drawing dye solutions by suction through the region lacking xylem (Curtis, 1925). In a later experiment with *Rhus*, however, it was found possible by the same method of suction to draw a dye solution through the region lacking xylem but this movement seemed to be limited to the latex tubes. It seems that sieve tubes have rather pliable and non-rigid walls, very different from those of the xylem. An attempt to force liquids through such tubes by methods used by Birch-Hirschfeld, or by cutting across them and applying solutions under pressure at one end, may fail largely because of this lack of rigidity. Any one who has attempted to force liquid or gas by either pressure or suction through such a nonrigid, thin-walled, rubber tube will recognize how such flexibility, allowing for the collapse of the tube, may be the chief difficulty that can be overcome only by using some method to hold the tube open. Dixon (1933) by using higher pressures than have previously been used, that is about 3 atmospheres, has reported injection into sieve tubes for distances up to about a centimeter.

A normal sieve tube with its high solute content is likely to be highly turgid and distended by the internal turgor pressure which will, of course, be dissipated when the tube is cut. It is even possible that the walls are sufficiently elastic and the internal pressures so great that ordinary mounts of phloem tissues give a decidedly wrong impression as to the normal size of the sieve-tube lumen, the thickness of its walls, and the size of the sieve pores. Crafts (1932) has recently observed that the supposedly large pores that have been described in sieve plates of *Cucurbita* are not large pores but extremely minute pores less than 2μ in diameter and seemingly completely filled with protoplasm. Schmidt (1917) also failed to find pores through the sieve plates. What has appeared as large pores, Crafts finds in his fresh specimens to be callose masses which may have been dissolved out by fixing reagents or which may have appeared as pores because of lack of staining or improper focus. Although Crafts has failed to find real pores of the size that have been assumed to be present in sieve plates, the fact remains that in making mounts for observation the phloem system has always been cut into and high internal pressures have been released so that perhaps no one has yet observed sieve tubes and plates in their normal, distended condition.

Although externally applied pressure or suction has failed to cause appreciable flow through phloem tissues, there is fairly clear evidence that internally applied pressure may, and at times does, cause considerable flow. For example, many plants will show an exudation from the phloem when that tissue is cut (Hartig, 1860, 1861; Münch, 1930; and many others). The volume of exudate is so great that much of it must have passed longitudinally through the phloem for a considerable distance (Crafts, 1931; Dixon, 1933; and others). Therefore internally applied pressures are capable of forcing materials through the seemingly impervious phloem. Furthermore this offers rather conclusive proof that either the pores of the sieve plates are actually open and allow for mass flow of solution through them or that Crafts (1931) is correct in his suggestion that such flow occurs within the cell walls themselves. The former alternative seems to me much more likely.

Any hypothesis explaining transport through the phloem must take into consideration not only the structures of the system through which transport takes place but also it should be adequate to account for movement of carbohydrates at rates which actually obtain. A number of investigators, especially Birch-Hirschfeld (1920), Dixon (1922), Mason and Lewin (1926), Tincker (1928), and Crafts (1932, 1933) have reported calculations of rates at which materials must be transported.

Although until recently (Münch 1926, 1927, 1930) no adequate mechanism has been proposed to account for unidirectional mass flow of solutions through the phloem, it has been tacitly assumed by many botanists that such movement of phloem contents does take place. Others have definitely stated, or at least implied, that diffusion accounts for the transfer through the phloem, but movement by diffusion alone would be altogether too slow to account for transport at the usual rates.

27. Older Hypotheses and Suggestions.—Hartig (1858, 1860, 1861) had observed exudation from cut phloem and assumed that there was a mass flow of sieve-tube contents. Nägeli (1861) agreed with this and suggested that pressures of neighboring cells caused the flow. Others suggested that bending movements brought about by winds would favor such flow. Sachs (1863) thought proteins might move by such a pressure flow but that sugars moved principally through parenchyma cells by diffusion. This idea of diffusional flow through parenchyma was supported by Schimper (1885). Although deVries as early as 1885 pointed out the complete inadequacy of diffusion alone to account for movement, others have stated or implied that it was adequate. Rywosch (1908, 1909, 1911) attempted to support the diffusion hypothesis, but the evidence presented is based largely on gradients in disappearance or reappearance of starch, and to support it, phenomena are cited which bear no relation to diffusion gradients. Furthermore, although in the 1911 paper evidence is given indicating that diffusion of glucose from a cell may be hastened by the presence of sucrose, the main criticism of the inadequacy of diffusion alone is not met. DeVries (1885) presented calculations of Stefan who had estimated that by diffusion alone it would take 319 days for 1 mg. of sodium chloride, one of the most rapidly diffusing salts, to move a distance of 1 m. from a 10 per cent solution. This calculation was based on the assumption of a column of pure water at the beginning into which the salt was diffusing. Similar calculations indicated that for a similar quantity of sugar to diffuse the same distance under similar conditions it would take 2 years and 7 months and for a soluble protein 14 years. Of course, after the solute has established a gradient over the distance and if the concentration is maintained at zero at the meter distance and a steady state of diffusion obtains, then sucrose, according to Fick's law, should pass the plane a meter distant from a 10 per cent solution at the rate of 1 mg. in about 10 hr. (595 min.). This, however, is too slow to account for normal solute movement. DeVries observed active streaming, of both the circulation and rotation types, in the companion cells and parenchyma of the phloem of a number of different kinds of plants and suggested that the streaming might account for a much more rapid movement than would occur if restricted to diffusion. Hartig (1858) had previously suggested that the movement of protoplasm which he had observed in living cells might actually be the moving nutritive sap. Velten also (1872) had observed and described streaming in sieve tubes and many other types of living cells. This hypothesis seems to have been largely discarded after a few years when investigators failed in attempts to observe streaming in mature sieve tubes.

A few years later Lecomte (1889) stated that no problem is more important to the life of the plant than transloca-tion and none has been more neglected by botanists. In explaining the possible mechanism of transport he stated that he had observed streaming of a rotational type, passing from one end of the cell to the other in young cells, but in older cells, when the protoplasm is limited to a parietal layer, this type of activity ceases. He opposed the views of Sachs and Van Tieghem that the protoplasm is dead and the sieve tubes are merely passive, but he considered that the tubes are physiologically active in the transport of materials, and he thought that, at least in those forms with open pores between the cells, there is a mass movement of albuminous material from one cell to another in one direction. He pictured sieve tubes of several plants showing droplets passing through the pores from one sieve-tube segment to another. He described several as passing toward the base of a plant, but in a young subterranean shoot of *Rubus idaeus* the position of the globules indicated a movement toward the apex. In a long branch rooted at the tip the position of the globules indicated a movement toward the base of the mother plant in the main part of the branch, but near the tip the direction of movement was toward the newly developing roots. Though he observed streaming in companion cells and young sieve tubes and emphasized the importance of diffusion between cells, he evidently considered that the movement in mature sieve tubes is by mass flow chiefly in one direction, and not of the circulation or cyclosis type. He considered that the high turgor in the sieve tubes, changes in temperature, and the removal of translocated material in the growing and storage regions are of importance in favoring rapid diffusion and increased mass movement of these substances. It is worth noting that, in his figures (Figs. 3, 5, 7, Plate 21), which show this mass movement of cell contents through pores, the protoplasm is strongly retracted from the lateral walls of the sieve tube. This would indicate a collapse due to the treatment, which might also easily account for an abnormal squeezing of the contents through the pores. In order to relieve the internal pressures and prevent this flow in some cases he cut and mounted the material in 3 to 5 per cent sugar solutions. Although such treatment may somewhat reduce the rapid flow resulting from cutting, it could not completely obviate abnormal pressure changes. It is also interesting that in the same drawing he has indicated by arrows the streaming of protoplasm in the companion cells, and these cells do not appear collapsed or plasmolyzed.

Though Lecomte considered this squeezing of albuminous globules through the sieve pores as an indication of normal movement, he clearly recognized that cutting may cause an abnormal flow for considerable distances. For example, he discusses the work of Fischer (1885) who demonstrated that the appearance of the slime plug on one side of the sieve plate was an artifact due to cutting or other injury, and he states that such an effect of cutting may be evident at a distance of 2 to 12 cm. in the petiole of *Cucurbita*. Whether Lecomte's observations and drawings represent a real and normal unidirectional flow of sieve-tube contents or whether the apparent flow resulted from the method of treatment, cannot be settled from the evidence now available. I am of the opinion, however, that it is not a normal condition.

Several had suggested that protoplasmic connections or plasmodesma are of importance in transmitting stimuli of one sort or another. Kienitz-Gerloff (1891) accepted these and suggested further that the plasmodesma serve as a path for rapid transfer from cell to cell of protoplasm, colloidal material and soluble materials of large molecular size, and although he seemed to think that most soluble materials, including sugars, could pass readily through plasmatic membranes, his suggestion as to the path of transfer is valuable, even if one does not accept his suggestion as to mass flow. It has long been recognized and repeatedly demonstrated that plasma membranes are relatively impermeable to many solutes, especially sugars and even simple salts and ions. Steward (1930) has clearly demonstrated this low permeability of living cells to sugars. The presence of plasmodesma, however, forming connections between living cells, would allow for ready exchange between them without necessitating a movement through surface membranes, whereas a surface membrane would interfere with such movement between the same cells and nonliving, water-conducting cells or any surrounding solution. This may explain the seeming contradiction that living cells are only slightly permeable to sugars and yet sugars must move readily and rapidly from cell to cell within the plant.

On the other hand, Weevers (1931) has recently claimed that the low permeability to sugars of the outer plasma membrane has been overstressed. He thinks that the low permeability is chiefly restricted to the tonoplast or vacuolar membrane and that methods used which show low permeability involve permeability of this inner membrane and not of the outer one. The rapidity with which yeast absorbs and ferments sugar and the readiness with which algae and leaf parenchyma tissues store starch when floated on sugar, he cites as evidence of rather high permeability of the outer membrane to sugar. Fungi and bacteria obviously must necessarily receive all their organic solutes through surface membranes and may have a different type of surface membrane, but with chlorophyll-bearing organisms this surface membrane seems to be much less permeable. It is true that parenchyma tissues can absorb sugar from bathing solutions or lose it to them, but the indications are that the rate of this absorption or loss through the surface membrane is much less than the absorption by storage tissues connected by living cells to supplying tissues, or the loss from the supplying tissues to receiving ones.

It is possible, on the other hand, that the differences in rates of exchanges between living cells and those between living cells and a nonliving environment are not related to differences in permeability but to relative surfaces exposed. There is evidence also that the conditions of aeration may partly account for slow movement to or from a bathing solution. Puriewitsch (1898) and Grünfeld (1926) have found that emptying and refilling of endosperms and cotyledons are dependent upon favorable aeration and Parkin (1899) has found that sugar absorption, as tested by starch deposition in leaf tissues floated on sugar solution, is dependent upon adequate aeration.

I am of the opinion that outer plasmatic membranes are relatively impermeable to sugars and that the plasmodesma offer ready channels through which diffusion from cell to cell may take place without passage through surface membranes. Kienitz-Gerloff considered that moving protoplasm is concerned in actually carrying organic material from cell to cell in all parts of the plant and that such flow is not restricted to sieve tubes where connections from segment to segment are relatively coarse. He claimed to have demonstrated that, with the exception of guard cells, all parts of a given individual are interconnected by plasmatic strands thus forming a single unified organism. He stated that movement seems not impossible, for the strands in many cases are no finer than the visibly moving strands in the hairs of *Cucurbita*. He suggested that protoplasmic contents may actually be withdrawn through these connections from maturing vessels, sclerenchyma fibers, and cork cells and that the autumnal emptying of leaves takes place largely through these connections. The failure of guard cells to empty when placed in the dark or during autumnal emptying, he explained as due to the complete absence of these connections. In a later paper (1902) he reported the finding of plasmodesma in guard cells thus confirming the observations of several others who had reported them subsequent to his earlier paper. It seems significant that the plasmodesma when found in guard cells are restricted to pits and are not scattered over the surface as in ordinary epidermal or parenchyma cells. His contention that protoplasm actually moves through the plasmodesma seems not to have been accepted but on the contrary has been specifically denied. I am of the opinion, however, that it is definitely worth reinvestigating. Miehe (1901) has reported the movement of nuclei and protoplasm through plasmodesma in response to wound stimuli. Münch (1930) (see Sec. 28) assumes that there

is a mass flow through these plasmodesma which is due
to a turgor pressure gradient, but he seems to consider it a
flow of food solution and not protoplasm. For a considerable period since the time of Lecomte's papers no
great attention was directed toward solution of the problem
concerning the mechanism of transport.

Mangham (1917) suggested a hypothesis by which he
attempted to explain the movement of sugars through
phloem cells as if it were controlled by adsorption. He
pointed out the probable continuity of colloidal protoplasmic material from sieve tube to sieve tube through
the sieve pores and between these and other cells through
plasmodesma. Then, recognizing the fact of a dynamic
equilibrium between adsorbing colloidal material and an
adsorbed substance, he suggested that the removal of
sugar molecules from the adsorbent in a receiving cell
would upset this equilibrium and result in a disturbance
which would be propagated as a wave of readjustment
through the continuous mass of colloidal material thus
tending to move the sugar along such a mass through its
entire length. He suggested that the rate of propagation
of this wave would depend upon the degree of approxima-
tion of the adsorbing particles. Mangham's hypothesis
is, however, based on a wrong assumption, for he failed to
realize the fact, that adsorbed molecules are not attracted
to the adsorbent from a distance but diffuse to the surface,
and that they would be hindered in their movement by a
stationary adsorbent and not hastened. When a molecule
or ion is adsorbed by a colloidal mass, its diffusion through
that mass tends to be retarded and not accelerated as
can be easily demonstrated in experiments on the relative
rates of movement of adsorbed and nonadsorbed solutes
through gelatin, agar, filter paper, and such colloidal
masses. Kidd (1918) has published a short note criticizing
Mangham's interpretation.

One distinctly valuable suggestion of Mangham's is that
offering an explanation for a rapid interchange of materials,
such as sugars, between one living cell and another, whereas

an interchange, either absorption or loss, between a living cell and neighboring dead cells or the external environment is extremely slow. This movement through plasmodesma was previously suggested by Kienitz-Gerloff (1891), though the latter did not emphasize the low permeability of surface membranes to sugars. This is a highly important suggestion of Mangham's, even though the mechanism that he proposed to account for the actual movement is untenable. Although Mangham implied adsorption on a stationary colloidal surface, it requires no great alteration of his adsorption hypothesis to adapt it to adsorption at an interface between liquids where the material is actually carried in the moving film. As thus modified, the hypothesis is far from untenable and would agree with the protoplasmic streaming hypothesis or a modification of it suggested by Van den Honert (1932) (see Sec. 37).

28. The Hypothesis of Münch.—Münch (1926, 1927, 1930) has recently revived the hypothesis that there is a unidirectional mass flow of sieve-tube contents which is due entirely to a fall in pressure in one direction. Though there are some very serious and perhaps insurmountable weaknesses in the hypothesis, there are a number of points that strongly favor it. His hypothesis is based fundamentally on the fact first stated by Pfeffer that if solutes are distributed unequally in an osmotic chamber, there will be an absorption of water by that side of the chamber where the concentration is high and a secretion of water from that side where the solution inside of the membrane is weakest, and that this will result in a mass flow of solution within the chamber from the region of high concentration toward that of lower concentration. Recognizing the fundamental principle but not realizing that Pfeffer had already proposed it, I set up a series of osmotic cells, consisting of atmometer shells impregnated with copper ferrocyanide membranes, connected with small tubes, and by this apparatus I demonstrated this fact of unilateral secretion through a closed system, where there was a high concentration at one end of the cell or system and a low concentration at the other. This work was reported at the Baltimore meeting of the Botanical Society of America in 1918, but it was never published. At that time I suggested that a similar mechanism might account for root pressure. A comparable mechanism is also described by Blackman (1921), and Ursprung and Blum (1925) have described a method whereby a unilateral suction tension resulting from such a condition can be measured in living plant cells.

The basic principle of unilateral flow is indicated by Münch in a diagram similar to Fig. 9. Membrane A

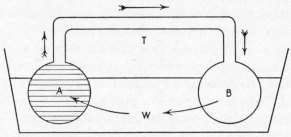

Fig. 9.—Diagram to demonstrate basic principle of osmotic flow. *A*, osmotic membrane with high concentration; *B*, osmotic membrane with low concentration connected by open tube *T*. Feathered arrows indicate flow of solution from cell or part of cell with high concentration to that with low. Plain arrows indicate direction of flow of water. (*From Münch.*)

contains a solution of high osmotic concentration. The tube T is filled with water as is also membrane B. Both membranes A and B dip into water W. Because of the steep diffusion gradient across the membrane at A, water moves in by osmosis developing a pressure in A. This develops a pressure throughout the system, and, since solutes are lacking in B, or their concentration is low in that region, there will be little or no resistance to the diffusion of water through the membrane B to the external water. As a result there will tend to be a mass flow of solution from A through the tube toward B. As the solute concentration in B rises, there will be a rising resistance to the diffusion of water from B to W, and the pressure in the system will increase. Such a gradual rise in pressure was actually demonstrated in a working model I described in 1918. If, on the other hand, the solute is removed in some way when it reaches B, water will continue to pass out readily through the membrane, and solution will continue to flow into B.

Münch applies the same principle of unilateral secretion to the plant. He suggests, for example, that the chlorenchyma cells of the leaf manufacture sugar from carbon dioxide and water, both of which readily diffuse through protoplasmic membranes. The cell membrane is not easily permeable to the sugar, so an osmotic pressure is set up in the cell. Plasmodesma, however, which connect such chlorenchyma cells with other similar living cells and eventually with sieve-tube cells, are assumed to allow for a mass flow of sugar solution into the sieve tubes which, with their larger pores, allow for continuous flow for some distance. That side of a cell abutting on the dead water-supplying cells would not be permeable to sugar; for on that side there would be a limiting protoplasmic membrane. The comparatively large pores of the sieve tubes should allow for a relatively rapid mass flow of solution through them. The receiving cells, such as the cambium, by removing the sugars from solution through respiration, deposition in cell walls, or other conversion to insoluble material, or to materials of higher molecular weight, would tend to have a low osmotic concentration and would therefore readily give up water through their semipermeable membranes; very much as B in the diagram, will lose water to W.

A simplified diagrammatic representation of the system as it may occur in plants as suggested by Münch is presented in Fig. 10. Münch gives diagrams and descriptions of the possible working of such a mechanism of transport under three widely differing sorts of conditions: (1) Transport under conditions of suppressed transpiration and water absorption; the figure is similar to that here given, but the two cells at the base are omitted and no water is lost from the cell P to the atmosphere. (2) Transport in a defoliated tree or in the stump and roots of a felled tree.

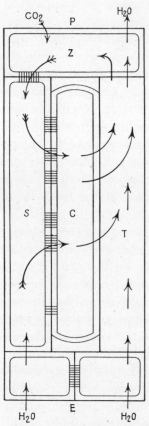

In this the cell at the top of the diagram is omitted and water entering T would tend to bleed from the cut stump or be forced toward the defoliated twigs. (3) Transport in a complete normal plant as indicated in the diagram here presented. He also gives diagrams indicating transport to fruits. Münch claims the system will work under any conditions of water supply; for, even if water is deficient, reducing the turgor in the leaf or supplying cell, P, he claims that to an equal extent there would be an increase in the tension of the cohesive xylem water in T, and this would be transferred to the cambium, so that the sum of the suction and turgor pressures of the receiving and supplying cells, which are responsible for the pressure gradient and circulation of sap, is as great as before a reduction of turgor took place and is equal to the osmotic concentration of the supplying leaf cell. More exactly, the pressure difference would be equal to the difference between the osmotic concentration of the supplying and receiving cells and would not be equal to the osmotic concentration of the leaf. In the fundamental scheme diagrammed in Fig. 9, the pressure gradient would depend on

FIG. 10.—Diagrammatic representation of transport by an osmotic flow as proposed by Münch. Diagram adapted from Münch with slight alterations. T, xylem tube; P, leaf parenchyma; S, sieve tube; C, cambium; Z, sugar; E, endodermis of root. Simple arrows indicate direction of movement of water, single-feathered arrows direction of carbon dioxide movement, double-feathered arrows direction of movement of sugar solutions.

the difference between the concentrations in membranes A and B.

29. Points Favoring the Hypothesis of Münch.—There are a number of points, both theoretical and experimental, that strongly favor the hypothesis developed by Münch, but there are also several serious weaknesses. One highly intriguing suggestion proposed by Münch is that the plasmodesma allow for rapid movement from living cell to living cell of those solutes, especially sugars, to which the surface membrane is highly impermeable. This same point was previously suggested by Kienitz-Gerloff (1891) and by Mangham (1917), and, though it is an important one, its acceptance does not necessitate the acceptance of the hypothesis, that the movement is a unilateral mass flow through either these plasmodesma or the larger pores of the sieve plates.

That materials can for a short time be forced through the phloem by internally developed pressures seems definitely proved by the fact that phloem contents will rapidly exude from a cut stem. This has been reported by a number of investigators, especially Hartig (1860, 1861), Münch (1930), and Crafts (1931). The exudation from *Cucurbita* that has been widely observed, though it comes from sieve-tube-like cells, comes, at least in part, from tissues very similar to latex tissues. Unless Crafts is correct in suggesting that the material moves within the walls, which is doubtful, this exudation demonstrates that the pores of the sieve plates are sufficienty large to allow for a flow. It is also possible, however, that the flow from the cut phloem is strictly abnormal and due solely to opening the tissues and thus developing an abnormally steep pressure gradient.

Perhaps the strongest direct experimental evidence for this hypothesis is that exudation from the phloem has been demonstrated, and it has been reported that exudation soon ceases if a second cut is made through the phloem above the first one, that is between the first cut and the supplying region, while exudation may continue for some time if the second cut through the phloem is made below. The second cut, if made above the first, may stop the flow at a distance up to 1 or even 5 m. (Hartig, 1860; Büsgen and Münch, 1929, p. 134; Münch, 1930, p. 124).

The secretion of water from the cambial surface, when separated from the xylem, as reported by Münch, is additional evidence strongly supporting the hypothesis. Weevers and Westenberg (1931), however, were unable to confirm a secretion from the cambium. Even if the secretion of water is proven, such secretion has not been demonstrated to bear a relation to food movement. Such secretion from the cambium may be comparable to the bleeding from cut stumps or to that occurring in normal guttation. There is no clear indication that these secretions are related to rapid food translocation, as would be the case in food transport to storage tissues or meristematic cells. Such bleeding, it seems, may occur under conditions when one would expect no storage and little or no meristematic activity. It may be true that this secretion is related to meristematic activity or food deposition, but it would not necessarily follow that the water results from a mass flow of solution through the phloem, for unequal distribution of solutes in secreting cells alone may cause water secretion and this may bear no relation whatever to the mechanism of transport.

The postulated secretion of water into the xylem might well account, as Münch suggests, for the refilling of the xylem with water, after high transpiration has reduced the content or even ruptured the cohesive columns and filled certain of the tubes with air. He suggests that such a mechanism may explain the necessity of living cells for maintaining a continuous column of water for transport, according to the cohesion theory of water rise. No other satisfactory explanation has been given for the seeming fluctuations in the water content of the trunk. I say *seeming* fluctuations because it is possible that the low water content of sapwood, observed by Jones *et al.* (1903), Craib (1918), Büsgen (1911), MacDougal, Overton, and Smith (1929), and others during periods of high transpiration or low water supply in the soil, as contrasted with the higher water content during rainy periods, may be in large part due to the fact that during dry periods the water is likely to be under greater tension so that cutting into the trunk while taking samples will rupture the columns, which will then be almost instantly replaced by air. Such a replacement of water by air can be easily demonstrated if, during a period of deficient water, the bark is removed to expose the wood and then a notch is cut into the wood. The sudden change in appearance of the wood is due to rupture and withdrawal of the water columns.

30. Weaknesses in the Hypothesis of Münch.—1. This hypothesis would not allow for what seems clearly indicated in the experiments reported in Chaps. II and III, that is, that both upward and downward movement of solutes occur simultaneously through the same phloem system. It might account for an upward movement from the leaves at a given level, for example to the apical meristem, and a simultaneous downward movement from the same leaves to the trunk, cambium, and roots. It might account for an upward or downward movement into defoliated regions of the stem as in the experiments described in Secs. 7, 8, and 9, or possibly into the isolated flaps of bark described by Mason and Maskell (1928a), but it would not allow for a simultaneous upward and downward movement through the same part of the conducting system, as for example a simultaneous upward movement of nitrogen and downward movement of sugars through the phloem of the trunk. Local reversals in side twigs may be easily accounted for, but even a daily alternation in direction of movement in the main conducting tissues would seem highly improbable.

In the scheme proposed by Münch, any nitrogen or salts reaching the leaves from the roots must necessarily pass exclusively through the xylem, for there would be a uni-directional flow, backward only, through the phloem of the main stem as long as the leaves were supplying foods to the roots. Under such a system, nitrogen or salts taken into the living cells in the root or stem could reach the top only through the transpiration stream. Eckerson (1924), Thomas (1927), and others have shown that, in some plants

at least, much or all of the nitrogen is converted into amino-
acids or proteins before leaving the roots. The only way
for these to reach the leaves would be through their resecre-
tion into the transpiration stream, but their amounts in
the xylem sap are extremely low and I know of no evidence
showing that living cells of higher plants readily excrete
organic nitrogen; although Mason and Maskell (1931,
p. 149) observed the organic nitrogen content of tracheal
sap taken from the cotton plant to be 4.43 mg. per 100 cc.,
while the nitrate nitrogen content was 5.36, and ammonia
nitrogen 2.37. When the nitrogen supply in the soil is
high, it is conceivable that some nitrate would more easily
get across the living tissues into the transpiration stream
and be carried to the leaves, but when it is low it would
seem that the living cells of the roots and those along the
conducting tract would remove all available nitrogen from
the nonliving transpiration stream (see Sec. 14). The
readiness with which living cells remove nitrate and certain
other ions from a very weak solution has been demonstrated by Osterhout (1922), Hoagland (1923), Steward
(1932), and others.

2. a. The pressure gradient that would seem necessary
to account for the movement especially for any great distance, as for example from the leaves of a tree to the roots
at a distance even as low as 10 m., would seem to preclude
the possibility of the movement being solely dependent
upon such a mass flow. Calculations by Crafts (1931)
indicate the necessity of great pressures to cause such a
flow.

b. If solution enters the receiving cells by mass flow
through plasmodesma, as postulated by Münch, this
resistance would be added to that of flow through sieve
plates, and still more pressure would be necessary. Furthermore, in addition to all these resistances that must be
overcome by pressure to cause a mass flow, it would be
necessary to develop sufficient pressure in the receiving
cell to force water from this cell into the xylem. This
pressure must exceed the difference between the osmotic

concentration of the receiving cell and the suction tension (turgor deficit) of the solution in the xylem. This latter is likely to approach zero; therefore solution must be forced into the receiving cell with sufficient pressure to develop an internal hydrostatic pressure in this cell greater than the osmotic value of the cell contents on the face next to the water-conducting tracts. To maintain this excess pressure, the turgor in the sieve tubes must be exceedingly high and the turgor in the supplying leaf cells must be still higher; for it is at this point that the high pressure gradient is initiated and maintained. Since the receiving cell is assumed to have a low osmotic concentration, either because the materials are used up in respiration and formation of cell parts or because their osmotic concentration is reduced by condensation into storage products, the pressure necessary to force water out of this cell into xylem is supposed not to be great. Experimental evidence presented under (3), however, demonstrates high osmotic concentrations in receiving cells.

c. For transport, according to the hypothesis of Münch, pressures at the source must increase directly with the distance to which the material is to be transported. Pressures may seem great enough to force phloem contents a few centimeters or even decimeters, but in order to bring about flow over great distances, as in our tallest trees or in vines where distances up to 100 m. or more are concerned, excessive pressures would seem to be necessary. Although in trees there seems to be a tendency for an increase in osmotic concentration of leaves at greater heights, this increase is not uniform, is at best not very great, and seems to bear no relation to the distance through which foods must move. MacDaniels and I have obtained a few data bearing on this point. By use of the freezing-point method the osmotic concentrations of grape leaves on shoots arising 5 to 8 m. from a short trunk were compared with those on shoots arising directly from the trunks. The data are presented in Table 18. Although in all but one case the leaves at a greater distance had somewhat higher concentrations than those close to the trunk, the differences were slight. On the average the leaves at the greater distances could have a maximum pressure of only 1.15 atmospheres above those close to the trunk and yet they were from 5 to 8 m. farther from the trunk or roots to which they were sending sugar. This would indicate a gradient of less than 0.2 atmosphere per meter, which seems inadequate.

TABLE 18.—FREEZING-POINT DEPRESSIONS OF SAP OF GRAPE LEAVES FROM SHOOTS GROWING ON CANES 5 TO 8 M. FROM A SHORT TRUNK AND FROM THOSE GROWING DIRECTLY ON THE SHORT TRUNK

Leaves from long canes...	0.805	0.975	1.07	0.880	0.995	0.870	
Leaves from short canes..	0.845	0.825	0.825	0.815	0.875	0.840	
Diff. long−short........	−0.040	+0.150	+0.245	+0.065	+0.120	+0.030	+0.095 av.
Max. diff. in pressure, atmosphere...........	−0.48	1.81	2.95	0.78	1.45	0.36	1.15 av.

Münch's own observations and those of Haller (1931), that apple fruits on defoliated branches at a distance of 5 ft. or more from leaves grew as well as other fruits close to the leaves, would be difficult of explanation on a pressure gradient hypothesis.

3. *a.* Disregarding the seriousness of the criticism that the pressure gradients that might be available may not be adequate to overcome the resistance to be met in causing a flow through the phloem and into the receiving cells, there still remains the added difficulty that the naturally existing pressure gradients, or concentration gradients, may not lead in the same direction as the movement of materials. The Münch hypothesis demands a higher turgor pressure in the supplying cells than in the receiving cells so that there will be an actual pressure gradient in the proper direction. To maintain such a pressure gradient, the supplying cells must ordinarily have an osmotic concentration greater than that of the receiving cells. Possible exceptions to this rule will be discussed shortly. Experimental evidence, however, demonstrates that receiving cells frequently, and, when storage tissues are supplying growing tissues, may consistently have higher osmotic

concentrations than the supplying cells. Fernald (1925) found that the osmotic concentration near the growing point of rapidly growing shoots was distinctly higher than that of the leaves which were obviously supplying the foods necessary for growth. In potato tubers also, the osmotic concentrations of the sprouts were regularly much higher than those of the tuber from which the foods were coming. Although this evidence seems fairly conclusive, that receiving tissues may have higher osmotic concentrations than the supplying tissues, certain doubts may arise concerning it. Fernald's freezing-point determinations were made with sap that was first extracted from the tissues, but Carrick (1924) has given evidence showing that the freezing point of extracted sap or of killed tissue is likely to be very different from that of the living tissue. Although the younger tissues which had the higher concentrations were chiefly growing tissues and therefore were receiving materials from the older leaves or storage tissues, they also included some cells that were perhaps mature, and, furthermore, no precautions were taken to exclude light so the possibility of photosynthesis, especially in the leafy stems which were exposed to full light, may have partly accounted for the high concentrations in the younger parts.

In order to test more critically the possible bearing of an osmotic gradient upon the Münch hypothesis, we have grown various types of material in complete darkness so as to insure a transport from storage tissues to receiving tissues (Curtis and Scofield, 1933). The osmotic concentrations have been determined in three different ways. The freezing points of the tissues have been determined directly by inserting thermocouples into the tissues to be tested. This made it possible to determine the freezing point without first killing the tissue or extracting its sap, and also to restrict the determinations to younger, more nearly meristematic regions. Freezing-point determinations were also made on samples of extracted sap. With onion tissue the osmotic concentrations were also estimated by the plasmolytic method, using sucrose as the plasmolyzing agent. Various types of storage and receiving tissues were tested, including cotyledons and the developing seedlings, tubers and their sprouts, bulbs and their developing leaves and roots, and old leaves of *Bryophyllum* and *Byrnesia* and the plantlets developing from them.

As shown in Table 19, the receiving tissues in all instances, and by three methods of testing, had higher osmotic concentrations than the supplying storage tissues. Not only have the receiving tissues the higher osmotic concentrations, but the data from the onion (given in the original paper but not here) show a progressive change in concentration increasing from the older outer scales toward the younger scales, with the highest concentrations in the growing tissues which are receiving solutes from the storage scales. The outer scales with lowest concentration empty first and lose their contents to tissues with higher concentrations. That the osmotic concentration gradient is always in a direction the reverse of that demanded by the Münch hypothesis has not been demonstrated. But in all of these determinations where the supplying tissue was a storage tissue and the receiving tissue a growing organ, the concentration gradients have been in the wrong direction to satisfy the Münch hypothesis.

Only under special conditions, where the receiving cells may have highly extensible walls and are therefore incapable of developing much turgor, or where the receiving cells are exposed to a desiccating environment reducing their turgor, would it be possible for them to maintain a higher osmotic concentration than the supplying cells and still receive solutes by the proposed mechanism. Ursprung and Blum (1924) have given evidence that growing cells are likely to have low turgor pressures, although the low turgor pressure actually calculated may have been excessive and may have resulted from release of pressures incident to cutting the tissues for observation (Curtis and Scofield, 1933). The second alternative, that is a desiccating environment, seems highly improbable. Even an assumption that the receiving cells have highly extensible walls

TABLE 19.—AVERAGE MAXIMUM OSMOTIC PRESSURES IN ATMOSPHERES AS INDICATED BY DETERMINATIONS OF THE FREEZING-POINT DEPRESSIONS OF SUPPLYING AND RECEIVING TISSUES

Direct freezing points of living tissue were determined unless otherwise stated

	Onion	Onion, expressed sap	Onion, plasmo-lytic method	Onion, root tip and storage scales	Etiolated bean seedlings	Etiolated bean seedlings, expressed sap	*Bryophyllum,* mother leaf and plantlet	Squash seed-lings	Potato tubers and sprouts	*Byrnesia,* mother plant and plantlets
Growing tissue	14.19	8.79	13.24	12.88	17.92	9.03	12.14	14.99	28.60	7.47
Storage tissue	11.06	2.05	4.10	6.98	15.04	7.71	9.28	12.69	22.18	5.18
Difference	3.13	6.74	9.14	5.90	2.88	1.32	2.85	2.30	6.42	2.29
No. of determinations	12	3	6	15	14	4	15	8	6	3
Odds that difference is significant	9,999:1	458:1	9,999:1	4,999:1	207:1	241:1	9,999:1	87:1	138:1	21:1

would seem insufficient to account for a low turgor, especially when the receiving tissues are in direct contact
with water and the supplying tissues are not, as was the
case with the onion when the receiving roots were submerged in water and the storage tissues were in the air.   In
spite of the evidence to the contrary some may think
sugar transport from storage tissue may take place with
the transpiration stream.   This could hardly be involved
to account for transport from the flaccid onion scales to the
turgid roots submerged in water.

For the most part Münch assumes that water is excreted
by the receiving tissue and this excretion is due to the
pressure resulting from a flow of solution into the cells.
Under such circumstances the receiving cells must be at
their maximum turgor and must have a concentration
less than that of the supplying cells where the turgor
pressure is initiated.   These osmotic concentration measurements seem definitely to refute the Münch hypothesis.

b. Even if the supplying cells of photosynthesizing tissues
which have not been extensively tested should have
osmotic concentrations greater than those of receiving
cells, this would not insure a pressure gradient leading
toward the receiving cells, because the turgor of the exposed
leaf may be greatly reduced, especially during periods of
high isolation.   In fact the turgor of the leaf may be
reduced to such an extent on a bright day as to reverse
the pressure gradient.   This should lead to movement
into the leaf instead of out of it.   Without going to such
an extreme the reduced turgor in the leaf should reduce
the rate of transport during the day.   The available
data, however, clearly indicate greater transport during
the day than at night.   Mason and Maskell (1928*a*) found
greater transport into the cotton boll during the day, as
indicated by a gain in dry weight during the day about
four times that during the night.   Crafts (1931) estimated
transport from the leaves of *Phaseolus* during the day to
be a little over three times that in darkness.   Data on
relative turgors of supplying and receiving tissues under
such conditions are not yet available.

Although adequate quantitative data are not available for showing the influence of turgor of leaves on transport from them, it is obvious that turgid tissues may receive solutes from relatively flaccid tissues. The development of turgid sprouts on potato tubers in a dark cellar, when the supplying tuber is distinctly flaccid, is a case in point. Other examples of movement from flaccid to turgid tissues have been frequently observed in the emptying of other storage organs such as fleshy storage roots of beets, carrots, turnips, etc., the scales of an onion or other bulb and the cotyledons or endosperms of sprouting seedlings. In all the experiments reported in Table 19 the storage tissues appeared distinctly less turgid than the receiving tissues.

Münch, foreseeing the possible objection that turgor in the leaf may be reduced by transpiration, offers the explanation that, when the turgor of the leaves is reduced, the turgor throughout the entire plant is correspondingly reduced; for the entire water system would be put under tension so that the decreased pressure in the leaves would be counterbalanced by a corresponding increase in tension on the water passing out of the receiving cell. (This would be cell B in Fig. 9 and cell C or cambium in Fig. 10.) Although, in a simple system where the resistance to movement is slight and the walls are rigid, there might be such a rapid transmission of tension, I am not convinced that in a large plant this would be possible. Although a transmission of tension through the water-conducting system would meet much less resistance than through any other tissues and might therefore put the receiving cell, such as C in the diagram, under tension, *a failure to transmit such a tension from the receiving cell or cambium backward through the sieve tubes, along the entire path through which the sugar is moving from the flaccid leaf, would offset any advantage resulting from withdrawing water from the receiving cell, and reducing its turgor.* The walls of the phloem cells, furthermore, seem not to form a rigid tubular system, as in the xylem, and it seems unlikely that they would allow for transmission of such tensions. Without a uniform development of a tension throughout the full length of the sieve-tube system, any reduction in turgor of the supplying leaf cells would correspondingly decrease the rate of flow from these cells. Furthermore, with the osmotic gradient leading in the wrong direction, as discussed under 3 *a*, the proposed transmission of tension is of no avail.

c. The partial emptying of leaves just prior to leaf fall which has been observed by Swart (1914), Deleano and Andreesco (1932), and others would seem to be another instance of movement from a tissue of low osmotic concentration or low turgor to one of higher concentration or higher turgor. Deleano and Andreesco, however, found a marked increase in hexoses during this period and suggested that this increase maintained the turgor of the cells and favored transport from them. I know of no specific data, however, which actually give the relative osmotic concentrations or turgors of these tissues. Several investigators have observed that the lower leaves of a shoot are likely to have lower osmotic concentrations than the upper leaves. They also wilt more quickly when water becomes deficient. According to the scheme of Münch, these leaves should therefore be receiving foods from the more turgid leaves. Phloem contents should also move more readily to these leaves than to roots or cambium at greater distances. I know of no data on transport into or from the lower leaves, but from their continued low content it seems unlikely that they act as receiving organs. I have noticed the progressively increasing flaccidity of the older leaves of *Crassula portulaca* when these are supposedly giving up their contents to the young shoots developing in their axils. Schumacher (1931) observed an actual transport of 60 to 70 per cent of the nitrogen from wilting flowers in a period of 24 hr.

d. Still another problem related to translocation, which would be difficult of explanation according to the hypothesis proposed by Münch, is that bearing on the matter of dominance of one part over another, and of the seeming directive flow of solutes. If the direction of flow is determined chiefly by pressure or turgor gradients, and by the resistance to flow in the connecting channels, it would seem that those cells with the lowest turgor pressures and nearest to the supply, or those having the lowest resistance in the channels leading to them, should always receive the greater part of the food coming from the leaves or storage organs. This, however, seems not to be the case (see Sec. 42). Very commonly those tissues having the lowest concentration or those that are nearest to the supply fail to receive the foods which pass close by them and move to tissues much more distant and with higher turgor pressures. Maskell and Mason (1930*b*) report high flaccidity in unfertilized cotton bolls and much greater transport to fertilized bolls that were more turgid. To explain this, one might have to postulate that the receiving cells in some way control the flow to them by keeping the plasmodesma and sieve pores open, while in the others they are closed or the resistance to flow is in some way increased. While not an impossible supposition, the necessity of assuming special controls of this sort weakens the hypothesis. Furthermore, the actual emptying of materials from flaccid tissues, as mentioned under *b* and *c*, demonstrates that the conducting system has not become plugged.

4. The mechanism proposed by Münch seems not to offer a simple explanation for the movement of specific types of materials to special tissues or organs. A receiving tissue could steepen the osmotic gradient by removing sugars for example, but the resulting unidirectional mass flow would carry all the movable phloem contents toward that same tissue. Through selective permeability the receiving cells might, for example, prevent the entrance of the nitrogenous materials, but there must be some mechanism to remove these, for otherwise they would accumulate in the conducting channels outside of the receiving cells and thus lessen the osmotic gradient in the conducting channel or tend to clog it mechanically. The receiving tissue, according to this hypothesis, would

seem incapable of controlling the type of material moving toward it through the phloem, but could control only the rate of flow of the mixed contents through a control of the pressure gradient.

5. The explanation given by Münch accounting for the removal of water from the receiving cells seems possible when the latter are in the position of the cambium. In this case the receiving cells lie between the phloem which supplies the food solution and the xylem through which the water may be removed. The receiving cells at the apical meristem, however, are not in such an ideal situation in this respect, and an explanation of the removal of water seems more difficult. Furthermore, for cortical storage tissues a possible mechanism for removing the excess water is not obvious; for the phloem is between the receiving tissues and the tissues which might remove the water. In an exposed stem it is possible that evaporation from the outer surface might be effective, but in many plants the cortical storage tissues are subterranean, where water loss from the surface may become very slight. It is conceivable that solutions may enter through plasmodesma and water may move backward through the walls, but the rate of such movement must be rather low. Movement to tissues of this sort, therefore, seems difficult of explanation according to the hypothesis of Münch.

6. Another serious objection is that this hypothesis seems not to allow for a simple explanation of the inability of leaves to empty themselves when they are removed from the stems and their petioles placed in water. If Münch's hypothesis is correct, one would expect that such isolated leaves, or cut stems with leaves, would rapidly empty their sugar through the cut phloem into the water. The greatly shortened channel for transport and the increased water supply through the xylem should increase the steepness of the pressure gradient and empty the leaves of their sugar much more quickly than when left attached to the plant. The observations of Saposchnikoff (1893), Deleano (1911), and the unpublished findings of Miss Skaer (1931)

in our own laboratory show a much retarded emptying from such leaves. Emptying through cut sieve tubes with their relatively large pores would very likely be different from an emptying from cut parenchyma cells where the death of the cut cells at the surface would probably cause a very rapid formation of a surface membrane closing the plasmodesma. Experiment on microdissection by Chambers (1925) and others have demonstrated rapid reformation of a surface membrane at cut or punctured surfaces of cells. A comparable closing of cut sieve tubes might take place but would seem very improbable especially if a continued unilateral flow of the contents is normal, as postulated by Münch.

The phloem contents, especially in cucurbits, may coagulate into a gel within a few minutes after exuding from a cut. This coagulum might be expected to prevent further loss in much the same way as the coagulation of blood will stop its flow. Coagulation at the surface alone, however, which is effective in stopping blood flow would seem inadequate for stopping flow from the phloem; because internal pressures in the latter must be very high and the coagulum would have no firm anchorage. The average maximum pressure developed in the arteries of man does not commonly exceed 150 mm. of mercury, or about 0.2 atmosphere, while that in the capillaries where surface coagulation is effective does not commonly exceed 27 mm. or about 0.035 atmosphere. In the phloem of plants, on the other hand, the osmotic concentrations are probably such as to allow minimum turgor pressures around 2 to 5 atmospheres. Münch (1930, p. 134) estimated the phloem exudate from *Quercus rubra* and *Robinia pseudoacacia* to have osmotic concentration values at 15°C. equivalent to 20.9 to 37.5 atmospheres, and Dixon (1933) reports similar concentrations for exudate from *Fraxinus excelsior*. These pressures are nearly a thousand times that occurring in blood capillaries. There is the possibility of coagulation of contents in the tubes for some distance from the cut, but why this should occur if unilateral mass flow is normal does not appear obvious.   If unidirectional mass flow is abnormal, this cutting resulting in such a flow, accompanied by frictional and other disturbances, might easily induce coagulation at some distance from the cut, or the more solid particles may accumulate against the sieve plates and thus clog the pores.   Furthermore, in many types of plants the sieve-tube contents do not readily coagulate (Lecomte, 1889; Münch, 1930; Crafts, 1933).

7. Another difficulty is that, if there is a unidirectional mass flow through the sieve tubes, as postulated by Münch, it is not clear why a local application of anesthetics or local chilling should stop the flow (Curtis, 1929, see also Sec. 39). His hypothesis might easily explain a failure to move through a dead stem, for the killing would be likely to result in a complete plugging of the sieve tubes.   It is, of course, possible that either chilling or anesthetics may cause temporary or reversible coagulation or such a great increase in viscosity as to stop the flow.   Crafts (1932) has made a few tests to determine the effect of chilling on the exudation from the phloem of cut stems of cucumber and has found that a temperature of 2 to 5°C., which apparently stops normal emptying of bean leaves, reduces this exudation only 25 to 50 per cent or less.   His data indicate a gradual and continuous retardation as the temperature is lowered from 25 to 2°C., whereas I found that the effect on carbohydrate transport from the leaves of beans seems to be rather abrupt, first appearing at a temperature near 6°C.   This would suggest that exudation from cut phloem cannot be taken as an indication of normal movement. The method of flow, direction of flow, and rate of flow from such cut tissues may all three be strictly abnormal and due to the cutting.   The danger of interpreting as normal those movements in a tissue which take place after that tissue is cut open may be as serious when applied to the phloem as when applied to the xylem.   This has already been discussed in Sec. 19.

8. Still another difficulty attendant upon the hypothesis of Münch is that a pressure causing a unidirectional mass

flow of solution through pores, such as plasmodesma or sieve pores, must necessarily have a tendency to carry materials that lie across these pores. In other words, the outer layers of protoplasm and the protoplasm within the pores themselves, unless it were highly porous and allowed the solution to filter through it readily, would thus be forced from cell to cell. This would favor the transport of the outer layers of protoplasm, would not allow for its return, and would not allow for direct transport of vacuolar contents where much of the osmotically active material, particularly in parenchyma cells, is probably located, and yet it is the osmotically active material which, according to the hypothesis, is responsible for the transport and is itself transported. It is true that plastids manufacturing or storing carbohydrates are not located in the vacuole but the osmotic concentration of the vacuole must equal or exceed that of the cytoplasm. Münch, though he pictures the protoplasmic layer as the moving layer, seems not to consider this as a difficulty. In the sieve tubes, however, if the sieve pores are so large that they are merely lined with protoplasm, thus leaving the vacuole continuous, this criticism would not apply, but it would seem to apply to movement out of the parenchyma cells and into the receiving cells of any and all kind of plants, and even in sieve tubes it has not been definitely demonstrated that the vacuolar contents are continuous. Although sieve pores have been described as having a parietal layer of protoplasm (Hill, 1908), that this is universally true or even occasionally so has not been conclusively demonstrated. In fact, Crafts (1932) has failed to find any indication of continuity of vacuolar contents.

To allow for mass flow of the sort postulated it would seem that those types of phloem that have few or only occasional sieve tubes, as well as those in which the sieve pores are filled with protoplasm (see Lecomte, 1889; Schmidt, 1917; and Crafts, 1932) would not be very effective as channels for transport. Furthermore, sieve tubes often are imperfectly developed close to the shoot and root meristem to which food must move fairly rapidly.

These many weaknesses in the hypothesis of Münch, and the strong opposing evidence lead me to the conclusion that the hypothesis as it now stands is not tenable.

31. The Hypothesis of Crafts.—Crafts (1931, 1932, 1933) has proposed a mechanism that, in many respects, is similar to that of Münch. Its main difference lies in his assumption that the entire cross section of the phloem, including especially the walls, is effective as a channel for transport. He was led to this suggestion for several reasons. He found that a solution containing about 8 to 10 per cent dry matter exuded from the cut phloem of cucurbits. Kraus (1886) found approximately the same concentration of material, while Münch (1930) found from 12.3 to 23.7 per cent dry matter (14 to 31.2 per cent if expressed as per cent of water as he gives it) in material flowing from cut phloem of several species of trees. Crafts estimated that this material flowed through the phloem of *Cucurbita* at an average linear rate equal to a linear displacement of 0.3 cm. per minute through the total phloem. On first cutting, a rate nearer 1 cm. per minute was obtained. The sieve-tube lumen occupies less than 20 per cent of the total phloem area and the pores only 8 per cent of this, or not over 1.6 per cent of the total phloem area. As a result of more detailed studies of the sieve plates (1932) he concluded that the pores were not actual openings but were completely filled with protoplasmic strands with a much smaller cross section than this estimated area. Applying Poiseuille's formula and assuming the sieve pores to have a diameter of 2μ, which was larger than what he actually found, he calculated that, in order to bring about a flow of solution through the sieve pores at the rate at which material was actually collected, a pressure gradient of 0.2 atmosphere per centimeter would be required. No such pressures, however, seem available.

Measurements before and after dehydration of the phloem demonstrated that the fresh phloem walls contain over 50 per cent water and also occupy over 30 per cent of the total cross-sectional area of the phloem. He therefore suggested that the space occupied by this water in the walls might act as a channel through which the solution is forced. Assuming all this water of the walls filled a single tube, he calculated that a pressure gradient of only 6.1×10^{-5} atmosphere per centimeter would be adequate to cause a flow at the rate observed. Of course, the space occupied by water cannot behave as a single pore but the pressure gradient calculated is sufficiently small to allow for considerable correction for increased resistance. His calculations, he suggested, allow for an increased resistance of about 4,400 times that of the single pore.

When the cut is first made the material is exuded from the phloem at a linear rate of 1 cm. per minute or faster. This flow is rapidly reduced but on repeatedly cutting thin sections from the end it approaches a rather steady rate of around 0.3 cm. per minute or 18 cm. per hour. "Calculations show that this is approximately the rate that would be required to deliver the volume of solution necessary to form the fruits of these plants. Since rates of this magnitude cannot be accounted for on the basis of flow through the sieve tubes, it is suggested that the solution has passed through the phloem walls." Similar rates varying between 13.5 to 19 cm. per hour through the walls of the phloem alone, he estimated, would account for the observed rates of transport of carbohydrates from the leaves of *Tropaeolum majus* and *Phaseolus multiflorus*, as well as the materials necessary to account for the observed seasonal increase in dry weight of the stem of Bartlett pear.

Since other mechanisms that had been proposed seem inadequate and since actual flow from cut phloem was so rapid as to seem to preclude the possibility of flow through the sieve pores, Crafts first suggested (1931) that the walls of phloem cells constituted the major path of transport. In his second paper (1932) he suggested that transport takes place through both walls and lumen. By the time he wrote the third paper (1933) he had come to realize the high resistance to flow through walls and suggested that the lumen is the major path. He suggested further that sieve-tube protoplasm is completely permeable, so flow from cell to cell may take place through end and lateral walls, and is not restricted to flow through pores or plasmodesma. For actually causing the flow he proposed an osmotic gradient scheme similar to that proposed by Münch. His scheme differs, however, in that the materials are not supposed to be forced into the phloem or from the phloem into the receiving cells through the plasmodesma by a pressure gradient. The receiving cells are assumed to be able to remove sugars from the wall through the surface membrane against a concentration gradient.

The chief advantage claimed by Crafts for the superiority of his hypothesis over that of Münch is that it proposes a large increase in the cross-sectional area through which materials may be forced, and therefore seemingly reduces the pressure gradient necessary to cause the flow. He found that the pores through sieve plates in fresh material are more minute than commonly observed in fixed material, and that they are completely filled with strands of protoplasm. Therefore they do not offer tubes for unobstructed flow. Exudation from the peduncle of a cucumber was found to continue at a normal rate even after the sieve tubes were heavily calloused and the sieve pores were apparently closed. It seemed therefore that the exudate could not have come through the sieve pores. He also claims that his hypothesis does not demand a lower osmotic concentration in the receiving cells as does the Münch hypothesis, for he assumes that the receiving cells can readily absorb solutes through these surfaces against a concentration gradient.

32. Weakness in the Hypothesis of Crafts.—At first (1931) Crafts proposed that the high water content of the phloem walls should make them suitable channels for transport. The area of the wall available as a channel he assumed to be indicated by the water content of the wall, which in his determinations was approximately 50 per cent. When one realizes, however, that a tube filled with a 2 per cent agar gel does not allow for ready mass flow of solution, even though 98 per cent of the volume is water, he is led to doubt whether a cellulose matrix with only 50 per cent water would be less resistant. Crafts suggested that the structure of cellulose, forming perhaps a regular lattice system might offer much less resistance than ordinary colloidal gels. These capillaries, however, are at best submicroscopic and may be of molecular dimension, but even if all the space occupied by water were in the form of fine capillaries with none of the water fixed as water of hydration, the resistance to mass flow must be very great.

One cannot safely apply Poiseuille's formula to tubes of such fine dimensions, for the formula assumes that the flow takes place chiefly in the free space at a distance from the wall of the capillary, and that the flow is nil at the wall. In capillaries of such fine dimensions there may be no free flow whatever, or at a certain small radius there may be slow but steady flow with no change in rate with further reduction in size. In this latter case the movement is more probably a diffusional one, and the volume rate of flow may not vary as the fourth power of the radius. Assuming, however, that the law does apply at these dimensions, and also assuming that half of the cross section of the fresh wall is wall material and half is capillary pores, and that the capillaries are of the same dimensions as those calculated for silica gel, namely $5m\mu$ in diameter; then in order to force a 10 per cent sugar solution through the walls of the phloem to a potato tuber at the rate calculated by Crafts, a pressure gradient of 23 million atmospheres per centimeter would be required. With the free space as small as it must be in hydrated phloem walls, movement is probably largely restricted to diffusion. Equally great pressures would be required to cause a diffusional flow at the required rate.

In his second paper (1932) Crafts calculated the minimum diameter of capillaries that would deliver sap at a linear rate of 0.3 cm. per minute, which he estimated to be the normal rate, through a distance of 50 cm. at a pressure

gradient of 7.0 atmospheres (0.14 atmosphere per centimeter) would be 3.3µ. If the flow were taking place
through spaces between parallel planes for a similar rate
and pressure gradient, he estimated a distance between
planes of 2.04µ. Since these demands of pore size are
obviously larger than can be expected in cell walls, he
concluded that part of the flow must take place through
the lumen of the phloem cell. Steward and Priestley
(1932) have given a clear presentation of the weaknesses
in Crafts' earlier calculations of the resistances to be met
in flow through phloem walls.

By the time he wrote his second paper, therefore, Crafts
was beginning to appreciate the difficulties attendant on a
flow restricted to cell walls and suggested that part of the
flow might take place through the lumen. In this paper
he reports an apparently unobstructed flow from the
phloem of the cut peduncles of cucumber fruits, even when
the sieve plates are covered with thick callous plates. There
are also interesting calculations on rates of flow and
valuable material on the anatomy of *Cucurbita* phloem.

When he finally realized the impossibly great pressures
necessary to force solutions along through the walls and
when further investigations led him to conclude that sieve-
tube protoplasm is completely permeable, he modified his
first proposal and suggested (1933) that the entire cross
section of the phloem would act as the channel of transport.
In this later paper he proposes that the principal path of
transport is the lumen of the sieve tubes, while the flow
from cell to cell may take place not through sieve pores or
protoplasmic strands but by filtration across any end or
side walls of the sieve tube that might intervene. He
assumes that the sieve-tube protoplasm is different from
that of other cells in that it is completely permeable. The
basis for this assumption is that in sections mounted for
observation the mature sieve tubes do not behave as young
sieve tubes or other living cells in that they fail to accumulate neutral red, stain easily with analin blue, and are also
incapable of being plasmolyzed. It is possible, however,

that this peculiar behavior of sieve tubes is abnormal and is the result of injury due to cutting and loss of contents by exudation. Calculations of rates of transport through potato stolons, as well as rates of flow from cut phloem of cucurbits, have led him to conclude that it is not possible for solutions to flow through the pores of sieve plates at the rate required for transport or actually observed in exudation. He suggests, therefore, that they must pass freely across walls at all points. The finding of rapid exudation from very young tips of shoots and roots, where differentiated sieve tubes with visible pores are absent, has given added impetus to this interpretation, although he seems to disregard his observation that young sieve tubes do not show this high permeability.

A number of investigators have reported rapid exudation from young undifferentiated tissues when these are cut into. Sachs (1887, p. 362) had observed the exudation of sap from the cut surface of turgid parenchyma and remarked on the fact that the amount of exudate was so great that it could not all have been contained in the cells that were cut open but must have come from cells at some distance from the cut. He points out that this is not so easily explained as the exudation from cut sieve tubes or latex vessels, for in the parenchyma cells the fluid must filter through the protoplasmic linings. Münch (1930) reports exudation from exposed cambium, though he has assumed this was mostly water. Crafts (1931, 1932, 1933) has observed ready exudation from immature cells near the shoot and root tips of *Cucurbita* and *Solanum* in which sieve tubes had not become differentiated. James and Baker (1933) have observed similar exudation from the cambial region of *Acer pseudoplatanus*, and explain the bleeding, observable in many stems, as having originated from the cambial and other immature cells as a result of flow of cell contents according to the Münch mechanism. They claim the exudate does not come from the xylem as is usually assumed. Münch and his followers interpret this flow as indicating a normal translocation flow through

plasmodesma and sieve pores. Crafts, because he finds
the plasmodesma and sieve pores so small, interprets the
flow as coming from the walls or from the completely
permeable sieve tubes. It seems to me, however, that it
may be strictly abnormal exudation of cell contents through
breaks in the surface layer or through plasmodesma that
have become greatly distended as a result of cutting.
Such cutting would release the external pressures which
normally would prevent the distention of thin-walled cells
having high osmotic concentrations. Miehe (1901) reports
having observed nuclei to pass through plasmodesma
when immature parenchyma or epidermal tissues are
wounded. It is conceivable that this movement may
have resulted from sudden release of pressure and distention of plasmodesma.

Although Crafts claims that, according to his proposals,
there need be no pressure gradient between supplying cell
and receiving cell, as is required by the Münch hypothesis,
his hypothesis does require a pressure gradient through the
phloem, and no mechanism is obvious that will account for
secretion into the permeable sieve-tube system at the supplying end and removal from the walls at the receiving
end. For the latter he says "The ability of living non-
photosynthesizing cells to produce a low concentration
within their walls is all that is necessary." Too much
space would be necessary adequately to discuss the essen-
tials and the difficulties involved in a system that would
be effective in introducing sugars into the phloem and in
maintaining a pressure gradient that could cause a flow in
the proper direction through the phloem which has a completely permeable sieve tube system, but which must
prevent leakage through the walls or through accidental
breaks. Special difficulties are also involved in accounting
for absorption of the sugar through their surface membranes
by the living cells at the receiving end, and since a unidirectional flow of solution is assumed, there must be some means
also for getting rid of the water that is carrying the sugar.
Unless the pressure on the solution in the phloem at the

surface of the receiving cell is in excess of the maximum osmotic pressure in the phloem, water will be drawn across the living cell into the phloem instead of being forced out of the phloem.

Although Crafts claims an advantage for his hypothesis because of the greater cross-sectional area allowed for transport, and because it is supposed not to require that the receiving cells have lower turgor than the supplying cells, the hypothesis still retains most of the serious weaknesses of the Münch hypothesis. These have already been discussed under 1, 2, 4, 5, 6, and 7 of Sec. 30 and need not be repeated. The modifications proposed, although they are supposed to overcome some of the weaknesses of the Münch hypothesis, because the proposed channel for transport is larger than that of the Münch scheme and the receiving cells can have a higher turgor than the supplying cells, really result in loss of much of the simplicity of the Münch hypothesis and introduce other serious difficulties. Crafts' scheme also seems to be based on more unproved assumptions than that of Münch. These major unproved assumptions are: (1) that the supplying cells can in some way introduce sugars into the phloem in such a manner that they will develop a pressure gradient leading to the receiving cells; (2) that the sieve tubes are completely permeable and offer a minimum of resistance to flow of solution through the lumen and across walls at all points, and yet that phloem is so enclosed by cambium and phellogen as to prevent leakage; and (3) that the receiving cells can absorb sugars against a gradient with such rapidity as to lower greatly the concentration within the wall outside of the living membrane. Because of the many weaknesses in the hypothesis of Crafts and because the necessary assumptions are not merely unproved* but seem highly improbable, I at no time have accepted his hypothesis and still feel that the hypothesis, even as modified to include transport through the cell lumina, is untenable.

* Phillis and Mason (1933) have, however, demonstrated accumulation of sugar in the phloem against a concentration gradient.

Although I have never accepted Crafts' suggestion that the walls form an important path for transport, or that the sieve tubes are completely permeable so that the entire cross section is available for transport, or that exudation in any way indicates a normal flow, or that the proposed mechanism accounts for the flow, I think these probably mistaken interpretations should not blind one to the fact that his evidence indicates that the exudation from cut phloem, as well as from cut cambium and young meristematic tissue, can hardly have come from normal sieve pores or plasmodesma if these are of the size observed in fresh cut material. The exudation from *Cucurbita* stems, in which most of the phloem had heavy callus on the sieve plates, indicates that the exudation perhaps does not come from sieve tubes. This is supported by his observations, and those of others, on the exudation from young tissues in which the sieve tubes have not become differentiated. Although Crafts obviously has accepted the translocation mechanism proposed by Münch and suggested, first that the walls, and later that the entire phloem might be the channel, because his measurements and calculations pointed to the inadequacy of the sieve pores or plasmodesma to allow for the exudation observed, it seems to me that his findings really tend to throw doubt on the validity of the hypothesis of transport by a pressure flow. If, on the other hand, sieve pores and plasmodesma are distended under natural conditions and much larger than observed in cut material, many of the calculations may be misleading.

Crafts is not the first to have suggested that walls may form the path of transport. Bokorny (1890) found iron to be deposited in the thick-walled elements of both xylem and phloem when the plants had previously been supplied with a solution of iron sulphate. He concluded that this supported the earlier suggestion of Sachs that water rose through the walls by imbibition. Priestley (1929) proposed a flow of solution within walls to supply the shoot meristem and Scott and Priestley (1928) proposed that the soil solution penetrates along the walls of the root cortex cells. Neither of these types of cells have the peculiar thick walls of the phloem region. As has been stated in Sec. 22, the flow within walls of the root cortex is based chiefly on the meager evidence of the staining of the walls. The suggested flow within the walls into the meristem is also largely assumption with little or no supporting evidence. Priestley's chief reasons for suggesting the walls as the channel for transport are that living membranes show high impermeability and that a rapidly developing cell would be unlikely to allow necessary foods to pass through to other cells. If solutes diffuse from cell to cell through plasmodesma and not through surface membranes, the first reason offered loses its force as does perhaps the second reason also. Furthermore the mechanism suggested by Priestley to account for forcing the sap into the meristem is not based on very positive evidence.

The mechanism, as I understand it, is that an isolated, maturing xylem element, or group of elements, as it becomes permeable, releases a rather concentrated solution which draws water osmotically across the membranes of enclosing cells. This sap, rich in foods, is thus forced within the walls to the meristem. This explanation of the method of the nutrition of the growing point is based on three assumptions each of which appears to me not only unsupported by direct evidence but even highly improbable. In the first place it is assumed that the xylem elements, in maturing and losing their protoplasmic membranes, release a relatively concentrated solution. To me it seems more likely that by the time the cell approaches death or loss of its membrane it has used up practically all of its available organic material in respiration and in forming the cell wall; thus little or none would be left either for developing the pressure necessary to force the solution along the walls or for nourishing the meristem. In the second place it is assumed that this solution would be forced toward the meristem, but it is not clear as to what would prevent its leakage in all directions away from as well as toward the

meristem.   Some additional mechanism for bringing solutes
into the meristem must be necessary because each crop of
new cells can hardly depend upon the foods released by the
maturing ones for their nutrition, even if the mechanism
were so perfect as to allow no loss whatever by leakage.
In the third place evidence demonstrating that solutions
can or do flow within the walls of such meristematic cells
is lacking.   Steward (1930) has given evidence that points
very clearly to the complete inadequacy of diffusion along
walls for supplying growing tissues with necessary solutes.

**33. Hypothesis Accounting for Transport by Moving
Protoplasm.**—The hypotheses thus far discussed assume
that there is a mass flow of solution through the phloem
cells, Münch suggesting that the flow is through the lumen
and Crafts suggesting that the entire phloem cross section,
lumen, protoplasm, and cell wall form the channel.   Among
the older proposals we find the suggestion that moving
protoplasm itself may carry the solutes.   Hartig (1858)
was among the first to observe protoplasm moving within
cells and suggested that it might be moving nutritive sap.
DeVries (1885) pointed out that diffusion alone is altogether
too slow to account for translocation and suggested that
protoplasmic streaming would greatly hasten the movement.   He observed and measured the rates of streaming
in companion cells and phloem parenchyma.   The hypothesis that this protoplasmic streaming would account for
translocation seems to have been rather generally dropped
shortly after its proposal, however, for Lecomte (1889),
Strasburger (1891), and others found that streaming,
though active in the individual sieve-tube elements when
they are young, is no longer visible after the cytoplasm
forms a thin layer next to the wall and the pores appear
to open between sieve-tube segments.   This is just the
stage at which one would expect the tubes to become
functional, but since movement was not observed after
this stage, it was assumed that there must be some other
mechanism concerned in transport.

As was pointed out in an earlier paper, however (Curtis,
1929), it seems highly possible that the failure to observe

protoplasmic streaming in mature sieve tubes has been due to the fact that, in preparing the material for observation under the microscope, the sieve-tube contents are greatly disturbed by cutting open the system which normally has a high internal pressure. Assuming that streaming does occur in sieve tubes at rates of the order of those found in internodal cells of *Nitella* or *Chara*, then it would seem to offer a possible mechanism for the transport of solutes in plants. In such a system of tubes containing streaming protoplasm it is conceivable that a diffusion gradient of 1 per cent per centimeter may be maintained over a distance of a meter when the actual difference in concentration at the two points, a meter apart, is only 1 per cent. If streaming is sufficiently rapid, the distance over which actual diffusion takes place may be largely determined by the sum of the thicknesses of the various membranes through which diffusion must take place. If this total thickness of cross walls in a stem a meter long is 2 cm., then the real diffusion gradient would be determined by the actual distance over which movement is limited to diffusion. According to the assumption above, this would be 2 cm. Thus the very slight diffusion gradients reported by Mason and Maskell (1928*b*) which would be meaningless if the movement were left to diffusion alone might well account for considerable movement if the total thickness of the membranes through which diffusion must take place is slight and protoplasmic streaming is carrying the solute from one end of the tube to the other.

Diffusion across thin membranes is extremely rapid as compared with that over the long distances used by deVries in his calculations, for, as A. V. Hill (1926) has emphasized, the time before appearance of a given amount of solute which is moving by diffusion into a medium lacking the particular solute, is inversely proportional to the square of the distance. Thus taking Stefan's calculation, that it would take 319 days for a milligram of sodium chloride to diffuse past a plane at a distance of one meter, the time to carry a similar amount a distance of 10μ (more nearly the thickness of the cell wall) would be 3.19×10^{-12} day, or about 0.003 sec., ten billion times as fast.   Of course, one would not expect so steep a gradient as this in conducting tissues, but it is evident that diffusion over short distances is extremely rapid.   The large number of strands traversing the sieve plates or those connecting one living cell with another through plasmodesma, although they offer but a small total cross-sectional area, should be highly effective in allowing movement from one cell to another by diffusion, as was pointed out by Brown and Escomb (1900).

A rotating stream of the type postulated could readily carry salts, proteins, or any soluble or adsorbed material from the roots in one direction in the same cells that are carrying sugars in the opposite direction from the photosynthetic organs.   In such a system the direction of movement of a given solute would be determined by concentration differences* between the region of supply and that of use, and the amount of solute moved would be determined by the combined influence of concentration difference, the rate of streaming, the number of cross walls, and perhaps also the effectiveness of the strands in preventing mixing of the streams going in opposite directions.   It is conceivable, therefore, that movement might be more rapid between two points a decimeter apart than that between two points a centimeter apart, when the actual concentration difference is the same in both systems. For, if the elongated cells connecting the receiving and supplying regions over the longer distance all show active streaming, whereas the protoplasm in the cells over the shorter distance is not streaming; then, since the total cross-wall thickness through which diffusion must take place over the decimeter distance would probably be much

---

* These concentration differences might appear as actual positive gradients, or, where living cells are capable of concentrating certain solutes or ions against a concentration gradient, they may appear negative when comparing the receiving cell or tissues and the source of supply.   Taking into consideration the actual dynamic equilibrium conditions, however, the gradient along the path should always be positive.

less than 1 cm., the rate of transfer might be greater than over the shorter distance where movement is limited to diffusion. The steepness of diffusion gradients between supplying and receiving cells alone, therefore, may be of minor importance in determining solute distribution. If there is a continuous series of active streaming cells between supplying and receiving cells and if there is actual flow through sieve pores, as seems likely, then the distance between the regions becomes a minor factor.

Points favoring the hypothesis that transport through the phloem takes place by a combination of diffusion with protoplasmic movement of the nature of rotation or streaming are as follows: (*a*) Such movements could account for transport at a rate immensely faster than can be accounted for by diffusion alone. (*b*) Such a mechanism would allow for simultaneous transport in both directions, and considerable evidence points toward such simultaneous transport, although for specific substances the movement may be almost exclusively in one direction (see Sec. 38). (*c*) It could also account for the selective transport of special substances to special tissues (see paragraph 4 of Sec. 28). (*d*) The postulated mechanism could easily account for transport to particular tissues where, because of the distance from the supply or because of only slight diffusion or pressure gradients, other suggested mechanisms would seem not to be adequate. (*e*) This mechanism also seems to offer a simple explanation of the mutual interchange of material between a pair of active organs such as root and leaf or root and shoot (see Sec. 42). (*f*) This hypothesis does not demand great pressure differences which are indispensable for the hypotheses of Münch and of Crafts. (*g*) It could also account for ready transport to a receiving tissue independently of whether that tissue had a higher or a lower osmotic concentration or turgor pressure than the supplying tissue. It could thus account for an emptying of flaccid storage tissues into turgid receiving tissues as well as for a rapid transport from leaves during the day when their turgor is greatly reduced (see paragraph 3, Sec. 30). (*h*) The sieve structures peculiar to phloem tissues seem of significance in that they should allow streaming protoplasm to move from segment to segment, but when a sieve tube is accidentally ruptured, the release of pressure, allowing an abnormal unidirectional mass flow, results in an accumulation of protoplasm or other semisolid material such as starch grains, which would effectively prevent continued bleeding. If unidirectional mass flow of sieve-tube contents due to internal pressure is normal, as claimed for the Münch and Crafts hypotheses, no such simple explanation can account for stoppage when the sieve tubes are cut or broken. (*i*) If solutes are transported by living protoplasm, the indication that living cells are necessary for transport is easily explained.

Any hypothesis postulating unidirectional mass flow, whether or not it involved the mechanism proposed by Münch or Crafts, would be likely to have most of the weaknesses mentioned in connection with the latter hypotheses, especially under paragraphs 1 to 7 Sec. 30, and would be likely to lack the advantages just mentioned under headings (*a*) to (*i*) of the protoplasmic streaming and diffusion hypothesis.

34. Weaknesses in the Hypothesis Accounting for Transport by Protoplasmic Streaming and Diffusion.—*a.* A serious weakness in this hypothesis is that the mechanism, though immensely more efficient than diffusion alone, still seems inadequate to account for the observed rates of movement. Data are not available from which one can make very accurate calculations, but the estimate of Crafts (1933) for the increase of dry matter in potato tubers attached to plants by stolons of known dimensions may serve as a satisfactory basis. He estimated that the tubers had increased in dry matter at a rate of 0.89 g. per day. Careful measurements were made of the cross-sectional area of various tissues in the freshly cut stolons. These are given in Table 20.

From these figures, Crafts estimated that, to carry 0.89 g. of dry matter through the stolon in 24 hr., it would require

TABLE 20.—AREAS OF MEASURED POTATO STOLON
(From Crafts)

	Sq. mm.	% of stolon
Stolon av	9.5	.....
External phloem	1.15	.....
Internal phloem	0.61	.....
Total phloem	1.76	18.5
Sieve tubes	0.40	5.7
Sieve pores	0.009	0.13
Walls of phloem	0.57	6.0
Cortex	.....	*36.5
Xylem	.....	*39.5
Pith	.....	*5.5

* Estimated from unpublished data.

approximately 9 cc. of a 10 per cent solution. This would have to move at a linear rate of 19 cm. an hour if the total cross-sectional area of the entire phloem, walls and lumen, were available as a channel $\left(\dfrac{0.89 \times 9}{0.0176 \times 24}\right) = 19$, or 83.0 cm. per hour if the flow were restricted to the sieve tubes. He estimated the total cross-sectional area of the sieve strands (pores) to be 2.3 per cent of that of the sieve tube. Through the sieve pores, therefore, the rate would have to be 3,609 cm. per hour. On the basis that 0.89 g. of dry matter was moving in the pure state, in which condition it would occupy approximately 0.6 cc., he estimated it would have to move at a linear rate of 1.42 cm. per hour if the entire cross-sectional area of the phloem were the channel. He points out that probably not more than 10 per cent of the phloem area could be occupied by streaming protoplasm and only half of this could be moving in one direction, so, on the assumption that protoplasm is carrying sugar in the pure state equal to its own volume, it would have to move at a linear rate of 56.8 cm. per hour, or 9.47 mm. per minute. The maximum rate of streaming he observed in stolon parenchyma was only 1.8 cm. per hour (0.3 mm. per minute), and since the above figure takes no account of the still greater restriction of the sieve pores, through which he estimated that sugar in the pure state must flow at a rate of 270 cm. per hour to carry the 0.89 g. in 24 hr., he concludes that protoplasmic streaming would be entirely too slow to act as a transporting mechanism.

On the other hand, it is probable that the estimates of rates required are too high because, as pointed out in Sec. 26, estimates of cross-sectional areas of sieve-tube lumen and sieve pores are probably too low. Crafts has found the sieve pores of *Cucurbita* to be smaller than commonly assumed. The open net-like appearance of sieve plates in *Ailanthus, Liriodendron,* and *Populus* figured by MacDaniels (1918), however, indicates that many kinds of sieve plates have large openings. It is true, on the other hand, that the reagents used in preparing these materials may have dissolved out callose layers and this enlarged the openings. It is probable that the cross section of the lumen of sieve tubes is normally much greater than appears when mounted for observation and measurement, because the marked reduction in turgor, which undoubtedly occurs when the system is cut and large amounts of exudate appear, is likely to result in considerable shrinking, especially if the walls are appreciably elastic. Crafts' findings (1931) that phloem cell walls contain about 50 per cent water indicate that they may be elastic, and measurements, by both Münch and Crafts, of the osmotic concentration of phloem contents demonstrate the probability of high turgor pressures. Measurements of osmotic concentration of phloem exudate from *Quercus rubra* made by Münch (1930) ranged from 20.9 to 23.7 atmospheres at 15°C. and from *Robinia pseudoacacia* between 25.8 and 37.5 atmospheres. It is, of course, likely that this phloem exudate does not have the same composition as the naturally moving components, but the rapidity of exudation and the high concentrations found clearly indicate high turgor. Schumacher (1933) has observed that the fluid first exuding from sieve tubes that were transporting fluorescein contained no fluorescein. This was restricted to the protoplasm and appeared later, perhaps when the dying protoplasm could no longer retain it. The exudate, therefore, may not be a true sample of the material moving in uninjured cells. Its high content of sugar, however, indicates that if some other part, such as protoplasm, is the carrier its content of sugar is also likely to be high. Crafts found the exudate to become weaker as successive samples were taken, as did also Frey-Wyssling (1932) for the exudate from the latex system of *Hevea.*

The very fact that rate calculations based on dimensions obtained from cut tissues have invariably led to seemingly impossible figures, adds weight to the suggestion that dimension measurements may be wrong. For example, the calculations of Birch-Hirschfeld (1920), Dixon (1922), Mason and Lewin (1926), Tincker (1928), and Crafts (1931, 1932, 1933) all point to the seeming impossibility of movement through the phloem. Ringing and xylem-cutting experiments, on the other hand, have conclusively proved that the materials do actually move at adequate rates through these tissues.

The seeming inadequacy of streaming, as indicated by calculations of necessary rates, may in part also be due to the low concentrations of sugar assumed to be moving. This does not apply to Crafts' calculations, for he assumed movement of pure sugar. Münch has found phloem exudate to contain as high as 23.8 per cent dry matter, of which about 88 per cent was sugar. An average of 22 determinations from 8 kinds of trees gave a dry-matter content of 17 per cent. Münch (1930, p. 132) expresses this as a percentage of water in which case the average is 20.5 per cent.

It is possible that rates of natural streaming in sieve tubes have been underestimated. It is true that observed rates of streaming in ordinary parenchyma cells and hair cells are rather low. DeVries (1885) reported streaming rates of 0.2 to 0.4 mm. per minute in companion cells, and I have observed rates of 0.25 to 0.36 mm. per minute at 18°C. in the companion cells and phloem parenchyma of a number of plants, and at 25°C. rates of 0.5 to 0.6 mm. per minute in the stamen hairs of *Zebrina*.   Rotational streaming in elongated cells of *Elodea, Nitella, Chara, Valisneria*, and the like, however, has been observed to take place at rates commonly running up to 1 to 2 mm. a minute. Ewart (1903) reports a maximum rate of 6 mm. a minute in *Nitella* at 40°C. and Lambers (1926) reports maximum rates of 5.5 to 7.9 mm. a minute in *Chara, Nitella*, and *Tolypella* at temperatures between 30 and 40°C.

Although rates of visible protoplasmic streaming in stamen hairs, leaf hairs, ordinary parenchyma cells, and phloem parenchyma cells are usually slower than those observable in large, greatly elongated cells like the internodal cells of *Nitella* and *Chara*, it is possible that the streaming in the specialized sieve tubes is as rapid as or even more rapid than the latter.   In observing streaming of protoplasm in the leaf cells of *Elodea*, one can often see that the more elongated cells near the midrib show a more active streaming than the other cells.   This strongly suggests that increased streaming activity is associated with increased length of cell units and increased translocation requirements.

In plants like *Nitella* there seems to be much less structural organization into fine moving strands than is evident in other parenchyma cells, but even here there is not a general unorganized rotational flow of the contents.   I have repeatedly observed differences in rates of movement of particles of different size in *Nitella*, the small particles moving appreciably faster than the larger ones.   As the size of the particles approaches the lower limits of visibility, rates about twice those of the larger particles are evident. Similar more rapid movement of the finer particles in *Elodea* is also apparent.   As Scarth (1927) has pointed out, what appears to be a revolution of the whole cytoplasm in *Elodea* really consists of a series of separately moving strands of kinoplasm carrying the chloroplasts.   It is possible that certain invisible layers of this kinoplasm move much more rapidly even than the finer granules which in turn can be seen to move faster than the chloroplasts. In the highly specialized sieve tubes, it is conceivable that the strands of protoplasm, or certain regions of them perhaps carrying sugars and other solutes, may be moving at still greater speeds.

Schumacher (1933) has demonstrated a movement of fluorescein through the protoplasm of sieve tubes at rates approximating 5 to 6 mm. a minute under optimum conditions. He suggests, however, that the dye is not carried by moving protoplasm (see Sec. 37), one reason being that streaming, with the exception of that observed in plants like *Chara*, is usually much slower than this. On the other hand, it seems significant that this observed rate of movement is within the range of possible streaming in specialized cells.

Although it seems generally agreed that there is no movement of protoplasm through the fine plasmodesma, it is possible that Kienitz-Gerloff (1891) was correct in suggesting that there is such movement. Ewart (1903, p. 30) claims that pressures necessary to cause flow through such pores would be so great that it is safe to conclude that no streaming movement in mass can take place through them. If the flow is due merely to differences in pressure at the two ends of the minute tube, his conclusion seems justified, but normal protoplasmic streaming seems not to be caused by such pressure differences. If normal streaming in fine protoplasmic threads is not due to pressure differences at the two ends of the thread, it is conceivable that flow through plasmodesma and especially that through the coarse connections of sieve pores may take place independently of ordinary pressure differences. Much of the resistance to flow through capillaries is, of course, due to friction, but when forcing liquids through capillaries filled with air or other liquids, a large part of the resistance may be due to surface tension. The surface tension and electrical conditions in flowing protoplasm may be such as to enhance flow and not resist it. The probability (denied by some investigators) that fine protoplasmic threads can pass through walls and thus connect protoplasts with one another which were not originally connected, tends to prove that protoplasm actually passes through these pores, and was not merely left behind as remnants or mere wall markings when the parent cell divided. Such penetration through walls is obvious where the connections are formed between cells that were not originally in contact, as in graft unions or wound healing. In fact, since there are connections on all faces of a mass of cells all of which came from the same parent cell, they cannot possibly have been left as remnants or wall markings at the time the walls were laid between dividing cells. New threads therefore must have penetrated through the walls (or new markings have developed in the walls if they are merely markings as seems improbable). Examples of haustorial penetration of host plants by parasitic fungi are well known and demonstrate the ability of protoplasmic penetration through walls. These strands, however, seem larger and more nearly the size of those in sieve pores. The ready movement of certain viruses from living cell to living cell and the failure of the virus to enter intact living cells from the xylem, as well as failure to move out into the xylem from these cells, as reported by Caldwell (1931), give added evidence that plasmodesma are actual protoplasmic connections which allow for movement of colloidal materials, and at least offer less resistance to penetration than does the surface membrane.

It seems probable that, especially in certain of the higher types of sieve tubes, as in the cucurbits and vines where the pores between sieve-tube segments appear large and the connecting strands are relatively coarse, there is active streaming of the protoplasm through the pores. It is possible that strands flow in one direction through some of the pores and back through other pores in the opposite direction. Possibly both currents pass through a single pore, for in observing protoplasmic movements one can frequently see a movement in both directions along a single narrow strand. Under such conditions a single rotating or streaming unit may be a decimeter or more long. This would necessitate less frequent diffusion across walls.

b. Another major weakness in this streaming hypothesis is that streaming has not been demonstrated in mature sieve tubes, except in such aquatics as *Elodea,* and in these the cells may not be typical or true sieve tubes. The facts that active streaming and rotational movements have been observed in practically all types of living plant cells, that this is especially noticeable in elongated cells, and that a not unreasonable explanation for failure to observe streaming in mature sieve tubes is at hand, as explained on page 174, all greatly reduce the seriousness of this weakness.

c. Tests with aquatic plants, like *Elodea* and *Vallisneria* which show active streaming, have not clearly demonstrated that streaming, even when it is known to take place, is effective in greatly hastening transport. Bierberg (1908) observed that transport was faster in plants showing protoplasmic rotation than in those in which streaming was stopped by ether. The increased rates, however, were only between three and four times those in the check plants and this seems rather insignificant. Although Bierberg states that he used potassium nitrate, sodium chloride, and lithium carbonate, he does not state which of these gave the reported results. Kok (1931, 1933), using pieces of *Vallisneria* leaves and *Drosera* tentacles, tested the influence of protoplasmic rotation on the transport of lithium nitrate and caffein. She was unable to detect any accelerating influence of rotation on transport, although both the reagents penetrated into the vacuoles.

A failure to demonstrate an accelerating influence of rotation on the transport of lithium salts or caffein is not conclusive proof that such streaming will not favor transport of other solutes. It is probable that lithium is not taken up by the streaming part of the system. Birch-Hirschfeld was unable to demonstrate transport of lithium through the phloem, yet it has been conclusively demonstrated that other solutes are rapidly carried through the phloem. Schumacher (1933) has offered rather conclusive proof that fluorescein is transported through sieve tubes with great rapidity, 5 to 6 mm. per minute, and that this is probably transported exclusively by the protoplasm (see Sec. 37). He suggests, however, that protoplasmic movement itself does not carry the dye.

d. If materials are transported through the phloem by protoplasmic streaming it would seem that different materials would move in opposite directions simultaneously, and it has not been clearly demonstrated that transport through the phloem does take place in both directions simultaneously. The exudation from cut phloem undoubtedly results from a unidirectional flow, but this may be strictly abnormal and due merely to opening a system which is under high pressure. The observations of Hartig (1861), however, that exudation ceases when a second cut is made above the first, but does not cease when the second cut is below, strongly points to a normal flow in one direction. If, on the other hand, simultaneous movement in both directions is demonstrated, the mechanisms which demand a unidirectional flow, such as those of Münch and Crafts, would have to be abandoned. If, however, unidirectional transport is proven the protoplasmic streaming hypothesis falls down or would require modification. It is, of course, conceivable that the protoplasm moving in one direction is different, perhaps bearing a different charge from that moving in the opposite direction and may thus carry a given substance in one direction only. There is some evidence strongly pointing to a unidirectional movement of specific substances. Bennett (1927) reports experiments in which the leaf curl virus of raspberries is shown to move through the phloem in but one direction, and this direction seems to be determined by the direction of major movement of carbohydrates. Caldwell (1931), working with a virus on tomato, has demonstrated simultaneous movement in both directions and at approximately equal rates. However, it seems that this virus moves rather slowly and may move exclusively through parenchyma cells and not through the phloem.

Van der Wey (1932) has given almost incontrovertible evidence that the growth substance of *Avena* coleoptiles is carried in one direction only and he gives strong evidence that its transport is independent of protoplasmic streaming. This growth substance is probably carried through phloem parenchyma cells of the coleoptile, but whether it is also carried through sieve tubes is not known.

Went (1932) has proposed that specific substances, such as these growth substances, are carried cataphoretically under the influence of a constant electrical gradient in the plant. He suggests that these are carried in the companion cells, while the foods are transported through the sieve tubes by a pressure mechanism, such as that proposed by Münch. Although one might expect growth substances to be carried through the phloem by the same mechanism as food transport, this point is still far from settled.

Schumacher (1933) has observed that fluorescein moves almost exclusively in a basipetal direction through leaf petioles of *Pelargonium*, although when reaching the stem it more commonly spreads in both directions. Critical experiments clarifying this point, as to whether transport of solutes through the phloem is strictly unidirectional or not, would help greatly in our solution of the problem as to the possible mechanism of transport. (For further discussion of transport of special substances see Sec. 38.)

e. Another weakness in the streaming hypothesis lies in the possibility that movement might not be determined by a diffusion gradient. Whether this weakness is to be considered serious or not, will depend upon the outcome of investigations which should reveal the fact whether transport does or does not follow a diffusion gradient. Thoroughly adequate data on this point are at present lacking, although recently Mason and Maskell have presented rather conclusive evidence that sucrose is the sugar of transport and its movement through the sieve tubes is correlated with its diffusion gradient. A detailed discussion of concentration gradients and their bearing on the transport by protoplasmic streaming are considered in Sec. 35 and also partly in Sec. 42.

35. The Relation of Concentration Gradients to Transport.—Although Mason and Maskell appear to be the first investigators to give data that can be safely interpreted as indicating real concentration gradients, it seems desirable to consider briefly the works of a few others which give data that show indications of concentration gradients that can be compared with the findings of Mason and Maskell who have restricted their investigation to the cotton plant. Sachs (1863), Schimper (1885), Rywosch (1908, 1909), and others have observed the order of emptying and filling of leaves or storage organs and have interpreted these in terms of gradients, but they are of little help in the problem before us.

From results of many analyses of leaf blades, midribs, and stalks of several plants, but principally the mangold and potato, Davis, Daish, and Sawyer (1916) conclude that sucrose is the primary product of photosynthesis in all leaves and that this is introduced into the conducting tissue where, during transport to storage roots or tubers, it is gradually transformed into hexoses. They suggest that the sugar is finally absorbed as hexose by the storage organs, in the cells of which it is converted into the storage product, starch, inulin, sucrose, etc. Their analyses of leaf blades, midribs, and upper and lower parts of the leaf stalks showed a progressive increase of hexoses and a slight decrease in sucrose, with a marked decrease in proportion of sucrose to hexose. One set of analyses for sugars in the mangold showed the following contents expressed as percentage of dry weight at 4 P.M.

	Leaf	Midrib	Stalk
Sucrose.............................	4.38	6.08	5.26
Hexose.............................	7.00	22.60	26.30

Since their data are expressed only as percentages of dry weight, there is no way of knowing what the actual concentration gradients were. They assume that the percentage of dry weight indicates actual concentration gradients and imply a diffusional mechanism for transport. They say that Brasse in 1886 pointed out that if sugar moves as sucrose it must move contrary to ordinary laws, for the concentration in the receiving cells is higher and therefore movement would be expected in the opposite direction. Although Davis, Daish, and Sawyer themselves, imply a diffusion mechanism for transport and their data show a rather steep gradient for hexoses, they make no comment on the fact that the concentration gradient for these hexoses leads from the storage organ to the leaf and not in the direction of assumed movement. The sucrose gradient is less steep but does lead in the proper direction, that is toward the storage organ, and the concentrations show only slight daily or seasonal fluctuations. The hexoses, on the other hand, fluctuate greatly both with time of day and with season. Although they conclude that hexose is the translocation sugar, it is conceivable that the sugar was actually being transported as sucrose along a positive diffusion gradient and the variations in hexoses merely indicate temporary accumulation and depletion in nonconducting tissues.

If the percentages of dry weight indicate the relative actual concentrations, the total osmotic concentration due to carbohydrates becomes greater at greater distances from the leaf, for although total sugar, as percentage, varied only slightly between upper and lower parts, the hexose increased markedly at greater distances from the leaf blade. This would be contrary to the requirements of the Münch hypothesis. The hexose gradient is also contrary to the requirements of the diffusion hypothesis. The sucrose gradient within the midribs and stalks, however, seems in agreement with the diffusion hypothesis. The leaf concentrations, on the other hand, are low and the concentration in the receiving organ is not given. Since all data are based on mass analyses of a mixture of tissues and not of individual tissues and since they are expressed as percentages of dry weight, further discussion of the implications would seem unprofitable.

Belval (1930), from analyses of banana material, came to conclusions similar to those of Davis, Daish, and Sawyer, that is, that sucrose is produced in the leaf, that this enters the conducting tissues where it is progressively transformed into hexoses which increase in amount at greater distances from the leaves, and that sugars enter the fruits as hexoses and are then transformed into starch.

Weevers (1924) has determined the hexose and sucrose contents of green and white parts of twelve different kinds of variegated leaves. His data are all expressed as percentages of dry weight. In only one of the twelve did he find any reducing sugars in the white parts and in that one the content was low as compared with the amount in the green parts. The hexose gradient, therefore, undoubtedly led from green to white parts. For sucrose, six of the species showed higher contents in the green parts, five showed higher contents in the white parts, and with one there was no difference between the two. Since the white parts had a higher water content than the green parts, it is probable that several that showed a higher sucrose content in the white parts when expressed as percentage of dry weight would have shown a reverse gradient if expressed as percentage of water. The indications are, therefore, that the sucrose gradient as well as that for hexoses is in the direction of transport.

Bruns (1925) has presented analytical data from leaf tissues that have some bearings on sugar gradients and transport. Using leaves of *Helianthus* and *Nicotiana* he determined the sugar contents of the larger veins and those of the mesophyll. Analyses were made of leaves immediately on harvesting after a bright day and of similar leaves that had been stored in the dark for two days. Of those stored in the dark some were stored as entire leaves while others were separated into main veins and mesophyll.

There were also two conditions of storage, moist and dry. For the most part the data are expressed as percentages of dry weight, but since the water contents are also given the sugar contents per 100 g. of water can be easily calculated. Expressing the data in this way the freshly harvested leaves of *Helianthus* showed 0.643 g. sucrose and 0.443 g. hexose per 100 g. water in the mesophyll, and 0.566 g. sucrose and 1.71 g. hexose in the veins. Those for *Nicotiana* were 0.583 g. sucrose and 0.414 g. hexose in the mesophyll, and 0.502 g. sucrose and 1.58 g. hexose in the veins. In the entire ten sets, five each of *Helianthus* and *Nicotiana*, whether analyzed immediately or after moist or dry storage and independently of whether the mesophyll and principal veins were or were not isolated before storage, the sucrose gradients in all but one instance with *Helianthus* were found to lead from mesophyll to veins. The hexose gradients, on the other hand, with but one exception with *Nicotiana*, led in all cases from veins to mesophyll. Maltose was found in the mesophyll in all cases, but in only the entire leaves in dry storage where the leaves became considerably wilted was there any maltose found in the veins.

Bruns also presents one set of analyses of variegated leaves of *Hedera helix* in which the white parts of the leaves were separated from the green. The green parts contained a larger proportion of veins which tends to complicate the data somewhat, as the veins have a higher water content, a higher hexose content, and a lower sucrose content than the mesophyll. But in spite of this the sucrose per 100 g. of water in the green parts was 2.94 g., while that in the white parts was only 1.19 g. The reducing sugars also had a higher concentration in the green parts, but this may have been due in part to the greater proportion of veins.

Mass analyses of general stem or leaf tissues, however, as were obtained by these investigators may give an entirely wrong impression as to which of the constituents found are actually being transported. The seeming gradient in one direction for sucrose and in the reverse direction for hexoses may not actually obtain in the conducting elements themselves.

The studies of Mason and Maskell (1928*b*, 1934), Maskell and Mason (1930*a*, 1930*c*), and Phillis and Mason (1933) give a much clearer picture as to the form in which carbohydrate is transported and the concentration gradients in the phloem. Other investigators had determined concentrations of sugars by analyzing entire veins or petioles, which therefore included xylem and parenchyma tissues with the phloem. Mason and Maskell not merely separated bark from wood but subdivided the bark into outer, middle, and inner portions.

The distribution of the phloem is not uniform throughout these regions of the cotton bark but increases markedly in proportion to the general parenchyma as one approaches the cambium (see Fig. 11). The phloem with its attendant sclerenchyma forms wedge-shaped groups with the base of the wedge facing the cambium, while between these groups are wedge-shaped masses of general parenchyma with the base of the wedge facing the outside. The inner layers of bark, therefore, contain a relatively high content of phloem and low content of cortical parenchyma, while outer layers contain high cortical parenchyma and low phloem. The outer phloem is also older and much of it may therefore be nonfunctional.

Data showing the radial distribution in the bark of sucrose and reducing sugars as well as of several nitrogen fractions are given in Table 21 and Fig. 11. These clearly indicate that sucrose is the predominant sugar in the inner tissues which are chiefly phloem proper, and reducing sugar is predominant in the outer cortical parenchyma. The phloem region is also richer in crystalloid nitrogen, the significance of which is briefly discussed at the end of this section. Not only does the high sucrose content of the phloem (which they call "sieve tubes") indicate that this is the transport sugar, but this is supported by their finding that any marked changes in sugar content of the

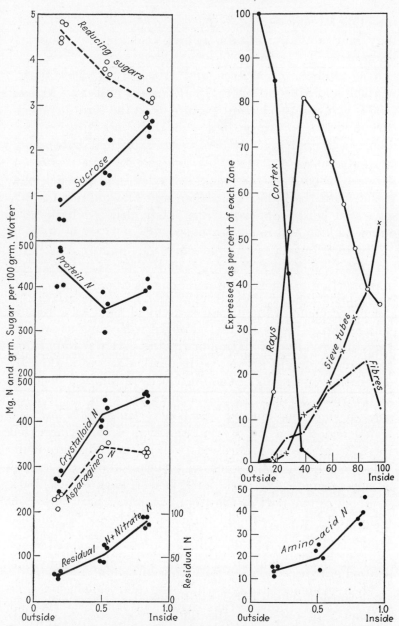

FIG. 11.—Radial distribution of bark tissues and of sugars and nitrogen fractions.
(*From Maskell and Mason.*)

TABLE 21.—RADIAL DISTRIBUTION OF SUGARS AND NITROGENOUS
COMPOUNDS IN THE BARK
Milligrams per 100 g. water
(*From Maskell and Mason*)

	Outer fraction	Middle fraction	Inner fraction
Total nitrogen............................	708.1	766.6	846.3
Protein nitrogen..........................	442.5	348.3	390.0
Total crystalloid nitrogen................	265.6	418.3	456.3
Asparagine nitrogen......................	222.9	346.1	329.0
Amino-acid nitrogen.....................	14.2	20.3	39.3
Residual nitrogen +⎰ Nitrate nitrogen ⎱	28.5	51.9	88.0
Sucrose..................................	762.0	1,607.0	2,565.0
Reducing sugars.........................	4,610.0	3,651.0	3,082.0
Total sugars.............................	5,372.0	5,258.0	5,647.0

bark following various treatments are to be ascribed
chiefly to changes in sucrose content of this inner region.
These changes were normal changes with time as well as
those induced by defoliation or ringing.   It was found that
the radial gradient of sucrose in particular was altered by
defoliation or ringing.   Defoliation resulting in a decrease
in transport of sugar caused a marked falling off in total
sucrose and the sucrose gradient.   Ringing below the
tested region so as to prevent removal of sugar increased
the concentration of sucrose as well as the radial gradient.
When conditions were such as to bring about movement
of sugar from leaf to bark, bark to leaf, bark to boll, bark
to wood, or one part of the stem to another part, above or
below, they always found diffusion gradients for sucrose
in the respective tissues to lead in the proper direction;
and, furthermore, where rates were estimated, these rates
showed a high correlation with concentration gradients.

Their evidence strongly supports their conclusion that
sucrose is the translocation sugar and that the rate and
direction of translocation are determined by diffusion
gradients.   The observed rates of movement through the
phloem, however, would give a diffusion constant for

sucrose about forty thousand times as great as the diffusion constant in a 10 per cent solution of sucrose in water. This, they point out, "is almost identical with the diffusion constant for molecules of the size of the sucrose molecule diffusing in air."

In their analyses of sugar concentrations in the bark and the boll of cotton, Mason and Maskell found in the bark a concentration of 2.441 per cent reducing sugars, and 2.647 per cent of sucrose (estimating the amounts in the "sieve tubes" or phloem proper these would be 1.019 reducing sugar, and 4.992 sucrose). The concentrations in the boll were 4.870 per cent reducing sugar and 0.626 per cent sucrose. It is obvious, therefore, that the concentration gradient for sucrose would tend to cause its diffusion toward the boll. That for hexoses, however, would tend to cause them to be carried back toward the leaf tissues unless one postulates, as do the authors, that there is the equivalent of a membrane between the "sieve tube and other tissues of the boll, permeable to sucrose but impermeable to reducing sugars." (See Sec. 42 for additional data on gradients.) If the sugars pass readily from cell to cell through plasmodesma, however, unless these have also the properties of membrane semipermeability, it would seem that the hexoses would pass back into the sieve tubes, and be rapidly carried back to the supplying cells by the same protoplasmic streaming mechanism that brought sucrose from the supplying cells. One can be certain, however, that protoplasmic streaming is rarely if ever a simple mass stirring of cell contents, but that there is considerable structural organization (see especially Scarth, 1927) which may be highly effective in controlling the movement of special constituents. This structural streaming in narrow strands can be readily seen in many living cells and especially in phloem cells. The different solutes, whether merely different carbohydrates or different in other respects, may occupy different parts of the living cell. Thus certain solutes, such as sucrose, may be present in the moving parts while others, such as hexoses, may be present in the relatively quiet parts, perhaps in the vacuole where they may be present as temporary storage materials.

Phillis and Mason (1933) have presented evidence that is of considerable importance in its bearing on concentration gradients and transport. They analyzed saps expressed from various parts of cotton leaves which were divided into lamina (excluding midribs), veins, and petiole. The petiole was also further subdivided into "outer bark," "inner bark" (principally phloem), and "wood." In their

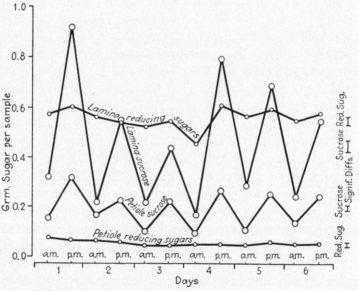

Fig. 12.—Daily variations in sugars (grams per 40 leaves) of lamina and petiole. (*From Phillis and Mason.*)

analyses they distinguished between sucrose, glucose, fructose, and an unidentified polyglucoside. As shown in Fig. 12, they found marked daily fluctuations in sucrose and but slight fluctuations in the other constituents. They present strong evidence that sucrose is the transport sugar, and, what is of special interest to the present subject of discussion, they found what seems conclusive evidence that the sucrose concentration of the veins is much higher than that of the mesophyll from which sugar is received. There is therefore a reverse gradient, and it seems that there must be some mechanism by which phloem can accumulate sucrose against a steep reverse gradient. They suggest that the companion cells and the enlarged companion-like cells that surround the sieve tubes in the fine veins may be responsible for the accumulation of sucrose in the sieve tubes. Schimper (1885) gives evidence indicating that these cells are capable of absorbing sugar against a concentration gradient. After entering the phloem it seems that sucrose moves along a positive gradient. This is shown in Table 22.

TABLE 22.—CONCENTRATIONS IN VARIOUS PARTS OF LEAF
Grams per 100 cc sap
(From Phillis and Mason)

	Lamina		Petiole	
	Mesophyll	Vein	Bark	Wood
Sucrose..............	0.61	1.04	1.06	1.13
Glucose..............	0.41	1.15	0.42	0.71
Fructose.............	0.23	0.20	0.09	0.29
Polyglucoside.........	0.29	0.02	0.05	0.01

In order to reverse the sugar movement they darkened 10 per cent of the leaves, then a day later ringed the bases of the plants, and followed by taking, for a period of 4 days, daily samples of those leaves that were darkened and those that were illuminated. The changes in composition over the 4-day period are shown in Table 23. It is indicated by these data, as well as by others presented in the original, that sugar has moved rather freely into the petioles and veins of the darkened leaves but only very slightly into the mesophyll. In fact, the small gains recorded may have been mostly in the finer veins. This evidence also supports the suggestion that there is some mechanism effective in moving sugar into the sieve tubes against a concentration gradient, and in preventing its movement back into the mesophyll.

In material not as yet published Scofield and I have obtained considerable evidence that growing tissues receiv-

TABLE 23.—PERCENTAGE INCREASE OF FINAL DRY WEIGHT OF MESOPHYLL
AND VEIN ON INITIAL DRY WEIGHT
(From Phillis and Mason)

Illuminated mesophyll............................ 47.15
Illuminated vein................................. 30.89

Darkened mesophyll.............................. 4.53
Darkened vein................................... 10.44

ing sugar from storage tissues may have concentrations
of both sucrose and reducing sugars distinctly in excess
of the supplying storage tissues. Whether the concentration in these tissues is higher or lower than in the
phloem or transporting tissue we have no evidence. It
would seem, therefore, that meristematic tissues, whether
they are elongating shoots or roots or growing storage
tissues, can receive sugars from supplying storage tissues
when the latter have lower concentrations. This ability
seems independent of whether the receiving tissue is basal
or apical to the storage tissue and the movement therefore
seems fundamentally distinct from the polar movement of
growth substance. If direction of flow is determined by
ability of receiving cells to concentrate against a diffusion
gradient—and this seems to be indicated by the available
evidence—actual concentration gradients, except within
the sieve tubes themselves, may have little to do with
direction of movement. It seems probable that the direction of movements within the phloem is actually determined by the concentration gradient in this tissue, as has
been so ably demonstrated by Mason and Maskell. On
the other hand, the actual concentration within receiving
and supplying cells outside of the conducting system proper
may not determine the direction of movement, while the
ability of the receiving cells to accumulate against a gradient or to prevent loss may be of major importance. If
living cells other than those of the phloem differ in their
abilities to absorb sugars against a gradient, it is conceivable that the living phloem cells themselves might
differ also, in which case they also may be able to transport
against a diffusion gradient. According to this line of

reasoning, a mechanism of transport depending on streaming protoplasm does not invariably demand transport along a diffusion gradient.

Although Mason and Maskell's studies of concentration gradients and transport of sugars are rather convincing, their attempts to find the form in which nitrogen is transported have been much less successful (Maskell and Mason, 1929a, 1929b, 1930a, 1930b, 1930c; Mason and Maskell, 1934; and Mason and Phillis, 1934). Their difficulties in this line are due in part, as they suggest, to the fact that the nitrogen compounds may rapidly change from one form to another and may also be carried in more than one form. There is also the complicating factor of static gradients of storage or protoplasmic nitrogen. These same difficulties apply to determinations of gradients of carbohydrate but are greatly minimized in the latter because there are fewer forms, only sucrose and reducing sugars, that seem to be concerned in carbohydrate transport, whereas for nitrogen there are many forms that may be concerned. During their studies they have determined total nitrogen, protein nitrogen, crystalloidal nitrogen which has been fractionated to determine amino-acid nitrogen, ammonia nitrogen, nitrate nitrogen, asparagine nitrogen, and residual nitrogen. Although nitrogen will not disappear en route while carbohydrate may disappear through respiration, the amounts of carbohydrate moved are greatly in excess of the nitrogen, so gradients may be more easily determined.

What seems to me a major difficulty in determining nitrogen gradients appears to have been completely overlooked by Maskell and Mason and this oversight seems greatly to weaken their interpretations (see also Sec. 14, p. 81). They assumed that all nitrogen moves through the xylem to the leaves from where it moves through the phloem to other parts. Thus in a normal stem they assume nitrogen is moving only downward through the phloem. In their attempts to reverse the movement of nitrogen through the phloem (1930a) they treat shoots in a fashion much like that shown in shoot 1 of Fig. 1. In this case, however, a second ring is placed at R^1. In one set they have leaves at the base with the upper part defoliated as here indicated, and in the other the leaves are in the upper part just below the upper ring while the lower part is defoliated. They assume that all nitrogen moves first to the leaves and then moves down through the phloem when the leaves are above. When the upper part is defoliated and the leaves are below, they assume they have reversed the direction of flow of nitrogen through the phloem.

When the leaves are above, however, and the defoliated region below, it is probable that some of the nitrogen as it passes the ring through the xylem will be immediately absorbed by the living cells of the rays which in this region would be gorged with carbohydrate. From here it may move over to the phloem and up through this defoliated region and not down. Eckerson (1924) and Thomas (1927) have rather clearly demonstrated that tissues of roots and stems may convert nitrate to organic nitrogen. Maskell and Mason's assumption that all the nitrogen in the bark must have come from the leaves above is certainly not well established. Their "increased negative gradient" for several forms of nitrogen in this region, therefore, may be in fact an increased positive gradient of nitrogen moving to the leaves or to the growing apex. I do not doubt that in ordinary stems some nitrogen moves to the leaves through the xylem. My own experiments as well as those of Mason and Maskell have demonstrated that conclusively. There are indications that, when nitrogen is in excess, or when the tissues are starved for carbohydrates, rather large amounts may move through the xylem. But it is far from established that all the upward moving nitrogen is carried exclusively through the xylem, and, unless movement through the phloem is strictly unidirectional, it would seem highly probable that some of the nitrogen after it passes the ring will be absorbed by the phloem, especially when it is gorged with carbohydrate.   The increase with time in "negative gradient" (that is, higher nitrogen near the base and lower above) in both bark and wood of nitrogen-starved cotton plants, as reported by Mason and Phillis (1934), would to me seem *more likely to be due to a retention by the carbohydrate-filled tissues, of nitrogen that has never reached the leaves.*   Actually Maskell, Mason, and Phillis have no conclusive proof, except perhaps where it is entering bolls or an isolated flap or defoliated region above leaves, as to the *direction* of movement through the phloem, so it is not surprising that they have difficulty in determining which constituent or constituents are directly concerned in transport through the phloem.   They give data (1929b) which clearly indicate that the conducting phloem is especially rich in crystalloid nitrogen, particularly amino-acid nitrogen and asparagine (see Table 21 and Fig. 11), and if one is not misled by their assumption of a transport restricted to downward movement through the phloem, their data clearly point to these as the translocation forms of nitrogen.

This oversight on their part, it seems to me, is a serious weakness attendant upon most of their extensive discussions in which they attempt to interpret their data on concentration gradients for nitrogen as well as for potassium, phosphorus, and calcium.   Since they have not established beyond a doubt the direction in which these materials are actually moving through the phloem, the data can hardly be handled with confidence.   If their assumption, namely, that nitrogen and ash constituents under normal conditions all move directly from the roots to the leaves and then down only through the phloem, is true, their data could be interpreted as they do.   If the mechanism of movement proposed by Münch is correct, one might expect upward movement of salts from the soil to be limited to the xylem and the downward flow would take place exclusively by way of the phloem.   In that case, however, concentration gradients of individual constituents would be meaningless because the flow would be dependent on a pressure gradient determined by osmotic concentration and not by individual concentration gradients.   According to the Münch hypothesis any minerals that might diffuse from the xylem across to the phloem would be carried along with the other phloem contents. Mason and Maskell, however, seem to assume that there is no such absorption from the xylem by the phloem.   Any such diffusion across, if in appreciable amounts, would seem hopelessly to complicate attempts at interpreting concentration gradients in terms of transport.

In their first paper on nitrogen transport (1929*a*) they find that flaps of bark receive nitrogen from above, which is clear proof that the nitrogen has moved down from above. When the bark is connected with the wood, the wood contains more nitrogen than when the bark is separated from the wood.   They interpret this as proving that the nitrogen has moved from the bark to the wood.   Such an interpretation is not unreasonable, but an alternative explanation is just as reasonable, that is, when the bark is raised from the wood, the wood fails to receive sugar; therefore it is less likely to absorb nitrogen from the transpiration stream or even retain that which it had originally.   The fact that the separated flap does not contain more nitrogen than the normal is in opposition to their contention that less has been transported to the wood, though of course this point might be otherwise explained as resulting from injury.

36. The Surface Tension Hypothesis of Van den Honert. It has been observed that a substance which lowers the interfacial tension between two immiscible liquids tends to spread rapidly over the interface between them, moving from the region of its application, where the surface tension is lowered, toward a region of its absence where the surface tension is high.   Van den Honert (1932) describes an apparatus in which he has observed the rapid spread of potassium oleate over the interface between water and ether.   The rate of spread was such as to give a movement approximately 68,000 times that calculated for diffusion. This rate is of the same order of magnitude as that found by Mason and Maskell for the transport of carbohydrate.

Furthermore, since the lowering of the surface tension is dependent on the concentration of the interface-active substance, the rate of transport is a function of concentration gradient. This also is in agreement with translocation along a concentration or diffusion gradient. It is tentatively suggested by Van den Honert that the interface boundary between protoplasm of the sieve tubes and the vacuole might serve as the boundary between two immiscible liquid phases, where any substance lowering the interfacial tension would tend to spread along this interface until concentration differences are equalized. He says, "This should of course be accompanied by protoplasmic streaming which could, however, be the consequence instead of the agent of the transport. The primary cause of the transport would be only the concentration-difference of the substance to be transported."

It has long been recognized that surface tension phenomena might account for the observed streaming of protoplasm (see especially Ewart, 1903; Tiegs, 1928) and that the streaming may account for the transport of materials. It is therefore highly interesting that Van den Honert suggests that protoplasmic streaming is the result of transport and not the vehicle itself. If transport is brought about by spread in an interfacial film, it is not clear why this moving film should result in a streaming of the more viscous protoplasm without causing an even greater flow of the more liquid watery phase. The latter, however, appears stationary (Ewart, 1903; Scarth, 1927). It is conceivable that the surface film of protoplasm itself may move faster than other layers (see Sec. 34*a*) and may then be the vehicle of transport. In such an event there is no real difference between the mechanism proposed by Van den Honert and the protoplasmic streaming hypothesis.

Even accepting his suggestion that the more rapid interfacial movement carries surface-active materials, it is at the same time conceivable that the visibly moving protoplasm itself also carries some of the transported substances.

The evidence, however, is as yet inadequate to prove in which region the major transport of sugar or other materials takes place. The observations of Schumacher (1933) on the transport of fluorescein and those of Van der Wey (1932) on the transport of growth substance are of great interest, both for the data given and for the bearing of these on the problem of the mechanism of transport. Their findings might be interpreted to support this hypothesis.

37. Schumacher's Observations on the Transport of Fluorescein.—Schumacher (1933) has reported some extremely interesting experiments on translocation in which he used the vital stain, fluorescein. Most of the experiments were carried out with specimens of *Pelargonium* which had been forced into vigorous growth by growing them in partial shade at high humidity, and by removal of all flower buds. The fluorescein was introduced by placing on the scraped surface of a leaf vein or stem a drop of 5 per cent gelatin containing a 0.1 per cent solution of the potassium salt. The presence of the dye was detected by fluorescence when longitudinal sections were mounted in paraffin oil and examined in a dark room using light of short wave lengths. He found that fluorescein is strongly absorbed by the protoplasm of sieve tubes as well as that of parenchyma cells. The green fluorescence is observable in the nucleus, protoplasmic threads, outer protoplasm, and starch grains of both leucoplasts and chloroplasts. The walls and vacuoles appeared totally dark and devoid of fluorescein. The protoplasm of dead or injured cells does not stain, and the stain is lost from the cells as they approach death. It spreads with great rapidity through the cytoplasm of sieve tubes and much more slowly in that of parenchyma cells. He made the interesting observation that, as the fluorescein was entering the sieve tubes from the gelatin, the companion cells were commonly more intensely fluorescent than other cells. This supports the suggestion of Czapek (1897) that these cells are especially concerned in carrying substances to and from the sieve tubes. After entering the sieve tubes, rapid spread is almost exclusively through the sieve-tube system. The companion cells, however, practically always fluoresce also. Shortly after application of the dye, he observed a marked concentration gradient in the sieve-tube system, grading from strong to faint fluorescence within a few centimeters. He also noted with surprise that the cambiform cells directly adjacent to the sieve tubes were totally dark and remarked on the possibility of peculiar permeability of the sieve-tube walls on these faces. It is interesting to note in this connection that Kienitz-Gerloff (1891) and Fischer (1886) both failed to find plasmodesma connecting cambiform cells with sieve tubes, though between cambiform cells and ordinary parenchyma there are abundant plasmodesma. Later Kienitz-Gerloff (1902) reports his own observations agreeing with those of Kohl, of Kuhla, and of Strasburger to the effect that in some plants plasmodesma, usually restricted to pits, are observable in the walls between sieve tubes and cambiform and companion cells. It is highly interesting and possibly of considerable significance that plasmodesma connecting sieve tubes as well as guard cells with their adjacent cells are rare or restricted to small groups in pits. Both in guard cells and in sieve tubes the cells are able to concentrate sugars at concentrations much in excess of those found in the adjacent cells. Unrestricted and unspecialized protoplasmic connections, if highly permeable to sugars, would seem to mitigate against accumulation of sugar or other solutes in one cell over that in adjacent cells. In fact, this very difficulty led me to the finding of the reports of Kienitz-Gerloff on plasmodesma of these specialized cells. Schumacher attempted to determine whether transfer from cell to cell takes place through plasmodesma. Although in epidermal cells and in sieve plates of *Pelargonium* he could occasionally see what appeared to be connecting fluorescent strands he could not be certain of it. The strands through sieve plates of *Curcurbita*, however, were clearly fluorescent and here the strands were obviously the path of movement.

When introduced through leaves, with but rare exceptions even in half-grown leaves, fluorescein moved down-

ward only through the petiole to the stem from where it
moved upward only, downward only, or in both directions.
For the most part the movement was chiefly toward the
growing point, and during June and July it was exclusively
in that direction, but the dye never entered even the
youngest leaves. In some of the other species of plants
tested this polar movement was not so marked.

The rate of movement was markedly influenced by
temperature. In a warm room at 30°C. the fluorescein
had passed through an entire petiole in one hour. Several
measurements indicated rates of from 30 to 35 cm. an
hour. In a cool room at 11 to 12°C. it required 3 to 4
hr. for detectable amounts to pass into the veins, while at
1 to 4°C. it took up to 10 hr. before movement into veins
could be detected. After this long period movement sud-
denly commenced and the dye was carried throughout the
plant but at a slow rate, only 1 to 3 cm. an hour. If first
placed in a warm room, the dye was quickly absorbed and
carried into the petiole, but if the plant was then placed
in a cold room, movement stopped. Therefore the delay
in movement in a cold room is not due to a failure to
enter the sieve tubes.

The rate of movement of fluorescein seemed almost
completely uninfluenced by the narcotics, chloroform,
ether, phenylurethane, and ethylurethane, unless they
were at concentrations sufficiently high to cause death.
Furthermore, the movement appeared to be uninfluenced
by wilting, was insensitive to light, and seemed in no way
dependent upon the movement of carbohydrates or nitrogen compounds. In his earlier paper (1930) Schumacher
found that carbohydrate transport from the leaf became
clearly apparent after 2 to 3 hours in darkness. After
24 hr. in darkness both carbohydrate and nitrogen transport from leaves were active, but after 3 days nitrogen
removal was complete. With fluorescein he found no
difference in rate of transport from leaves in light as
compared with that from leaves which had been in darkness for from a few hours up to 7 days.

Schumacher suggests that movement through sieve tubes takes place in the protoplasm and not in the vacuole or the walls, but that it is not carried by moving protoplasm. His chief reasons for thinking that moving protoplasm is not concerned are that the rate of movement is much faster than that observed in ordinary parenchyma cells and that the sieve tubes did not show one-sided staining, which would point to a returning, unstained stream of protoplasm. The first objection is not necessarily very serious. His data indicate that, under optimum conditions, the dye moved through the sieve tubes at rates running up to 5 or 6 mm. a minute. It is true that streaming in ordinary parenchyma cells and hair cells is nearer one-tenth of this rate, but as is pointed out in paragraph *a* of Sec. 34, streaming rates of 5 to 6 mm. a minute have been observed in certain much elongated cells, and it is conceivable that the specialized sieve tube may have equal or even greater rates of movement.

The second objection also is not very serious, for, even in glandular cells where moving strands of fluorescent protoplasm were observed, he found no indication that advancing strands were more deeply stained than others. He found that each cell, as the staining progressed, showed first a fluorescence in the nucleus, and then the protoplasm along the walls showed a gradually increasing light. Even in long cells there was no visible difference between the intensity at the two ends, which he suggests is due to a very rapid spreading of the dye after entrance. Of course, this gradual increase in intensity may have been due to a rapid spread of slowly entering dye along the protoplasm independently of the movement of the latter, or it may have been due to a rapid lateral redistribution from one strand to another by diffusion. Over such short distances diffusion across from one strand to another might be faster than movement of a part of the strand itself from one end of the cell to another. The entrance of the dye may have been so slow that the protoplasm could make a complete circuit before enough entered to develop distinct

fluorescence. The fact that the nucleus shows lighting
before the cytoplasm, points to a gradual accumulation
which can be as easily explained on a basis of streaming as
by a rapid and almost instantaneous spread through the
cell. The fact that the rate of movement of the fluorescein
through parenchyma cells was immensely slower than
through sieve tubes and is more nearly of the order of
observed protoplasmic streaming in these cells, lends
weight to this interpretation. Schumacher suggests that
mere penetration into the protoplasm does not determine
movement but that some secondary, unknown factor,
perhaps one concerned with polarity phenomena, determines movement.

Schumacher is strongly opposed to the Münch hypothesis
as to the mechanism of movement. He concludes that
protoplasm is the path of movement, but that the streaming protoplasm is not concerned in the movement. As
has just been pointed out, however, it seems that the
motion of the protoplasm may be responsible or that
movement may take place by a mechanism like that
proposed by Van den Honert, which may be considered
as a special case of protoplasmic streaming.

Although I am thoroughly convinced that Schumacher's
experiments and observations demonstrate the effectiveness of the sieve tubes as transporting cells and that
materials may be carried by the same mechanism by which
the dye is carried, I hesitate to conclude without more
extensive evidence that the rate, direction, and mechanism
of movement through the sieve tubes of carbohydrates,
nitrogen compounds, and such solutes will be strictly
comparable to those of fluorescein. As is made clear in
Chaps. IV and V, the movement of solutes such as dyes
that have been introduced into xylem tissues has led to
false conclusions relative to the normal tissues concerned
in movement as well as to rates and direction of movement.
It is perhaps equally possible that fluorescein movement
through sieve tubes is also misleading. It is true the
movement of fluorescein through sieve tubes seems much

more normal than, for example, backward flow of dyes through the xylem, but at one time the latter seemed normal to many botanists. Introducing a dye into cut xylem is abnormal in that a foreign substance is introduced under conditions that alter or even reverse natural pressure or tension gradients. The introduction of a dye that is taken up by protoplasm may disturb in a comparable manner the normal interfacial relations within the sieve-tube contents.

The spread of fluorescein through protoplasm, even if it were clearly demonstrated to take place by the mechanism proposed by Van den Honert, does not necessarily signify that sugar and such solutes are carried by the same mechanism. It is conceivable that cells produce a substance that is active at protoplasmic interfaces and thus causes protoplasmic streaming. This streaming protoplasm may in turn be the vehicle for carrying other solutes, perhaps sugar. The alternative, suggested by Van den Honert, is also possible, that is, that the sugar itself, or some substance into which it is transformed, may be the surface-active material which causes the streaming, and the streaming is then the result of sugar transport and is not the vehicle. A foreign substance like fluorescein, therefore, may be transported because of its activity at the interfaces, or it may be carried in a moving stream of protoplasm activated by some other agent. In a similar way sugar may be active at an interface causing transport, or it may be carried in a stream activated by some other agent. Another alternative may be that fluorescein and certain substances are carried by one of the methods, either active or passive, and sugars and certain other substances by the other method. It is also conceivable that there is a rapid interfacial spread of a substance like fluorescein that is not accompanied by protoplasmic movement.

The very fact that Schumacher found fluorescein to move out and not into young developing leaves when sugars and other materials were almost certainly moving into them would indicate that sugars are carried by a different mechanism or that there is a simultaneous flow in both directions. In the latter case it would seem that the surface-active substance causing the flow would move in one direction and other substances would be passively carried in the opposite direction, perhaps in the resulting stream of moving protoplasm. Possibly the electrical charge or the molecular configuration or solubility of different substances will determine which of the moving streams they will enter and thus determine the direction of their movement.

38. Relations between the Transport of Viruses and Hormones and That of Foods.—Studies on the transport of viruses may be of considerable assistance in solving normal translocation problems; for with but few possible exceptions (Grainger, 1933) it has been rather clearly established that natural transport of viruses is restricted to living tissues and rapid movement takes place in the phloem. Bennett (1927) describes experiments which clearly indicate that transport of the leaf curl virus of raspberries takes place through the phloem, and that the movement is unidirectional and in the direction of the major transport of food. That is, in plants with well-formed leaves, the transport is downward only, while in new shoots, drawing their food supply from diseased roots or the older diseased canes, the transport is upward. Growing shoots that had appeared above the surface of the soil and were probably sending foods back to the roots failed to become infected from the roots, even though the shoots continued growth and were susceptible to direct inoculation.

On the other hand Caldwell (1931) working with the virus producing yellow mosaic of tomato demonstrated simultaneous movement in both directions and at approximately equal rates. Later (1934) using Johnson's No. 1 mosaic of tobacco and the aucuba or yellow mosaic of tomato, he found movement throughout both tobacco and tomato plants to be independent of the position of inoculation and independent of the direction of major transport of foods.[*] The virus spread throughout the plants at approximately the same rate whether it was introduced into older basal leaves or young apical leaves or into young axillary shoots. To vary the probable direction of food movement he placed entire plants in darkness for 48 hr., inoculated an older leaf, and then placed the plant in the light keeping the inoculated leaf in darkness. The virus spread as rapidly and as completely from this darkened and starved leaf as from a similar mature leaf exposed to light or from a very young leaf near the apex. As he says, this movement of virus from a darkened leaf, that is probably receiving sugars from the tissues to which the virus is moving, rather clearly indicates a movement of virus independent of the movement of carbohydrate. It is possible, however, that even this starved and darkened leaf was losing its contents to other parts of the plant and was receiving nothing, for leaves that are about to die or abscise still lose their stored foods to other tissues (see Par. 3, Sec. 30), and Schumacher (1931) has demonstrated the removal of nitrogen from such darkened leaves. The spread from a darkened axillary shoot of tomato, however, would seem to demonstrate a movement of virus out of a tissue that was almost certainly receiving foods unless in inoculating the axillary shoots Caldwell inoculated leaves that perhaps receive no food when darkened. His description of these experiments is not sufficiently detailed to make this point clear.

Holmes (1932) reports experiments on the movements of the tobacco virus in *Nicotiana tabacum* which rather clearly demonstrate that the virus follows the same path as that taken by carbohydrates. The virus leaves a leaf, however, at about the same rate whether the leaf is supplying carbohydrates to other parts of the plants or has been darkened during the experiment. This is comparable to the observation of Schumacher (1933) that transport of fluorescein from a leaf is independent of carbohydrate or nitrogen transport. If all other leaves were removed and the inoculated leaf was exposed to light, however, Holmes found a somewhat earlier appearance of virus symptoms

in the apical growing parts but this was not clearly proved
to be due to more rapid transport.   There seemed to be an
approximate relation between the completeness of spread
of the virus and the relative amount of food supplied by
the inoculated leaf to the rest of the plant.   That is, if the
inoculated leaf was shaded and other leaves not shaded,
the subsequent distribution of virus throughout the plant
was markedly unsymmetrical, perhaps indicating a small
amount of inoculum, whereas if the inoculated leaf was
not shaded the unsymmetrical distribution was greatly
reduced, and when two other leaves were shaded so that
the inoculated leaf was supplying a large part of the
carbohydrate for the plant, the unsymmetrical distribution
was completely lacking.   In these experiments of Holmes
there was no way of determining the actual velocity of
movement for the time necessary for incubation and
entrance of the virus into the phloem was included in the
total time necessary for movement.

Samuel (1934), working on the movement of tobacco
mosaic in tomato plants, found the virus to move from the
point of inoculation on a leaflet near the middle of a plant
to the root at a distance of about 60 cm. within 12 hr.
after the entrance into the phloem.   But, contrary to the
type of behavior observed by Bennett, the virus during
the next 12 hr. or less moved rapidly from the roots to the
younger tissues at the top of the plant, a distance of
approximately 90 cm.   This would indicate a movement
between 1 and 2 mm. per minute.   This movement from
the root would seem to be in the reverse direction of that
of the major movement of food.   The direction of movement seemed to bear no relation to the time of day and
would seem for this reason also to be unrelated to food
movement.   Movement during the first 12 hours seemed
to be in the direction of food movement, for the virus
usually moved into developing fruits independently of
whether they were below the point of inoculation or one
or two internodes above.

The fact that viruses seem to move out of older leaves
even when they have been darkened and are exporting

little or no carbohydrate, and move into them only slowly or not at all even though they may be receiving carbohydrate, and that they move rapidly to growing tissues independently of the position of the growing tissue, might be interpreted as indicating that the growth condition of the tissue is more important than the direction of movement of carbohydrate. Schumacher (1933) found that outward transport of fluorescein was in like manner unrelated to carbohydrate transport. The fact that viruses are negatively charged may be a factor in determining their distribution. It is possible that the direction of movement of both virus and certain solutes is determined by the movement of protoplasm of a certain type, whereas other material, perhaps bearing a different electrical charge or held in different layers of protoplasm, may be moving in the opposite direction. Although movement may be partly determined by electrical charge, the effect may be different from that on growth substance for the movement of the latter seems to be strictly polar. Smith (1931) reports the interesting fact that in experiments on the behavior of a mixed virus in tobacco, although the x strain develops more rapidly at the point of inoculation, the y strain seems to travel to distant parts much more rapidly. Bennett (1932) reports a comparable case in which, of two types of raspberry mosaic both of which are probably transported through the phloem, one moves much faster than the other. Whether these observations mean that the different strains of virus move in different cells, in different parts of the same cell (perhaps in different layers of moving protoplasm), or one is delayed more at obstructions of course is not known, but they seem to oppose the concept of a unidirectional mass flow of all phloem contents.

The various transportation studies with viruses may prove to be of great value in helping to solve general translocation problems. But until they are supported by other evidence I rather hesitate at present to accept them as indicating normal movements, for some of them bring about phloem necrosis and other abnormalities and it may be their movement is unrelated to normal solute movement. Furthermore the amounts transported are probably minute in comparison with the transport of carbohydrates, nitrogen compounds and mineral nutrients.

Among the many investigations on special hormone-like substances there has accumulated a fair amount of literature dealing with their transport. It is not within the scope of this work to discuss these interesting contributions further than to touch very lightly on a few of the more recent papers in so far as they deal chiefly with transport through living tissues. Went (1932) seems to accept the Münch hypothesis as satisfactory for explaining the transport of sugars through the sieve tubes. The direction of this transport, he agrees with Münch, is determined by the pressure gradient which, in turn, is controlled by ability to supply or remove osmotically active material. He emphasized, on the other hand, that the transport of various growth substances is more strictly polar. These, he suggests, are electrically charged and are carried cataphoretically under the influence of an electrical potential whose direction remains constant. Negatively charged substances, like the growth substance of *Avena* coleoptiles, move basally only, while positively charged substances move apically only. He suggests that these substances are probably carried in companion cells of the phloem and not in the sieve tubes. The evidence offered, however, is very weak. Since their movement is polar, while sugar movement seems not to be, and since their rate of movement seems much slower than that of sugar, he concluded these special substances are carried in other cells than the sieve tubes, and since other functions of companion cells are not definitely known they seem to him very likely to be the path for this special transport.

Van der Wey (1932) has reported some interesting experiments dealing with the transport of the growth substance of *Avena* coleoptiles. He summarizes his findings very much as follows: (1) Both the velocity (the distance of movement in unit time) and the intensity (the amount of substance in unit time) are independent of the length of the coleoptile cylinder used. If diffusion accounted for movement, the intensity should be inversely proportional to the length of the cylinder. This was actually demonstrated to be the case when agar cylinders and not coleoptile cylinders were used. (2) The movement of the growth substance through the coleoptile is strictly polar, that is, it is carried only in a basal direction. It follows from this that, in equal times and with equal initial concentration in the agar plates, equal amounts will be transported through coleoptile cylinders to agar plates at the base independently of whether, at the start, the basal plate had no growth substance or a concentration of growth substance many times that in the upper plate from which it is moving. (3) With increasing initial concentration of growth substance the absolute transport intensity increases while the relative intensity decreases (according to diffusion the absolute transport intensity should be proportional to the concentration). The velocity of transport is independent of the initial concentration. (4) The velocity of transport in the coleoptile seems almost completely independent of the temperature. Below 40 to 45°C. the influence of the temperature on transport intensity displays an optimum curve comparable to that of a life process. (5) While (2) and (3) apply for coleoptile cylinders at 0°C. as well as at higher temperatures the transport in cylinders of various lengths at 0°C. behaves more according to a diffusion scheme, but the movement is still polar at 0°C. and in this respect is unlike diffusion.

Van der Wey states that it is not possible from his investigations to form a definite idea as to the method of transport. He says, however, that the evidence is clear that normal transport is a vital process, that movement is strictly polar, and that it is totally independent of protoplasmic streaming. The strongest evidence for its independence of protoplasmic streaming is that, if this accounted for transport, both velocity and intensity should be markedly influenced by temperature because the rate of protoplasmic streaming is greatly influenced by temperature, whereas actually the velocity seems entirely uninfluenced by temperature, while intensity is greatly influenced. He points out that the growth substance seems to be transported by a mechanism analogous to a carrier belt which moves at constant speed, the carrying capacity of which, however, is greatly influenced by temperature. He suggests that capillary electrical forces somehow account for transport. Points favoring this are that the growth substance is known to be a weak acid, bearing an electrical charge, and therefore will be moved by electrical forces; evidence presented by a number of investigators indicates that living plant cells maintain an electrical polarity, and Kögl (1933) has found that externally applied potentials alter the speed of the hormone movement. Transport of growth substance under such conditions may be a type of electro-endosmose or cataphoresis. With such an assumption, it is understandable why velocity is almost independent of temperature, while intensity is so strongly influenced, because the electrical charge would be independent of temperature while the effective path may be strongly influenced by temperature. The path of transport he suggests to be the plasma that permeates the walls of the parenchyma cells as well as the nonmoving protoplasm which lies at the surface of the wall. This cell-wall plasma, according to his opinion, is continuous from cell to cell through young walls and the connection is not restricted to the plasmodesma. He considers that the movement is not a mass flow of the sort proposed by Crafts but one dependent on electrical charge and potential.

If the findings and suggestions of Van der Wey for the transport of this growth substance are confirmed, it would seem that living cells may transport different substances along different paths and perhaps by different mechanisms. For example, Schumacher (1933) gives strong evidence that the velocity of transport of fluorescein is greatly influenced by temperature and that transport is very slow at temperatures approaching 0°C. Van der Wey, on the other hand, finds the velocity of transport of the growth substance to be independent of temperature, although the amount transported in unit time is influenced. These differences may be related to the fact that one was moving through sieve tubes and the other through parenchyma cells. Schumacher finds fluorescein is carried solely in protoplasm and does not permeate the wall excepting along plasmodesma, while Van der Wey suggests, but without much supporting evidence, that the growth substance is carried by wall plasm that in part permeates the walls. Sugar transport almost certainly is not polar and salt transport probably is not, while movement of the growth substance seems strictly polar. It is possible, however, that movement may have fixed polarity in coleoptiles and be reversible in other parts. The amount of the growth substance carried is obviously much less than that of carbohydrates, nitrogen, or other nutrient elements; for the initial concentration of growth substance used in most of his experiments was usually of the order 0.000001 normal, or 0.00003 per cent. A mechanism that is adequate for the transport of the growth substance, therefore, may not be adequate for transport of sugars.

The velocity of transport of the growth substance seems much slower than that of fluorescein, but this may be due to the fact that rates for growth substance seem to have been determined with parenchyma tissues, while the higher rates of movement of fluorescein were observed with sieve tubes. The data presented by Van der Wey indicate a transport of the growth substance of from 0.05 to 0.25 mm. per minute, while Schumacher estimated fluorescein to be carried through sieve tubes at about 5 mm. per minute. In hair cells, on the other hand, he found fluorescein to move about 0.05 mm. per minute. The velocity of normal sugar transport is not known. It is true that Münch and Crafts have estimated velocities of flow of phloem exudate, but both the rate as well as the mechanism of flow of exudate may be abnormal.   Mason and Maskell (1928*a*) found an increase in sugar content of the bark of cotton, at a distance of about 50 cm. from the leaves, to lag behind an increase in the leaves by about 2 hr.   This would indicate a linear transport at a rate of about 25 cm. per hour. Reported rates of transport of viruses which were supposed to be moving largely through phloem tissues have ranged from 0.25 mm. per minute and lower up to 25 mm. per minute. In many of these cases the calculated rates are not very exact because the total time between inoculation at one point and arrival at another was included, and there was no way of knowing the time at which the virus entered the phloem.   Some have used leaf hoppers for introducing the virus directly into the phloem and have thus a fairly accurate knowledge as to the time of entrance of the virus. By such a method Bennett (1934) has observed rates of movement up to 25 mm. per minute for transport of virus in sugar beets.

If movement through the sieve tubes of all substances being transported is unidirectional, this would point to a mechanism of the sort proposed by Münch. However, the movement of more than one substance in one and the same direction, such as virus and sugar, for example, does not mean that both are being carried by the same mechanism.   Sugar may be carried along a diffusion gradient where the movement is being hastened by streaming, while the virus, because of its electrical charge, may be carried cataphoretically or may attach itself only to that part of the protoplasm which is moving in the one direction. It is even conceivable that in special cases there may be unidirectional flow, as in a leaf or flower which is being emptied of certain materials before abscission, where the protoplasm itself may be actually withdrawing through the sieve tubes.   Kienitz-Gerloff (1891) has made a similar suggestion.   Such a withdrawal may be comparable to the withdrawal of the plasmodium of a myxomycete from the medium through which it had spread itself.   Such a withdrawal could take place by a mechanism very different from that proposed by Münch, and when the osmotic concentration of the emptying tissue is less than that of the receiving.

Growth responses involving matters of regeneration and dominance of the sort described in Secs. 41 and 42 have often been ascribed to transport of special hormones. The effects seem to be controlled in many cases by transport or transmission through the phloem. If they are due to transport of hormones, as often assumed, and since the direction of movement is often not the same as that of sugar movement, the evidence would point to transport in both directions simultaneously. This would seem to be in opposition to the Münch or Crafts hypothesis. Münch (1932) assumes different growth substances to be concerned in shoot growth and cambial growth, and suggests that growth may also be partly controlled by inhibitors. Since these growth substances seem to be transported through the phloem and not always in the same direction as the assimilates, he suggests that they do not move through the sieve-tube lumen because, according to his hypothesis the sieve-tube contents can move in but one direction at a time. He points out that Went's suggestion (1932), that they are carried in companion cells, is untenable because companion cells are absent in conifers. He thinks it probable that they are carried in the walls, as suggested by Van der Wey (1932), while the mechanism and direction of transport are controlled by their electrical charge. There seems to be no clear-cut evidence, however, indicating such movement along walls and both Van der Wey and Münch suggest the walls because they think moving protoplasm is not concerned or that movement can be in only one direction through the lumen.

Studies on the translocation of hormones, viruses, and fluorescein have been interpreted by several investigators as indicating a unidirectional movement through phloem and an outward transport only from mature leaves. Both fluorescein and viruses seem to move only outward from mature leaves even when darkened for varying periods, and

show no movement or only a greatly delayed movement
into them.   This evidence supports the opinion held by
many that movement through the phloem of mature leaves
is restricted to export only.   Phillis and Mason (1933),
however, observed a movement of sugar into darkened leaves
of cotton, and although this may have been restricted to
movement into conducting tissues only it does demonstrate
a reversal through the phloem of the petiole.   Furthermore
the fact that white leaves, which are occasionally met with
on many kinds of plants, continue to live and receive foods
from the rest of the plant (Weevers, 1923) offers conclusive
proof that some mature leaves can readily receive sugar
from the parent plant.   That they can remain alive and
continue to receive food if darkened has not been tested
so far as I know.   It would be of interest to determine
whether such white leaves receiving carbohydrates through
the phloem would at the same time export fluorescein or
viruses.   If they would do so, as might be expected, it
would seem to demonstrate simultaneous transport in
both directions through the phloem.   The continued export
of nitrogen (Schumacher, 1931), of fluorescein (Schumacher,
1933), and of viruses (Holmes, 1932; Caldwell, 1934) from
darkened leaves, at a time when sugar was probably moving
into the leaves, points rather strongly to a mechanism allowing simultaneous movement in both directions.   These
observations also indicate a mechanism that is active
independently of the presence or absence of material
to be transported.   It is true, on the other hand, that in
spite of the evidence for movement of carbohydrate into
darkened cotton leaves, as well as into white leaves, we
have not conclusive evidence that darkened leaves which
are exporting virus or fluorescein are at the same time
receiving carbohydrate.   As mentioned previously transport in leaves that are approaching death or are about to
abscise may be strictly unidirectional and outward only.
Evidence on this point and even on the matter of normal
movements into and out of leaves is very meagre.

   39. The Necessity of Living Cells.—That living cells are
necessary for, and take an active part in, translocation

through the phloem was strongly urged by Lecomte (1889) and has been fairly generally accepted by botanists since the work of Czapek (1897). He demonstrated that the killing of the petiole with steam or chloroform prevented the removal of carbohydrates from the leaves. He used the test for disappearance of starch as a criterion for removal. This, of course, is not always a conclusive test especially when used with leaves, yet under the conditions of Czapek's experiments seems to have been suitable. Deleano (1911), although he found that killing of the petiole with steam or chloroform distinctly retarded carbohydrate removal from the leaf blade, reducing it to one-third the normal, claimed that there was still a fairly rapid backward translocation through the dead petiole. His criterion for loss, however, was based on a change in dry weight or sugar content of the blade expressed as a percentage of the fresh weight. He assumed that the fresh weight of the attached and darkened leaf remained constant over a period of 26 to 48 hr. and that any change in dry weight expressed as a percentage of this fresh weight was a real change in total dry weight. In one experiment, for example, he found in the normal leaf a reduction of 3.49 per cent in dry weight expressed in this manner. It is probable, however, that much if not all of this change in percentage was due to an increase in water content of the darkened leaf and not to transport of solids. It is surprising how frequently a change in percentage composition is assumed to be due to a change in one constituent when the change in amount of any one or more of several other variables may have been responsible (see also Sec. 12, pp. 64–67). More recently, however (see especially Deleano and Andreesco, 1932), Deleano has published several papers dealing with movement of various nutrient elements including nitrogen, into and out of leaves of *Salix fragilis*, and has expressed the data on an absolute basis. For most of the mineral elements he has found that they increase until about June 1, remain practically constant until about Sept. 1 to 20, and just before leaf fall pass in appreciable quantities back to the stem, roots, and soil. Calcium behaved peculiarly in that it continued to increase until about June 20 and was not removed before leaf fall.

Failure to transport solutes through dead phloem tissues, however, is not conclusive evidence that living cells take an active part in the actual transport; for killing would certainly coagulate some of the proteins that are abundant in these tissues. Such coagulation would be expected to prevent or retard movement of any sort through these tissues, except perhaps diffusion. Czapek (1897) and others, moreover, have found that treatments which reduce certain forms of protoplasmic activity without killing the cells may hinder food transport. He found that exposure of petioles to chloroform which did not kill prevented, however, the removal of starch from the blade. Deleano (1911) also found chloroform to have a retarding effect similar to that of killing but claimed that transport was not completely stopped. As explained above, however, his claim of transport through dead or anesthetized stems is not well founded. Kruseman (1931) found treating the petioles of *Phaseolus* leaves with chloroform, to interfere with transport from the leaf. Schumacher (1933), however, found various anesthetics to have no effect on transport of fluorescein, unless used in amounts sufficient to cause injury. Possibly such injury occurred in the experiments of Czapek and Deleano and recovery was due to regeneration of new phloem cells.

McCallum (1905) found that local etherization of a stem would induce root development above the etherized part when the etherized part was not killed, Moore and Willaman (1917) found that local fumigation of a stem of tomato with hydrocyanic acid interfered with translocation even when the stem was not killed. The delay of starch removal from the upper part of the fumigated branch and the development of axillary buds below this part may be considered as evidence for an interference in translocation either of carbohydrates, nitrogen, and such solutes or of growth-controlling hormones, or both foods and hormones. The appearance of the stem and the fact that the axillary shoots stopped growing when the part above recovered demonstrated that the parts were not killed.

Child (1921) and Child and Bellamy (1919) found that local chilling of the stem of the scarlet runner or lima bean would induce the formation of shoots below the chilled portion. Similar local chilling of the runner of *Saxifraga sarmentosa*, they found, would induce the development of a plant at the runner tip. These regeneration effects are similar to those induced by ringing or by local killing or anesthesia of the stems. The writers concluded that there could have been no interference with movement of materials since the shoots did not wither and the growth of the runner tip seemed normal. Therefore they explained the effect of chilling as due to an interference in the transmission of an influence or stimulus comparable to an effect of local chilling on the transmission of a nerve stimulus. Although these regeneration phenomena are induced by cutting, killing, anesthesia, or chilling of the phloem tissues and may therefore be due to an interruption of solute movement, one is not justified in concluding from this that interfering with solute movement alone will fully account for regeneration. The same phloem tissue may take part in both transportive and transmissive effects. The fact that the phloem contains living cells with well-developed protoplasmic connections might be considered to favor both the transmissive and transportive explanations.

More recently it has been demonstrated (Curtis, 1929) that similar local chilling actually does interfere with the backward transport of carbohydrate from the leaf blades. Details as to procedures and results can be found in the original paper. The data presented in Table 24 represent the type of results obtained. It is clear that backward transport is checked or stopped when a part of the petiole or stem is chilled to a temperature somewhere between 0 and about 6°C. Later investigations indicate that it may be nearer 0 than 6°C. Temperatures somewhat above 6°C. had no significant effects on transport. Comparable effects on regeneration were reported by Child and Bellamy (1919). Although the data are not sufficiently complete to demonstrate just how abrupt the stoppage is or what the critical temperature is, yet they show very clearly that the influence of a fall of a few degrees at the lower range, somewhere around 4 to 6°C., is much greater than a similar fall in temperature at a higher range, such as between 10 and 25°C. It seems probable that the critical temperature will vary with the plant, its previous condition, and the time of exposure. This would follow if, as seems to me probable, the stoppage is related to stoppage of protoplasmic streaming. Ewart (1903) has observed protoplasmic streaming to cease when lowered to a few degrees above zero and then later begin again at the same temperature.

Kruseman (1931), though he found some retardation especially at the lower temperatures when he cooled the petioles of *Phaseolus* leaves, did not find the marked retardation that I did and disagrees with my interpretation. Most of the temperatures he used, however, were 5°C. or above, which is so near the critical temperature that streaming may not have been stopped all the time. Even though his temperatures remained fairly constant, in several instances the temperature rose for varying periods above the average temperature given. In my experiments a maximum-minimum thermometer placed in the line showed in most experiments a smaller range, a maximum of 4°C. and a minimum of 3°C. for the data reported in Table 24. He suggests that experimental errors in my method of using paired leaves may have accounted for the differences obtained. However, the differences were so great, the findings were so consistent with different individuals and in different experiments, and the statistical treatment showed such striking odds, that I am convinced the data are really significant. Stanescu (1933) obtained data indicating some retardation, but these effects also were much less pronounced than my own.

TABLE 24.—EFFECT OF CHILLING THE PETIOLE ON REMOVAL OF STARCH AND SUGARS FROM BEAN LEAVES
Plants in the dark 22 hr. after a bright day. Petioles chilled to 3 to 4°C. Check petioles about 18 to 23°C. Data are averages of eight sets. Two sets of four samples each were combined for sugar analyses.

Starch tests	Dry wt. as % of fresh wt.	Dry wt. g. per sq. dec.	Total sugar in 4 leaves, mg.	Sugar, mg. per g. fresh wt.	Sugar, mg. per g. dry wt.	Sugar, mg. per sq. dec.
Check................. Absent from all leaves	8.32	0.123	3.22	0.790	9.46	1.172
Chilled................ Abundant in all leaves	9.29	0.134	6.33	1.571	16.84	2.269
Chilled rel. to check.........	1.12	1.09	1.97	1.99	1.78	1.94
Odds that difference is significant...........	87:1	3,322:1	20:1	26:1	19:1	32:1

The calculated odds for sugar content are not in all cases clearly significant. This is due to the fact that in order to have enough material only two separate analyses were made consisting of 4 leaves each. There is every reason to believe that the large sugar differences are even more significant than the other differences which show significant differences when treated statistically.

The temperature at which he kept the petiole ranged from 5 to 7°C., which was almost certainly above the critical point at least for a part of the time, and this, I am sure, accounts for the lack of great differences. It is perhaps surprising that if materials are carried by streaming protoplasm, there is not more retardation at intermediate temperatures, for the rate of streaming must, it seems, be less at 8 than at 18°C. As pointed out in my earlier paper, however (Curtis, 1929), some factor other than rate of streaming may be limiting the amount of transport so that the rate of streaming does not become important until the lower temperatures are reached. Furthermore, these findings bear only on the amount of material transported, not on the velocity of transport.

Recent experiments of Schumacher (1930) give additional evidence that living cells are actively engaged in transport. By the use of eosin, which is toxic and which seems to have a specific effect on sieve tubes, inducing a formation of callose plugs on the sieve plates, he was able to interfere with translocation through the phloem. He claims this work proves conclusively that transport takes place almost exclusively through the sieve tubes because they alone develop the callose plugs, while the companion and parenchyma cells appear normal and show normal movements. Although the plugging of the sieve tube is clear and positive evidence, the evidence is not clear that the activity of the companion and phloem parenchyma cells is not also interfered with. Even though streaming continued in parenchyma cells, the ability of the protoplasm to absorb or carry normal solute may have been destroyed by the eosin. If the stoppage of translocation is due solely to plugging of the sieve tubes, the evidence does not directly support the contention that living cells take an active part in transport. It would be interesting to know if local chilling or anesthetics cause a temporary coagulation of the contents or the development of a callose plug. Dr. Knudson has brought to my attention the fact that temperatures below 11°C. may cause stoppage of bleeding from latex tubes of banana fruits. In a later paper Schumacher (1933) gives strong evidence that the living protoplasm in sieve tubes is essential for the transport of fluorescein.

The available evidence seems rather conclusive that translocation takes place through the phloem only as long as it is alive. Although experiments on chilling, anesthesia, etc., indicate that the cells must be not merely alive but take an active part in the transport, this evidence is not incontrovertible and this phase needs further investigation.

Final understanding as to the part played by living cells is closely linked with that of the mechanism of transport. A mechanism of streaming protoplasm is clearly dependent upon living and active cells. A mechanism of the sort suggested by Van den Honert (1932) would probably be dependent on living protoplasm in so far as living protoplasm is necessary for maintaining the active interface over which the materials are carried. In a sense, the mechanism may be considered as a special type of protoplasmic streaming in which the interfacial protoplasmic films move faster than the more granular visible protoplasm. A mechanism of the sort suggested by Münch seems independent of the activity of living cells, except as they may be concerned in furnishing the osmotic membrane at the source, in maintaining a gradient, in keeping the tubes in condition for transport, and in preventing leakage from the system. A mechanism of the sort proposed by Crafts seems entirely independent of living cells except for the introduction and removal of the sugars at the two ends of the system. According to the proposal of Crafts, the phloem must also be surrounded by living cells or something to prevent leakage. With such a mechanism a system of open or dead tubes more like that of the xylem would seem to be more effective.

The very facts that sieve tubes seem universally present in all types of plants in which rapid transport of solutes takes place, that they are more extensive and most highly developed in those vascular tissues demanding most effective transport, and that, so far as we know, they always contain living protoplasm; all point strongly to the conclusion that the sieve tubes take part in transport and that the living contents play a significant and active rôle. This evidence would strongly favor the protoplasmic streaming hypothesis, or the Van den Honert modification, as contrasted with those of Münch or Crafts. None of the hypotheses that have been suggested to account for transport through the phloem seems adequate, and it has not even been definitely established whether transport is or is not unidirectional at any one time and place.

SUMMARY

26. Because of the differences between structure and contents of the xylem tissues and those of phloem tissues, one would hardly expect methods that are effective in causing flow through the one to be effective in causing movement through the other. Differences in pressure applied externally at the ends of the tracheids or vessels of the xylem, either increased pressure at one end or reduced pressure or tension at the other, are effective in causing flow of solutions through the system, because it consists of rather thick-walled cells that resist collapse and contain little or no solid material that would obstruct the flow. With the sieve tubes of the phloem, on the other hand, the tubes are usually narrower, are less rigid, have rather frequent cross walls with but minute openings, and contain protoplasm and other solid or semisolid materials that would seem likely to obstruct free flow. Methods that have been found to be effective in causing flow through the xylem have not been found effective in causing flow through the phloem. This difference is probably related to differences in structure and content of the two types of tissues.

27. It had been suggested that diffusion accounted for transport of solutes through the phloem, but at an early date diffusion alone was demonstrated to be inadequate. It had also been suggested that moving protoplasm which had been widely observed might account for transport, but this suggestion was not widely accepted because observations indicated that protoplasmic streaming does not occur in sieve tubes when they are mature and supposedly active. Rather indefinite appeals were made to turgor pressures as the cause of flow, but no clearly defined hypothesis was formulated to explain the mechanism of flow. Several had recognized the possibility that an explanation of movement from cell to cell involved a transport through surface membranes which often show a very low permeability to sugars and which therefore seem to introduce added difficulties to finding a satisfactory explanation of movement. This difficulty has been met by some through suggesting that movement takes place through plasmodesma thus avoiding passage through a surface membrane. Others have suggested that it is only the vacuolar membrane of the cell that shows low permeability to sugar, and low permeability of the surface membrane offers no special difficulty.

28. Münch has suggested that there is a unidirectional flow of phloem contents that is brought about by a pressure gradient. This pressure gradient is established and maintained by differences in osmotic concentrations of supplying and receiving tissues. If within an osmotic system (a single membrane or a group of membranes connected by openings that will allow mass flow of solution) the osmotic concentration is high at one end or on one face and the concentration is low at the other end or on another face, and water is available at the end having a high concentration, there will be absorption of water through the membrane in the region of high concentration, a mass flow through the system, and excretion of water from the region of low concentration. In applying this to living plants it is assumed that a semipermeable membrane exists separating living cells from water in water-conducting tissues. Plasmodesma are supposed to allow for flow of solutions from one living cell to another, while sieve pores allow for similar flow through specialized sieve tubes. Therefore, if the supplying cells or tissues have a high osmotic concentration, the receiving cells a low concentration, and the plasmodesma and sieve pores allow for mass flow, there should be a transport of solution from the cells with high concentration and high turgor to those with low.

29. Several factors tend to support the Münch hypothesis. The fact of exudation from cut phloem proves the possibility of mass flow through this tissue. The observed cessation of such flow if a second cut is made above the first and the continued flow if the second cut is made below points to a mass flow of the sort postulated. An exudation of water from the cambial surface when left in contact with phloem so that it can receive material from the phloem, is added evidence, but evidence is presented by Weevers and Westenberg denying such an exudation.

30. There are many weaknesses in the Münch hypothesis. (1) The proposed mechanism would not allow for simultaneous movement in both directions through the phloem, yet there is a fair amount of evidence pointing to such a simultaneous movement. (2) Calculations indicate that the pressure gradients available are insufficient to cause a flow of solution through the conducting tissues into receiving cells and exudation of water from the receiving cells. This is true especially where receiving cells are at a great distance from the supplying cells, as is the case in certain trees or vines where the receiving roots may be a great distance from the leaves. (3) Naturally existing osmotic concentration gradients as well as turgor gradients have been demonstrated in many cases to lead in a direction the reverse of that required by the proposed hypothesis. The reduced turgor of leaves during the day should reduce transport, but available evidence indicates greater transport by day. Although it has been suggested that this reduced turgor of the leaves is offset by increased tension in the receiving cells, this would be effective only if the sieve tubes were rigid and could transmit such a tension throughout their length. Where tissues are competing for organic solutes often those with higher turgor receive the solutes, while those with lower turgor and nearer the source of supply fail to receive the solutes.   (4) The proposed mechanism seems not adapted to account for movement of specific substances to specific cells or tissues, but all must move together.   (5) The removal of water from the receiving cell if it is in the position of the cambium may be easily explained, but removal from apical growing points or from cortical storage tissues is not easily accounted for.   (6) If the proposed mechanism is correct, it is difficult to account for the failure of leaves, or stems bearing leaves, to empty carbohydrate when the cut petiole or stem is placed in water.   Under such conditions the pressure gradient through the phloem should be steepened because the distance of flow is shortened, the phloem is cut open reducing the resistance, and the supply of water through the xylem is increased.   (7) Local chilling of the petiole or stem does not stop exudation from cut phloem, yet it does prevent emptying when the leaf or stem is attached to the plant.   The method of flow, rate of flow, and direction of flow in cut phloem may be strictly abnormal.   (8) A pressure that would cause a unidirectional mass flow through plasmodesma or sieve pores would probably cause a flow of the protoplasm that lies across these pores, would not allow for its return, and would not allow for transport of the vacuolar contents where the osmotic pressure is supposedly developed.   Because of its many weaknesses the Münch hypothesis seems untenable.

31. From measurements of size of pores of sieve tubes, Crafts calculated pressure gradients much in excess of those available would be necessary to cause a flow of exudate at the rates actually observed with cut stems.   Since the total cross-sectional area of cell walls is greatly in excess of that of the sieve pores, and even of the sieve tubes themselves, and since their walls in the fresh condition are thick and greatly hydrated, he first suggested that the hydrated walls acted as the path of transport.   Because of the great resistance to flow through hydrated walls and since the protoplasm seemed completely permeable to solutes, he later suggested that flow takes place principally through the sieve-tube lumen, but that flow takes place freely across all side and end walls and is not restricted to flow through sieve pores. The actual flow through sieve tubes is supposed to take place by a mechanism similar to that proposed by Münch with the exception that it is assumed that neither flow out of supplying cells nor entrance into receiving cells takes place through plasmodesma.   The receiving cells are assumed to be capable of absorbing against a concentration gradient, and absorption is assumed to be independent of turgor.

32. Most of the weaknesses attendant upon the hypothesis of Münch apply equally well to that of Crafts. Attempts to obviate certain weaknesses of the former are based on assumptions with little supporting evidence and have introduced other weaknesses equally serious. The claim of low resistance to flow through walls is not substantiated, nor is the claim that the protoplasm of sieve tubes is completely permeable. Although his suggestions and conclusions seem not to be tenable, he gives valuable data on phloem anatomy and his observations and calculations on exudation, as well as those of others, can be interpreted to indicate that exudation from phloem and other cells is not normal but results from sudden release of pressures by cutting.   Various claims by others that solutes move chiefly along walls in the absorbing root or to the apical meristem are not well founded.

33. DeVries seems to have been the first clearly to formulate the hypothesis that protoplasmic streaming may be concerned in transport of solutes. Largely because of failure to observe streaming in mature sieve tubes, the hypothesis seems to have been discarded. Fairly satisfactory evidence has been presented that explains failure to observe streaming in sieve tubes. Several points seem to favor transport by streaming protoplasm. Such movements would allow for transport at rates immensely more rapid than by diffusion alone; it could account for selective transport to special tissues; it could account for transport to great distances without requiring excessive pressures or concentration differences; and it could account for transport out of or into tissues independent of the osmotic concentration or turgor of the tissues.

34a. Although protoplasmic streaming would seem to account for transport over considerable distances at rates immensely more rapid than would diffusion alone, calculations indicate that the mechanism is not adequate. These calculations, however, may be misleading because rates of streaming in specialized elongated cells may greatly exceed those observed in parenchyma cells on which the calculations are based; and the measurements of sieve pores and sieve tubes, which are based on observations of cut tissues, may be much too low because the cutting has released high internal pressures. It is also conceivable that strands of protoplasm may actually move through sieve pores, and possibly even through plasmodesma, and thus allow for more rapid transport.

b. Though protoplasmic streaming has not been observed in mature sieve tubes, its almost universal occurrence in other living cells and the fact that injury attendant upon observation would easily account for failure to find it in sieve tubes reduce the seriousness of this objection.

c. Tests with aquatic plants have indicated that protoplasmic streaming does not greatly hasten the transport of lithium and caffein, even though they penetrate into the vacuoles. This, however, may be due to the type of substance used which may not be taken up by the moving protoplasm. Fluorescein has been demonstrated to be carried in protoplasm, though it has also been denied that the moving protoplasm is concerned in its transport.

d. If materials are transported by moving protoplasm, it would seem that there might be simultaneous transport in both directions. There is some evidence for simultaneous movement and also for restricted unidirectional movement. The best evidence for unidirectional movement is that on the polar movement of the growth substance in *Avena* coleoptiles. There is also evidence for unidirectional movement of certain viruses and that this is not polar but in the direction of major movement of sugars. There is also evidence of a simultaneous movement of virus in both directions. In certain regions or under certain conditions fluorescein seems to move in but one direction but under other conditions in both directions.

e. It has not been demonstrated that the movement of materials is or is not in the direction of a diffusion gradient. Mason and Maskell have given strong evidence indicating that sucrose is the principal sugar transported through sieve tubes and that its movement is correlated with a diffusion gradient.

35. Most of the earlier data that might be considered as offering evidence on concentration gradients are of doubtful significance because they consisted chiefly of mass analyses of leaves and stem tissues in which the xylem, phloem, and cortical regions were not separated. Some also were expressed as percentages of dry weight which cannot be safely interpreted in terms of concentration gradients. Mason and Maskell, by analyses of bark tissue subdivided into outer, middle, and inner regions so as to compare parts with a high cortical parenchyma content with those having a high phloem content, found the cortical parenchyma to be rich in hexoses and low in sucrose, while those tissues that consisted chiefly of phloem were rich in sucrose and poor in hexose. The vertical gradients for sucrose were always in the direction of actual sugar transport, independently of whether the direction was natural or reversed by various treatments. The gradient of sucrose led to the receiving boll, while that for hexoses led from the boll to the bark. This would seem to lead to a transport from the boll of hexoses unless some mechanism is effective in preventing such loss. Such a mechanism is assumed to exist. Phillis and Mason give strong evidence showing that the phloem is capable of absorbing sugar from the mesophyll under conditions that build up a steep reverse gradient of sucrose leading back to the mesophyll. The attempts of Maskell, Mason, and Phillis to determine concentration gradients for nitrogen have been less successful. These determinations are complicated by the fact that nitrogen is present, in many forms of which some may be moving while others are static, and by the fact that the forms of nitrogen may quickly change from one to another. Another still more serious weakness which they overlooked lies in the fact that these investigators have not established with any degree of certainty the direction in which nitrogen is actually being transported. They assume, with almost no evidence to support the assumption, that all nitrogen first moves entirely through the xylem to the leaves, that the phloem receives none from the roots and none from the xylem, and that all which is moving through the phloem has come entirely from the leaves.

36. Van den Honert has demonstrated that a substance that lowers the surface tension between two immiscible liquids will spread rapidly over the interface; and he suggests that sugars may be transported in phloem tissues by a similar mechanism. The direction of such movement is determined by the concentration gradient, and the rate of movement seems to be of the same order as that calculated for sugar transport through the phloem. He suggests that movement of protoplasm may be the result of transport and not the vehicle. This rapid-moving surface film may be considered as a special type of protoplasmic streaming.

37. Schumacher has reported a rapid transport of fluorescein through the sieve-tube system. This dye does not appear in the vacuole but is seemingly absorbed and transported exclusively in the protoplasm. When introduced through leaves, the direction of movement is nearly always toward the stem from where it may move either down or up or in both directions. When moving up, it rarely passes into leaves, even into the young ones that are but half grown. Rates up to about 5 to 6 mm. a minute were observed at temperatures around 30°C. These rates were greatly reduced at around 11°C. and they became barely perceptible below 4°C. The rate seems entirely uninfluenced by anesthetics, and is independent of the movement of carbohydrates or nitrogen. He suggests that, although the transport of fluorescein takes place in the protoplasm, its movement is not dependent on moving protoplasm. The evidence for this latter conclusion is not strong. Although the movement of fluorescein through phloem tissues may be strictly comparable to that of sugars and other substances, it is possible that sugars may move by a different mechanism. The quantity of sugar transported seems immensely greater than that of fluorescein or growth substance.

38. Various hormones and viruses may or may not be transported in the same tissues and by the same mechanism concerned in food transport. There is evidence that growth substances are electrically charged and show strict polar movement only. Went has suggested that these substances are carried cataphoretically and that the movement takes place in companion cells. The evidence for the latter point is very weak. Van der Wey has given considerable evidence that transport of the growth substance of *Avena* coleoptiles is strictly polar; the velocity of transport is almost independent of temperature, but the amount transported is greatly influenced by temperature. The substance is supposed not to be carried by moving protoplasm and he suggests that it is carried in the protoplasm lying next to the walls as well as in that permeating them. There are similarities as well as striking differences between the reported transport of growth substance, of virus, of fluorescein, and of sugar. All are carried in living cells and seem to be under partial control of them. The velocity of movement of growth substance is about the same as that of fluorescein moving through parenchyma cells, and much less than that of fluorescein moving in sieve tubes by 20 to 100 times. Little is known about the normal velocity of sugar movement, although it is probably more nearly the same as that of fluorescein. The velocity of movement of growth substance seems almost uninfluenced by temperature while that of fluorescein is markedly influenced. Evidence is lacking concerning the influence on velocity of sugar transport. Movement of growth substance, at least in coleoptiles, is strictly polar, that of fluorescein and virus is mostly polar in leaves but not so in stems, while that for sugar is probably mostly nonpolar. The amounts of growth substance or virus normally carried are extremely minute, those of introduced fluorescein may be somewhat greater, while sugars are normally transported in great quantity. The evidence is inadequate to make clear-cut comparisons, but it seems to indicate that, in transporting the different types of substances here mentioned, different tissues (parenchyma, phloem sheaths, or phloem proper), different parts of the same tissue (sieve tubes, companion cells), or even different regions of a cell (vacuole or specific layers of protoplasm in sieve tubes) may be involved. It is also possible that the mechanism of transport may vary with the kind of material transported and with the tissue of transport.

39. Although denied by some the evidence is rather conclusive that appreciable transport does not take place through dead phloem. There is considerable evidence that anesthetics interfere with transport of sugars, but they seem to have no influence on transport of fluorescein.   Analytical data clearly demonstrate a marked reduction in carbohydrate transport through petioles chilled to a temperature between 0 and about 4°C.   That transport is reduced at these temperatures, that the effect appears rather abruptly, and that the critical temperature appears to be somewhere around 6°C. is indicated by these transport studies as well as those on bud inhibition. Some have failed to duplicate the temperature effects, but it seems that the material was kept too close to the critical temperature.   Although transport takes place through living cells, it has not been positively established that these cells take an active part in the transport or whether they are merely passive tubes.   Final understanding on this point is linked with an understanding of the mechanism of transport.   The universality of specialized sieve-tube structures containing living protoplasm in all plant tissues showing rapid transport would seem to point to a mechanism that requires living protoplasm to take an active part in transport.   The protoplasmic streaming hypothesis seems at present best adapted to meet the requirements of transport and to demand the structure and conditions that obtain in phloem tissues.

CHAPTER VII

POSSIBLE RELATIONS BETWEEN SOLUTE DISTRIBUTION AND BEHAVIOR

The probable importance of solute distribution in influencing or determining behavior in ordinary growth as well as in regeneration and related phenomena was mentioned in the introductory chapter. It is not my intention to discuss this topic at any great length, but it does seem worth while to point out the possible bearing of solute movements and factors influencing these movements upon these problems.

40. Relations between Solute Distribution and Amount of Growth.—It has been repeatedly observed since early times that if stems are ringed, the behavior of parts above and below the ring becomes appreciably different from the normal behavior. Of course, exceptions have been found in those plants with internal phloem or in monocotyledonous plants in which ringing does not result in cutting all of the phloem. Experiments and common horticultural practices demonstrating the influence of a change in distribution of solutes following ringing are so extensive and well known that it is not necessary to cite specific data or to discuss these effects in any detail.

One of the most striking effects of ringing is that the diameter growth, especially that immediately above the ring, is greatly increased, whereas secondary thickening below the ring ceases or is much reduced. This enhanced diameter growth above the ring seems obviously due to an increased supply of carbohydrates, or possibly other foods produced in the leaves, whose downward transport has been stopped by the ring. The reduced supply of carbohydrates, and possibly some special food, to the region below the ring also obviously accounts for the lessened diameter growth there. Fruits, if already present above the ring and accompanied by many leaves, tend to grow larger, sweeter, and brighter colored, and these changes are usually explained as resulting from the higher carbohydrate supply. The marked accumulations of carbohydrates above the ring, as demonstrated by qualitative and quantitative tests, accompanied by a corresponding deficiency below the ring, have been long recognized and support the generally acceptable explanation that these particular growth responses result from a disturbance in carbohydrate transport brought about by the interruption of backward flow by the ring.

Other changes in behavior also result when a stem is ringed. Elongation of shoots tends to be checked above the ring and favored below the ring. Although these changes in shoot growth are not usually explained on the basis of altered solute distribution, the evidence is fairly clear that a deficiency or at least relative deficiency of solutes from the soil, particularly nitrogen, may account for the decreased shoot growth above the ring and an enhanced supply, either absolute or relative, of these same solutes may account, at least in part, for the increased shoot development below the ring. The reduced tendency toward vegetative shoot growth above a ring is often accompanied by an increased tendency toward the formation of flower primordia, and this is usually explained as due to increased carbohydrate supply.

It has long been recognized that ringing results in a starvation of the roots and therefore a diminution of root growth, as well as a cessation of storage in subterranean organs and reduced growth of these organs. These responses, also, obviously result from a disturbance in normal transport of organic solutes.

41. Relation between Solute Distribution and Regeneration.—When a stem is ringed, roots are likely to be formed above the ring and shoots below. These perhaps develop more commonly from dormant or suppressed primordia, but in some cases they may be strictly adven-

titious. Exceptions will, of course, be found in some plants
which seem incapable of regenerating shoots or roots.
Although many of the responses to ringing, especially
changes in food content, diameter growth above and below
rings, growth of fruits, storage organs, and roots, obviously
result from an interruption of food transport and have
been usually so explained; other explanations have frequently been offered to account for regeneration phenomena. Some have proposed that regeneration or its
lack is controlled by inhibitors (Loeb, 1919; Reed and
Halma, 1919a, 1919b) or hormones (Kastens, 1924) which
are supposed to be carried in the phloem. Others have
attempted to explain the phenomena on the basis of the
transmission of a stimulus or influence through the phloem
(McCallum, 1905; Child, 1921). Still others have considered that movement of nutrient materials (Loeb, 1924)
may largely control the regeneration phenomena. I shall
not attempt to discuss these interpretations at length or
to weigh the evidence for and against them, but whatever
interpretation is considered, it should be clearly recognized
that cutting the phloem, though it may cut the channel
through which specific hormones or inhibitors may be
transported or through which a stimulus may be transmitted, it at the same time severs the tissues through
which normal solutes, sugars, proteins, and salts are being
or can be carried. Furthermore, it not only prevents
backward movement of solutes from the leaves but movement toward the apex also. Reed and Halma (1919a)
and Child (1921) failed to realize this possible upward
transport through the phloem.

Loeb (1924, pp. 137–139) claimed that the materials that
influence the mass of regenerated tissue move in both
directions past a region that has been ringed. In experiments to test this point, with *Bryophyllum*, the plant
Loeb used, I have been unable to duplicate his results
when the phloem was entirely cut. In ringing *Bryophyllum*
I have found that it is easy to remove an outer layer consisting largely of cortex, which treatment gave the stem

the appearance of having been ringed, but closer examination showed a layer of phloem was left intact and the regeneration response confirmed this. Loeb refers to but two layers which he calls cortex and wood.

The composition of a stem also influences the type of regeneration. A high carbohydrate content increases the tendency to regenerate roots (Curtis, 1918) and one with a low carbohydrate content to regenerate shoots (see also Kraus and Kraybill, 1918; Reid, 1924; and others). That extreme changes in composition alone will tend to induce regeneration does not seem to follow, for McCallum (1905) could induce no such regeneration in his attempts to cause such changes in composition. The methods used by McCallum, however, did not insure as extreme changes, perhaps, as were brought about by decapitation, ringing, or removal of roots. That adventitious root formation can be induced by high carbohydrate content without removal of active roots can be demonstrated by growing the plant with deficient nitrogen; and the development of an increased number of buds can be brought about by increasing the nitrogen and water supply and decreasing the carbohydrate. Whether the development of true adventitious buds can be so caused may be doubtful.

Evidence pointing to composition as more important than hormone or transmissive effects in causing regeneration has been obtained from experiments on double-ringing. I have found that defoliated parts between double rings have a strong tendency toward shoot development. Buds in these isolated regions developed shoots even more readily than buds below the lower ring, at which point any increased influence from the roots below or any increased supply of substances from the roots might be expected to be more effective. The carbohydrate supply in these isolated defoliated regions was exceptionally low, lower than that below the lower ring. These parts developed shoots in spite of their difficulty in getting water in competition with tissue below or above with high osmotic concentrations. It was also noticeable that apical dominance was distinctly less marked in these defoliated regions. In an experiment with *Ligustrum* similar to that shown in Fig. 1, 20 to 21 stems were treated in each of the ways indicated. Of the 20 treated as in No. 1, 4 developed strong shoots just below the upper ring, with no shoots elsewhere. Of the 20 treated as in No. 2 with two rings, 12 developed weak shoots at the node below the upper ring, 5 developed weak shoots immediately above the lower ring, and 4 developed strong shoots below the lower ring. Of 21 treated as in No. 3, none developed within the defoliated region, and 5 developed strong shoots at the node below the lower ring. It seems from these and other observations that a diminished absolute or relative amount of carbohydrate favors shoot growth and shoot regeneration, while an increased absolute or relative amount of carbohydrate favors root growth and root regeneration.

Although regeneration of a type can be brought about by changing the composition of the tissues, it can be more easily brought about by cutting or otherwise inactivating the solute-conducting tissue. That the interruption of solute distribution alone will always account for the various responses has not, however, been definitely established, and one is tempted sometimes to appeal to the possible transmission of a stimulus or hormones to account for the behavior. On the other hand, I know of no undoubted evidence that regeneration in plants is ever controlled by hormones or by transmission effects, and since there is abundant evidence that cutting, or otherwise inactivating the phloem, does interfere with the transport of nutritive materials, I rather hesitate at accepting the hypothesis, more easily formulated than proved, that regeneration phenomena are controlled by hormones, by specific growth substances or by transmission of influences of one sort or another.

42. Relation between Solute Distribution and Dominance.—Almost inseparable from problems of regeneration are problems of dominance. No simple explanation has been offered to solve the problem of competition between similar tissues.   It is difficult to see how solutes, such as nitrogen, for example, may be moving up a stem to a vigorous growing shoot at the apex, passing along the way weak-growing shoots which seem to be suffering from lack of nitrogen, and, although nearer the source of supply than are the apical shoots, yet fail to obtain adequate quantities.   Their low content of nitrogen and of other solutes, it would seem, should increase their ability to obtain these solutes when in competition with the apical shoots which supposedly have higher concentrations of these same solutes.   That is, the diffusion gradient to these weak side shoots must be steeper than to the vigorous apical shoots, yet they fail to get the materials.   A similar anomalous condition may be made out for the roots receiving carbohydrates from the leaves.   The lateral roots much nearer the supply may suffer for lack of sugar while roots at a great distance are receiving large supplies. Tensions or pressures in water columns, on the other hand, may be transmitted great distances; therefore inability to compete for water may be more easily explained on the grounds that the osmotic concentration of the side shoots may be low and thus make them incapable of competing with the other tissues for water (Chandler, 1914; Curtis, 1920*a*; Fernald, 1925).

There is evidence of a similar competition between fruits. For example, there may be several apples on a single spur, all of which, when the terminal blossom is removed, seem to be uniformly distributed so that at first no one fruit seems to have an advantage over any other, either as regards location on the spur, distance from the food source, or attachment to conducting tissue.   Yet if one flower is well pollinated or receives pollen which tends to produce more or larger seeds, this fruit may soon become successful in receiving the major part of the foods, and the others, which without the competition might have developed normally, may fail to receive enough food to allow for growth and may actually die or be cut off by an abscission layer (Heinicke, 1917).   I have seen no adequate explanation for the failure to obtain food. From the standpoint of diffusion gradients or turgor gradients one would expect solutes to move more readily to the fruit with a low food content and not to the one that already has a higher food content. Eventually the conducting tissues leading to the successful fruit may become better developed than those leading to the unsuccessful fruits, but this difference is probably developed after growth differences have taken place, not before, and is not in this sense causal. An indefinite appeal to influences, stimuli, or hormones merely seems to beg the question.

A possible explanation which seems to me more definite and possible of experimental test may be based on the assumption that translocation is actually carried on by the streaming protoplasm within the conducting cells. Starting with two blossoms with equal potentialities if one, *A*, is cross-pollinated with active pollen that induces the development of vigorous seed, while the other, *B*, is pollinated with ineffective pollen, then the more effective pollen will probably induce higher activity in the gynaecium of *A*. White (1907) found the respiration of gynaccia of 11 different species of plants to show a marked increase 4 to 5 days after pollination, while similar flowers not pollinated showed no such change. In one instance where abortive pollen was used there was no increased carbon dioxide production over that of the flowers not pollinated. One might expect this increased activity to increase the streaming or interfacial activity of the protoplasm of these tissues, which in turn would hasten the movement of foods. It is very possible that this increased activity in protoplasmic streaming is propagated back through the conducting tissues. I know of no direct evidence to this effect and this is a weak point in this explanation, but it should be capable of verification or disproval.* If the

---

* Heilbrunn (1928, p. 295) makes the following statement but cites no evidence: "A third aspect of protoplasmic activity . . . is the fact that whenever protoplasm is made active, the effect tends to be transmitted from one part of a cell to another, and from one cell to another."

protoplasmic streaming of the tissues leading to A is thus increased while that of the tissues leading to B is less active, then, other things being equal, solutes should be carried faster to A, thus allowing for continued greater activity of the growing tissue of the fruit. This greater activity would allow for more rapid transfer of solutes though the concentration of solutes at this receiving tissue were equal to, or even greater than, in B. Thus, although there may be actually a smaller difference in concentration between the source and the receiving tissue in A than between the source and that in B, so that the seeming diffusion gradient would favor B, the more active streaming in the conducting cells leading to A would tend effectively to reduce the distance through which movement is limited to diffusion, or would tend to increase the steepness of the diffusion gradient by more quickly carrying the solute from one end of the cell to the other. Thus, as was explained in Sec. 33, the effective diffusion gradient over a distance of a decimeter may be steeper than over a distance of a centimeter if in the former case streaming were active in the conducting cells and diffusion limited to occasional cross walls, while in the latter case movements were limited entirely to diffusion, or if the rate of streaming was very much reduced. The mechanism of transport proposed by Münch would not explain movement into A but would favor movement to B.

That a diffusion gradient alone accompanied by protoplasmic streaming of either the visible sort or a faster moving interfacial film does not fully account for transport into organs, such as these hypothetical fruits, is indicated by the fact that transport from the fruits that fail to receive food continues to take place, and therefore a translocation mechanism must still be active. This is indicated by the observations of Howlett (1926) that nitrogen is removed from the weaker fruits which later abscise. Schumacher's (1931) observations on transport of nitrogen from darkened leaves is a comparable case, as is also the emptying of leaves before leaf fall (Deleano and Andreesco, 1932).

Maskell and Mason (1930c) have approached this problem by actually determining concentration gradients between the bark and bolls, some of which were fertilized and others not. The bolls were divided into two samples, ovules and remaining portion. The gains over a 7-day period in dry weight, water, and nitrogen of the ovules

TABLE 25.—GRAMS DRY WEIGHT, NITROGEN, AND WATER PER 100 BOLLS
(From Maskell and Mason)
Ovules

Day	Normal group		
	Water	Dry Weight	Nitrogen
0	1.93	0.559	0.0318
2	3.11	0.802	0.0482
4	7.80	1.627	0.0900
6	21.78	3.667	0.1615
1	2.56	0.702	0.0430
3	4.76	1.123	0.0686
5	16.76	2.866	0.1414
7	43.60	6.635	0.2721
	Unfertilized group		
0	1.93	0.559	0.0318
2	2.93	0.784	0.0477
4	5.46	1.176	0.0707
6	11.27	1.985	0.1070
1	2.54	0.695	0.0432
3	4.71	1.124	0.0687
5	11.04	1.977	0.1066
7	22.84	3.565	0.1622

are presented in Table 25, while the progressive changes in sugar and nitrogen concentrations are shown in Fig. 13. From these data it is clear that by the fourth day the fertilized bolls diverged abruptly from the unfertilized, showing an increased rate of absorption of dry matter, nitrogen, and water. Up to the seventh day the sucrose gradient from bark to boll remained fairly constant for both groups, but the gain in carbohydrate was much faster

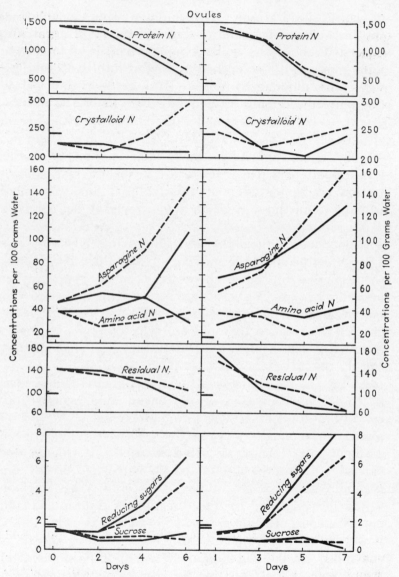

FIG. 13.—Change in sap concentration in the ovules of fertilized and unfertilized cotton bolls. Grams of sugar and milligrams of nitrogen per 100 grm. water in ovules of normal groups (continuous line), and unfertilized group (broken line). The average concentration in the bark of the fruiting branches is shown by the short horizontal lines on the left of the graphs. (*From Maskell and Mason.*)

in the fertilized group. This might well be explained on the basis of increased streaming activity, as tentatively suggested above. The backward gradient for reducing sugars was greatly steepened in the fertilized bolls and less so in the unfertilized bolls. During the 7-day period the unfertilized bolls gained steadily, but to a smaller extent, in both nitrogen and carbohydrates, so the period of removal observed by Howlett (1926) for apples had not set in. If the unfertilized bolls later lose nitrogen, this would point to a real reversal of movement, and concentration gradient studies on this material might be more valuable than those in which actual reversal has not been demonstrated (see Sec. 35).

It may be that the ability of the receiving cells to remove a given solute from the moving stream, thus determining the direction of the gradient, may be as important as maintaining an actively moving stream between the receiving and supplying cells. Phillis and Mason (1933) give clear evidence that phloem cells can remove sugars from living cells against a concentration gradient. If they can do this, it is obvious that the relative abilities of the receiving and supplying cells may be of greater significance in controlling direction of movement than actual concentration gradients. The seeming demand of the protoplasmic streaming hypothesis for a positive concentration gradient may therefore be eliminated. If sugars are carried in an interfacial film and the movement of this film is unidirectional in sieve tubes (see Sec. 36), the direction would be controlled by the direction of film spread and not by a concentration gradient. Van den Honert (1932), however, assumed that the direction of film spread is controlled by the sugar gradient itself. The demand of the Münch hypothesis for an osmotic gradient is not fulfilled in the case of transport from fruit or leaves that are about to abscise.

On the assumption that rapid translocation is brought about by streaming movements in living cells and that the activity of cells in a given tissue may induce increased

streaming in cells leading backward or forward to possible
sources of supply, one can readily formulate a hypothetical
scheme that seems to offer a fairly simple basis for partly
explaining .phenomena of dominance and regeneration.
If, for example, the chain of active cells leading to a
dominant shoot is severed, then other growing points are
no longer in competition with the dominant shoot. The
materials moving to the dominant region are stopped in
their movement and accumulate in sufficient quantity to
initiate the activity of one or more other growing points
and again one of these, becoming for one reason or another
slightly more active than its competitors, soon gains the
dominance.

On the same assumption, one might explain an increased
activity of two complementary tissues such as root and
shoot. If a given shoot gains supremacy and is drawing
upon the major part of the supply of soil nutrients through
increased protoplasmic streaming in the connecting phloem
cells, this same increased activity should not only favor
the movement of solutes to this particular shoot but should
also favor the transfer of carbohydrate from the leaves of
that shoot to the roots. Those particular roots, therefore,
that are perhaps in a rich pocket in the soil not only would
favor the growth of the particular shoots with which they
are connected but should also in turn be favored themselves, for the quickened activity of the conducting cells
should carry the solutes to the tops faster, and should also
return more rapidly the carbohydrates which favor root
growth.

Loeb (1915) observed that, if any part of the root of a
Bryophyllum plant was in water, root development of all
other parts ceased, whereas if the entire plant was suspended in moist air, roots would develop at many points.
He explained this lack of widespread root development as
due to an inhibiting effect of root pressure developed by
the roots in water. The same explanation had also been
given by others. A better explanation would seem to be
that when one set of roots touches water, their growth

would be favored by an adequate water supply. They could therefore use carbohydrates faster, which would steepen the gradient leading to them, and their increased activity might also favor more rapid streaming in the connecting phloem tissues. A similar explanation would apply to many other instances given by Loeb and others, where one active tissue becomes and remains dominant over others.

This hypothesis might also well explain the seeming conflict between the two concepts that solutes move to a tissue because it grows and that a tissue grows because solutes move to it. Any treatment that starts the activity of a group of cells, as in a shoot or root meristem or in a fruit or storage tissue, may establish a diffusion gradient leading to these cells and also initiate the streaming activity of the conducting cells leading to this particular region, thus establishing an active conducting system connecting the meristem or storage tissue with a supply of necessary solutes. The supply of these solutes to the particular tissue enables it to continue its activity and thus also to continue its connection with the source of supply. The solutes, therefore, move to this tissue because the tissue is active, and the tissue may remain active because foods are moving to it. The original activity may be initiated either by a greater supply of foods or other solutes or by any one or more of various other agents. The increased nitrogen absorption as well as the increased photosynthetic activity in plants sprayed with bordeaux, as reported by Mader (1934) and others, may be in part due to an effect of copper increasing the effectiveness of the translocation mechanism. This agrees nicely with the streaming hypothesis, for it is well known that traces of copper are highly effective in inducing or in hastening protoplasmic streaming.

The mechanism of food movement as proposed by Münch (1930) can also be adapted, as he suggests, to account for dominance. According to his hypothesis a receiving cell can cause materials to flow to it by keeping a low osmotic concentration and low turgor pressure. Those meristematic cells which are more active in removing solutes by respiration or by deposition as osmotically inactive protoplasm or as cell wall material, will tend to bring more solutes to themselves than will less active cells which may receive nothing if their turgor remains high. Storage cells which can remove osmotically active sugar, by deposition of starch, for example, will continue to receive a supply from the phloem so long as they are able to maintain a relatively low turgor pressure. Theoretically the mechanism seems well adapted to account for directive flow to tissues capable of removing solutes. The main obstacle to this interpretation, however, is the fact that the receiving cell frequently has a higher osmotic concentration or a high turgor, or both than the supplying cells (see 3a of Sec. 30). A directive flow of specific substances also cannot be accounted for either according to the Münch hypothesis or by the modification suggested by Crafts. Other weaknesses of the proposed mechanism have already been discussed in Sec. 30.

That distribution of materials, whether brought about by diffusion, by protoplasmic streaming, by spread in an interfacial film, or by pressure gradients, may be a factor in phenomena of dominance and regeneration is probable, but it also seems probable that it is perhaps only one of several factors. For example, the effect of gravity on the distribution of materials and on dominance is not easily explainable on the basis of rate or direction of movement as influenced by diffusion gradients, rates of streaming, or pressure gradients alone.

Reed and Halma (1919a) have reported a marked influence of gravity on dominance of buds on stems of the Chinese lemon. In horizontal stems apical dominance was greatly reduced and buds along the upper side of the stem developed shoots. If the stem were then turned over inverting the sprouts, these ceased growing and died as shoots from buds on the upper side replaced them. This may be partly explained on the basis that gravity influenced the activity of the meristematic cells which, in turn, influences the diffusion gradient and perhaps also the activity of the streaming protoplasm which connects the receiving cells with the source of supply. Effects of gravity seemingly less related to a gradient have been reported by Loeb (1920) who has given evidence showing that if isolated leaves of *Bryophyllum* are suspended vertically in a moist chamber, certain materials, which he calls "sap," tend to accumulate on the lower side. This is indicated by greater dry weight, greater pigment formation, and greater development of plantlets on this lower side. The pigment would point to greater sugar accumulation. Inadequate data obtained by MacDaniels and myself indicate that the upper sides of horizontal branches have relatively high nitrogen contents while the lower sides have higher carbohydrate concentrations (see MacDaniels, 1923). It is true, however, that mass analyses for total carbohydrates or total nitrogen are of little use in indicating diffusion gradients. This is well indicated by the observations of Mason and Maskell (1928*b*) that the diffusion gradient of sucrose in the cotton plant is toward the boll, whereas that of glucose is away from the boll.

That something other than food supply and initial activity influences meristematic activity or food movement is clearly indicated by the cambial activity of woody stems. It has been widely observed since very early investigations of ringed stems that diameter growth above a ring, if leaves are present above, is likely to become excessive, whereas cambial growth below a ring is greatly diminished. This decrease immediately below a ring may be marked even if there are leaves or side branches nearby from which a fairly adequate food supply would seem available. In fact, sufficient food may move into this region below a ring to allow for considerable starch deposition or considerable starch and sugar may already be present, as observed by Proebsting (1925), and yet cambial growth may be very weak. Some attribute the lack of cambial activity below a ring or on a defoliated branch to the lack

of some stimulus or a specific hormone.   There seems to be
a quantitative relation, however, between leaf area and
growth, so it would seem to be more controlled by food
supply unless there is also a quantitative response to a
hormone for which there is evidence.

It has also been demonstrated (Münch, 1930; Curtis,
1920*a*; Haller, 1931) that fruits on a completely defoliated
shoot may grow at approximately normal rates, which
proves that food is carried through these stems, and yet
cambial growth may come to a standstill.   Possibly the
movement of the substance necessary for cambial growth
is strictly polar.

As pointed out by MacDaniels and Curtis (1930), both
cambial development itself and also orientation of the
cells seem to be determined or at least influenced either
by lines of movement of necessary solutes, carbohydrates
from above and nitrogen from below, or by some sort of
electrical gradient through the phloem or cambium.   Lund
(1931) has given evidence that there is such a gradient
in stems and that ringing between two contacts alters the
electromotive force between the contacts.   It is conceivable that polarity and dominance may be partly under
the control of such gradients.   The ringing of a stem by
interrupting such a system may interrupt both the transport of materials through the conducting tract as well as
the continuity of a system showing electrical polarity.
That a cambium to become active merely needs to lie
within such a gradient and parallel to it is not adequate,
for if leaves are not allowed to develop on a defoliated
shoot, the gradient may be still present and yet cambial
activity ceases.   It would seem, therefore, that mature
leaves favor cambial growth partly by supplying carbohydrates and possibly partly by producing some other
specific substance which shows a polar movement.

There seems to be a common tendency to explain these
at present obscure phenomena as controlled by hormones,
and often a special hormone is assumed for each obscure
point.   The evidence seems conclusive that a hormone is

concerned in the growth of *Avena* coleoptiles, that this is widespread in nature and may be concerned in the growth of many cells other than those of the coleoptile test material used. But it seems to me that the evidence is far from conclusive that there is a specific hormone for growth of a shoot apex, another for cambium, another for roots, and others acting as inhibitors. By some it is claimed that special hormones move chiefly through the xylem, while many claim others move exclusively through the phloem. It is true that lack of conclusive evidence for such hormones does not prove their absence, but it seems there is danger of depending too much upon special hormones to account for phenomena that are not otherwise easily explained.

SUMMARY

40. It has long been recognized that ringing is likely to alter the composition and amount of growth of the tissues both above and below the ring. If many leaves are present above, carbohydrates accumulate in this part and there is an increased diameter growth of stems and increased growth and sugar content of fruits. A decreased sugar content and cessation of diameter growth in stems below rings has often been explained as due to a diminished carbohydrate supply, as has also the cessation of root growth as well as that of subterranean storage organs. Though diminished shoot elongation above rings and increased shoot development below rings may be due to altered distribution of carbohydrates and mineral elements, especially nitrogen, this behavior is usually explained on other grounds.

41. Attempts to explain formation of roots above rings and the development of dormant or adventitious buds below rings seem more commonly to be based on an assumed change in the distribution of special hormones, or inhibitors, or an interruption in the transmission of some influence. Evidence from several sources indicates that an increased supply of carbohydrate relative to that of nitrogen tends to reduce shoot elongation and favors root formation and growth, whereas an increased supply of nitrogen, especially an increase relative to carbohydrate, tends to favor shoot elongation or formation from dormant or adventitious buds. Effects of ringing on these regeneration and growth phenomena may be explained on the same basis, although it is also possible that the regeneration phenomena are controlled by hormones or stimuli that are transported or transmitted through the phloem. Conclusive evidence on these points seems lacking.

42. No satisfactory explanation has been given to account for the receipt of solutes, such as sugars and nitrogen, by dominant tissues when in competition with suppressed tissues, especially when the latter may have a lower concentration of the particular material moving and may also be nearer the supply. From the standpoint of diffusion gradients alone one would expect the weaker fruit or bud, or other growing part, to receive the material more rapidly.   It is conceivable, however, that within the phloem tissues leading to a dominant part, such as a pollinated fruit, there may be more active protoplasmic streaming than in those leading to the suppressed part, such as fruit that has not been pollinated.   Therefore, although the actual gradient may lead to the suppressed fruit, the higher activity within the conducting tissues leading to the other may in effect bring about a steeper gradient to the dominant fruit.   It is also possible that the dominant part may be more effective in removing the material from the transporting tissue.   Data on gradients leading to fertilized and unfertilized cotton bolls show no difference in gradient but a marked difference in rate of receipt. This would indicate a more effective transport system.   The reverse gradient for reducing sugars is greater in the fertilized bolls, which indicates that they have a greater ability to accumulate sugars.   A transport mechanism of the sort proposed by Münch can theoretically be adapted to account for many phenomena of dominance, regeneration, and growth correlation, but much of the available evidence points to an active movement in a direction the reverse of that required by the theory.   There are also several other weaknesses in the hypothesis.   A transport mechanism based on diffusion and streaming protoplasm seems well adapted to account in part for dominance of one part over another, for observed phenomena of regeneration and growth correlation as well as for other phenomena of behavior.

There are some phenomena bearing on food movement and utilization, however, such as the influence of gravity, which though not definitely in opposition to any theory of transport, yet are not easily explained by any of the theories.   That some substance or condition other than supply of carbohydrate and mineral elements is involved in growth and regeneration phenomena is demonstrated especially by the unexplained behavior of cambial growth.   Some of the growth responses following ringing are undoubtedly due to an interruption of the transport of foods and mineral elements.   It is also possible, though it seems not conclusively established, that some responses may result from an interruption of the transport of specific substances of the nature of hormones.   There is also evidence that such cutting may alter normal electrical gradients and it may influence the transmission of stimuli.

BIBLIOGRAPHY[1]

ACTON, E. H. 1889. The assimilation of carbon by green plants from certain organic compounds. *Roy. Soc. Lond. Proc.*, **47**: 150–175. [21.]

ANDERSSEN, F. G. 1929. Some seasonal changes in the tracheal sap of pear and apricot trees. *Plant Physiol.*, **4**: 459–476. [81, 120–123, 127.]

APPLEMAN, C. O. 1912. Changes in Irish potatoes during storage. *Maryland Agr. Exp. Sta. Bull.* 167: 327–334. [19.]

ARNDT, C. H. 1929. The movement of sap in *Coffea Arabica* L. *Amer. Jour. Bot.*, **16**: 179–190. [104, 106.]

ATKINS, W. R. G. 1916. Some recent researches in plant physiology. 328 pp. [9, 99.]

AUCHTER, E. C. 1923. Is there normally a cross transfer of foods, water and mineral nutrients in woody plants? *Maryland Agr. Exp. Sta. Bull.* 257: 33–62. [57.]

BAILEY, IRVING W. 1916. The structure of the bordered pits of conifers and its bearing upon the tension hypothesis of the ascent of sap in plants. *Bot. Gaz.*, **62**: 133–142. [111.]

———. 1930. The cambium and its derivative tissues. A reconnaissance of the vacuome in living cells. *Zeitschr. f. Zellforschung und mikroskopische Anatomie* **10**: 651–682. [42.]

BELVAL, H. 1930. Transformation of carbohydrates in the banana. I. Formation of starch. *Chinese Jour. Physiol.*, **4**: 365–372. [190.]

BENNETT, C. W. 1927. Virus diseases of raspberries. *Michigan Agr. Exp. Sta. Tech. Bull.*, 80: 38 pp. [186, 210.]

———. 1932. Further observations and experiments with mosaic diseases of raspberries, blackberries and dewberries. *Michigan Agr. Exp. Sta. Tech. Bull.* 125: 32 pp. [213.]

———. 1934. Plant tissue relations of the sugar-beet curly-top virus. *Jour. Agr. Res.*, **48**: 665–701. [218.]

BIERBERG, W. 1909. Die Bedeutung der Protoplasmarotation für den Transport in den Pflanzen. *Flora*, **99**: 52–80. [185.]

BIRCH-HIRSCHFELD, LOUISE. 1919–20. Untersuchungen über die Ausbreitungsgeschwindigkeit gelöster Stoffe in der Pflanze. *Jahrb. wiss. Bot.*, **59**: 171–262. [5, 10, 75, 88–94, 110, 113, 133, 181, 185.]

BLACKMAN, V. H. 1921. Osmotic pressure, root pressure, and exudation. *New Phytol.*, **20**: 106–115. [144.]

BODENBERG, EMMET T. 1927. Tissues involved in the transfer of mineral salts in plants. *Pub. Puget Sound Biol Sta.*, **5**: 231–244. [114.]

———. 1929. Lateral transfer of lithium nitrate in *Salix*. *Amer. Jour. Bot.*, **16**: 229–237. [115.]

[1] Numbers placed in brackets at the end of each citation indicate sections in the text where the item is mentioned.

BOEHM, JOSEF. 1883. Über Stärkebildung aus Zucker. *Bot. Ztg.*, **41**: 33–38, 49–54. [21.]

BOKORNY, T. 1890. Die Wege des Transpirationsstromes in der Pflanze. *Jahrb. wiss. Bot.*, **21**: 469–503. [116, 172.]

BROOKS, MATILDA MOLDENHAUER. 1926. Studies on the permeability of living cells. VII. The effects of light of different wave lengths on the penetration of 2,-6,- dibromo phenol indophenol into Valonia. *Protoplasma*, **1**: 305–312. [70.]

BROWN, H. T., and F. ESCOMB. 1900. Static diffusion of gases and liquids in relation to the assimilation of carbon and translocation in plants. *Roy. Soc. Lond. Phil. Trans.* B, **193**: 223–291. [176.]

BRUNS, ADOLPH. 1925. Untersuchungen zur Auffindung der Ursache der Amylumverminderungs-Beschleunigung im welkenden Laubblatt. *Bot. Archiv.*, **11**: 40–103. [20, 190.]

BÜSGEN, M. 1911. Studien über den Wassergehalt einiger Baumstämme. *Zeitschr. f. Forst-u. Jagdwesen*, **43**: 137–154. [148.]

BÜSGEN, M., and E. MÜNCH. 1929. The structure and life of forest trees. Transl. by T. Thomson, N. Y. 436 pp. [147.]

CALDWELL, JOHN. 1931. The physiology of virus diseases in plants. II. Further studies on the movement of mosaic in the tomato plant. *Ann. Applied Biol.*, **18**: 279–298. [184, 186, 210.]

————. 1934. The physiology of virus diseases in plants. V. The movement of the virus agent in tobacco and tomato. *Ann. Applied Biol.*, **21**: 191–205. [210, 220.]

CARRICK, D. B. 1924. Some effects of freezing on mature fruits of the apple. *Cornell Univ. Agr. Exp. Sta. Mem.* 81: 1–54. [153.]

CHAMBERS, ROBERT. 1925. The physical structure of protoplasm as determined by micro-dissection and injection. COWDRY *et al*, General Cytology, Section V. 237–309. [161.]

CHANDLER, W. H. 1914. Sap studies with horticultural plants. *Missouri Agr. Exp. Sta. Bull.* 14: 489–552. [29, 240.]

CHANG, HO-TSENG. 1932. The effect of light and darkness on the uptake and distribution of nitrogen in *Phaseolus vulgaris* L. Thesis Cornell Univ. 93 pp. [70, 78, 82–86.]

CHIBNALL, ALBERT CHARLES. 1923. Diurnal variations in the total nitrogen content of foliage leaves. *Ann. Bot.*, **37**: 511–518. [55, 64–67.]

CHILD, C. M. 1921. Certain aspects of the problem of physiological correlation. *Amer. Jour. Bot.*, **8**: 286–295. [223, 237.]

———— and A. W. BELLAMY. 1919. Physiological isolation by low temperature in *Bryophyllum* and other plants. *Science*, **50**: 362–365. [223, 224.]

CLEMENTS, HARRY F. 1930. The upward movement of inorganic solutes in plants. State Col. of Washington. *Research Studies*, **2**: 91–106. [58–60, 80.]

CRAFTS, ALDEN S. 1931. Movement of organic materials in plants. *Plant Physiol.*, **6**: 1–42. [10, 56, 57, 135, 147, 150, 156, 164–166, 166–174, 180, 181, 216.]

————. 1932. Phloem anatomy, exudation and transport of organic nutrients in cucurbits. *Plant Physiol.*, **7**: 183–225. [135, 162, 163, 164–166, 166–174, 181.]

————. 1933. Sieve-tube structure and translocation in the potato. *Plant Physiol.*, **8**: 81–104. [162, 164, 165, 168, 169, 178, 181, 186, 217, 227.]

CRAIB, W. G. 1918. Regional spread of moisture in the wood of trees. I. Deciduous-leaved trees during the period late autumn to early spring. *Notes Roy. Bot. Gard. Edinburgh*, **51**: 1–18. [148.]

CURTIS, OTIS F. 1918. Stimulation of root growth in cuttings by treatment with chemical compounds. *Cornell Agr. Exp. Stat. Mem.*, 14: 71–138. [22, 127, 238.]

————. 1920a. The upward translocation of foods in woody plants. I. Tissues concerned in translocation. *Am. Jour. Bot.*, **7**: 101–124. [12–14, 15–17, 17–20, 25–33, 34.]

————. 1920b. The upward translocation of foods in woody plants. II. Is there normally an upward transfer of storage foods from the roots or trunks to the growing shoots? *Amer. Jour. Bot.*, **7**: 286–295. [17, 118.]

————. 1923. The effect of ringing a stem on the upward transfer of nitrogen and ash constituents. *Amer. Jour. Bot.*, **10**: 361–382. [31, 47–53, 59, 63, 113.]

————. 1925. Studies on the tissues concerned in the transfer of solutes in plants. The effect on the upward transfer of solutes of cutting the xylem as compared with that of cutting the phloem. *Ann. Bot.*, **39**: 573–585. [36–44, 104, 114, 126, 134.]

————. 1929. Studies on solute translocation in plants. Experiments indicating that translocation is dependent on the activity of living cells. *Amer. Jour. Bot.*, **16**: 154–168. [162, 174, 223, 226.]

———— and H. T. SCOFIELD. 1933. A comparison of osmotic concentrations of supplying and receiving tissues and its bearing on the Münch hypothesis of the translocation mechanism. *Amer. Jour. Bot.*, **20**: 502–512. [153–156.]

CZAPEK, FRIEDRICH. 1897. Über die Leitungswege der organischen Baustoffe im Pflanzenkörper. *Sitzungsber. kais. Akad. Wiss. in Wien, Math. Naturwiss. Kl. Abt. I*, **106**: 117–170. [204, 221, 222.]

————. 1897. Zur Physiologie des Leptoms der Angiospermen. *Ber. deutsch. bot. Ges.*, **15**: 124–131. [204, 221, 222.]

DAVIS, A. W., A. J. DAISH, and G. C. SAWYER. 1916. Studies on the formation and translocation of carbohydrates in plants. I. The carbohydrates of the mangold leaf. II. The dextrose-laevulose ratio in the mangold. *Jour. Agr. Sci.*, **7**: 255–326, 327–351. [188–190.]

DELEANO, N. T. 1911. Über die Ableitung der Assimilate durch die intakten, die chloroformierten und die plasmolysierten Blattstiele der Laubblätter. *Jahrb. f. wiss. Bot.*, **49**: 129–186. [160, 221, 222.]

DELEANO, N. T., and M. I. ANDREESCO. 1932. Beiträge zum Studium der Rolle und Wirkungsweise der Mineral- und organischen Stoffe im Pflanzenleben. *Beitr. z. Biol. d. Pflanzen*, **19**: 249–286. [158, 221, 242.]

DENNY, F. E. 1930. The twin-leaf method of studying changes in leaves. *Amer. Jour. Bot.*, **17**: 818–841. [63, 67.]

DE VRIES, H. 1885. Über die Bedeutung der Circulation und der Rotation des Protoplasmas für den Stofftransport in der Pflanze. *Bot. Zeit.*, **43**: 2–6, 18–26. [137, 174, 181.]

DIXON, H. H. 1922. Transport of organic substances in plants. *Nature*, **110**: 547–551. [5, 10, 36, 94–99, 104, 125, 181.]

———. 1924. The transpiration stream. 80 pp. [95, 103, 125.]

———. 1933. Bast sap. *Roy Dublin Soc. Sci. Proc.*, **20**: 487–494. [134, 135, 161.]

——— and W. R. G. ATKINS. 1915. Osmotic pressure in plants. IV. On the constituents and concentration of the sap in the conducting tracts, and on the circulation of carbohydrates in plants. *Roy. Dublin Soc. Sci. Proc.*, **14**: 374–392. [99, 119.]

——— and ———. 1916. Osmotic pressure in plants. VI. On the composition of the sap in the conducting tracts of trees at different levels and at different seasons of the year. *Roy. Dublin Soc. Sci. Proc.*, **15**: 51–62. [99, 119.]

——— and N. G. BALL. 1922. Transport of organic substances in plants. *Nature*, **109**: 236–237. [94, 97, 110.]

——— and ———. 1923. On the extraction of sap from living leaves by means of compressed air. *Roy. Dublin Soc. Sci. Proc.*, **17**: 263–266. [99, 119.]

DRINKARD, A. W., JR., and A. A. INGHAM. 1917. Studies on methods of protecting ringing wounds on apple trees to promote their healing. *Virginia Agr. Exp. Sta. Tech. Bull.* 17: 147–160. [127.]

ECKERSON, SOPHIA. 1924. Protein synthesis by plants. I. Nitrate reduction. *Bot. Gaz.*, **77**: 377–390. [81, 149, 199.]

EWART, ALFRED J. 1903. On the physics and physiology of protoplasmic streaming in plants. Oxford. 131 pp. [182, 183, 203, 224.]

FERNALD, EVELYN I. 1925. The inhibition of bud-development as correlated with the osmotic concentration of sap. *Amer. Jour. Bot.*, **12**: 287–305. [153, 240.]

FISCHER, A. 1885. Über den Inhalt der Sierbröhren in der unverletzten Pflanze. *Ber. deutsch. bot. Ges.*, **3**: 230–239. [139.]

———. 1886. Neue Beiträge zur Kenntnis der Siebröhren. *Ber. Verhandl. Konig. Sächs. Ges. Wiss. Leipzig. Math. Phys. Kl.*, **38**: 291–336. [205.]

———. 1888. Glycose als Reservestoffe der Laubhölzer. *Bot. Zeit.*, **46**: 405–417. [99, 119.]

———. 1891. Beiträge zur Physiologie der Holzgewächse. *Jahrb. f. wiss. Bot.*, **22**: 73–160. [20.]

FREY-WYSSLING, ALBERT. 1932. Der Milchsafterguss von *Hevea brasiliensis* als Blutungserscheinung. *Jahrb. f. wiss. Bot.*, **77**: 560–626. [181.]

GARDNER, F. E. 1925. A study of the conductive tissues in shoots of the Bartlett pear and the relationship of food movement to dominance of the apical buds. *Calif. Agr. Exp. Sta. Tech. Paper*, 20: 1–26. [126.]

GAUWENTAK, CORNELIA A. 1929. Untersuchungen über den N-Stoffwechsel bei *Helianthus annuus* L. Dissertation Univ. Amsterdam. 95 pp. [67.]

GRAINGER, J. 1933. The movement of tobacco mosaic virus in its host. *Ann. Applied Biol.*, **20**: 236–257. [210.]

GRÜNFELD, OTTO. 1926. Über die Entleerung und Wiederauffülung isolierter Getreideendosperme, insbesondere von *Mais*, unter aseptischen Bedingungen. *Beih. J. Bot. Centralbl.*, **43**: 167–203. [21, 140.]

HAAS, A. R. C., and H. S. REED. 1927. Relation of desiccating winds to fluctuations in ash content of citrus leaves and phenomenon of mottle-leaf. *Bot. Gaz.*, **83**: 161–172. [75.]

HALES, STEPH. 1727. Vegetable statics or an account of some statical experiments on the sap in vegetables. 376 pp. [4, 6, 34, 91, 98.]

HALLER, M. H. 1931. The relation of the distance and direction of the fruit from the leaves to the size and composition of apples. *Proc. Amer. Soc. for Hort. Sci.*, **27**: 63–68. [35, 152, 250.]

HANSTEEN, BARTHOLD. 1894. Ueber die Ursachen der Entleerung der Reservestoffe aus Samen. *Flora* **79**: 419–429. [21.]

HANSTEIN, J. 1860. Versuche über die Leitung des Saftes durch die Rinde und Folgerung daraus. *Jahrb. wiss. Bot.*, **2**: 392–467. [8, 9, 28, 34, 88, 100.]

———. 1864. Die Milchsaftgefässe und die verwendten Organe der Rinde. 92 pp. [42.]

HARTIG, TH. 1858. Ueber die Bewegung des Saftes in den Holzpflanzen. *Bot. Zeit.*, **16**: 329–335, 338–342. [14, 28, 88, 136, 137, 174.]

———. 1860. Beiträge zur physiologischen Forstbotanik. *Allgem. Forst-u. Jagd-Zeit.*, **36**: 257–261. [8, 88, 135, 136, 147.]

———. 1861. Über die Bewegung des Saftes in den Holzpflanzen. *Bot. Zeit.*, **19**: 17–23. [88, 135, 136, 147, 186.]

———. 1862. Über die Bewegung des Saftes in den Holzpflanzen. *Bot. Zeit.*, **20**: 73–79, 81–87, 89–94, 97–100, 105–109. [28.]

HASSELBRING, H. 1914. The effect of shading on transpiration and assimilation of the tobacco plant in Cuba. *Bot. Gaz.*, **57**: 257–286. [71.]

HEILBRUNN, L. V. 1928. The colloid chemistry of protoplasm. 356 pp. [241.]

HEINE, H. 1885. Über die physiologische Funktion der Stärkeschiede. *Ber. deutsch. bot. Ges.*, **3**: 189–194. [116.]

HEINICKE, ARTHUR J. 1917. Factors influencing the abscission of flowers and partially developed fruits of the apple (*Pyrus malus* L.). *Cornell Univ. Agr. Exp. Sta. Bull.* 392: 43–114. [240.]

HILL, A. V. 1926. The physical environment of the living cell. *In* Lectures on certain aspects of biochemistry. H. H. Dale *et al.*, pp. 253–280. [175.]

HILL, A. W. 1908. The histology of the sieve-tubes of angiosperms. *Ann. Bot.*, **22**: 245–290. [163.]

HOAGLAND, D. R. 1923. The absorption of ions by plants. *Soil Sci.*, **16**: 225–246. [71, 79, 150.]

———, P. L. HIBBARD, and A. R. DAVIS, 1926. The influence of light, temperature and other conditions on the ability of *Nitella* cells to concentrate halogens in the cell sap. *Jour. Gen. Physiol.*, **10**: 121–146. [70, 73, 80.]

HOLMES, FRANCIS O. 1932. Movement of mosaic virus from primary lesions in *Nicotiana tabacum* L. *Contrib. Boyce Thompson Inst.*, **4**: 297–323. [211, 220.]

HOOKER, HENRY D., JR. 1924. Changes produced in apple trees by various types of pruning. *Missouri Agr. Exp. Sta. Res. Bull.* 72: 3–11. [130.]

HOPKINS, E. F.   1924.   Studies in potato storage.   *Bot. Gaz.*, **78** : 311–325. [19.]

HOWLETT, FREEMAN SMITH.   1926.   The nitrogen and carbohydrate composition of the developing flowers and young fruits of the apple.   *Cornell Univ. Mem.* 99: 2–79.   [242, 245.]

JAMES, W. O., and H. BAKER.   1933.   Sap pressure and the movement of sap.   *New Phytol.*, **32** : 317–343.   [169.]

JONES, C. H., A. W. EDSON and W. J. MORSE.   1903.   The maple sap flow *Vermont Agr. Exp. Sta. Bull.* 103: 43–184.   [6, 12, 19, 95, 117, 118, 148.]

KASTENS, EMMA.   1924.   Beiträge zur Kenntnis der Funktion der Siebröhren.   *Mitt. Inst. f. allgem. Bot., Hamburg*, **6** : 33–70.   [99, 130, 237.]

KIDD, F.   1917.   Translocation in plant tissues.   *New Phytol.*, **17** : 44–45. [142.]

KIENITZ-GERLOFF, F.   1891.   Die Protoplasmaverbindungen zwischen benachbarten Gewebeselementen in der Pflanze.   *Bot. Zeit.*, **49** : 1–10, 17–26, 33–46, 49–60, 65–68.   [139, 141, 143, 147, 183, 205, 218.]

————.   1902.   Neue Studien über Plasmodesmen.   *Ber. deutsch. bot. Ges.*, **20** : 93–117.   [141, 205.]

KNIEP, H.   1905.   Über die Bedeutung des Milchsafte der Pflanzen. *Flora*, **94** : 192–205.   [42.]

KNIGHT, T. A.   1801.   Account of some experiments on the ascent of sap in trees.   *Roy. Soc. Lond. Phil. Trans.*, **91** : 333–353.   [4, 7, 24, 34, 88.]

KÖGL, FRITZ.   1933.   Über Auxine.   *Zeit. f. Angew Chem.*, **46** : 469–473. [216.]

KOK, ALI C. A.   1931.   Über den Einfluss der Plasmarotation auf den Stofftransport.   *Proc. Kon. Acad. v. Wet. Amst.*, **34** : 918–929.   [185.]

————.   1933.   Über den Transport körperfremder Stoffe durch parenchymatische Gewebe.   *Recuil des Travaux botaniques Neérlandais*, **30** : 23–139.   [185.]

KRAMER, PAUL J.   1933.   The intake of water through dead root systems and its relation to the problem of absorption by transpiring plants. *Amer. Jour. Bot.*, **20** : 481–492.   [78.]

KRAUS, E. J. and H. R. KRAYBILL.   1918.   Vegetation and reproduction with special reference to the tomato.   *Oregon Agr. Exp. Sta. Bull.* 149: 1–90.   [238.]

KRAUS, GREGOR.   1886.   Über die Zusammensetzung des Siebröhrensaftes der Kürbise und alkalisch reagirende Zellsäfte.   *Abhandl. der Naturforsch. Ges. zu Halle*, **16** : 376–387.   [8, 164.]

KRUSEMAN, W. M.   1931.   De Invloed van Temperatuur en Narcose op het Transport der Assimilate.   129 pp.   (Dissertation Utrecht.)   [222, 224.]

LAMBERS, M. H. R.   1926.   Temperatur en protoplasmastrooming.   76 pp. (Dissertation Utrecht.)   [182.]

LECLERC, J. A., and J. F. BREAZEALE.   1908.   Plant food removed from growing plants by rain or dew.   *U. S. Dep. Agr. Yearbook*, 1908: 389–402.   [49.]

LECLERC DU SABLON.   1906.   Recherches physiologiques sur les matières de réserves des arbres.   *Rev. Gén. Bot.*, **16** : 341–368; **18** : 5–25, 82–96. [9.]

LECOMTE, HENRI. 1889. Contribution a l'etude du liber des angiosperms. *Ann. des Sci. Nat. Bot.*, **10**: 193–324. [3, 137–139, 162, 163, 174, 221.]

LINSBAUER, KARL. 1920. Bemerkungen über Alfred Fischer's "Gefässglykose" *Sitzungsber. Akad. Wiss. Wien (Math.-Nat. Kl. Abt.* 1), **129**: 215–229. [99, 119.]

LOEB, JACQUES. 1915. Rules and mechanism of inhibition and correlation in the regeneration of *Bryophyllum calycinum. Bot. Gaz.*, **60**: 249–276. [246.]

———. 1919. The physiological basis of morphological polarity in regeneration 1. *Jour. Gen. Physiol.*, **1**: 337–362. [237.]

———. 1920. The nature of the directive influence of gravity on arrangement of organs in regeneration. *Jour. Gen. Physiol.*, **2**: 373–386. [249.]

———. 1924. Regeneration from a physico-chemical viewpoint. New York. 143 pp. [237.]

LUND, E. J. 1931. Electric correlation between living cells in cortex and wood in the Douglas fir. *Plant Physiol.*, **6**: 631–652. [250.]

LUNDEGÅRDH, H. 1914. Einige Bedingungen der Bildung und Auflösung der Stärke. *Jahrb. f. wiss. Bot.*, **53**: 421–463. [20.]

MACDANIELS, L. H. 1918. The histology of the phloem in certain woody angiosperms. *Amer. Jour. Bot.*, **5**: 347–378. [180.]

———. 1923. The apple-tree crotch. Histological studies and practical considerations. *Cornell Univ. Agr. Exp. Sta. Bull.* 419: 1–22. [249.]

——— and OTIS F. CURTIS, 1930. The effect of spiral ringing on solute translocation and the structure of the regenerated tissues of the apple. *Cornell Univ. Agr. Exp. Sta. Mem.*, 133: 31 pp. [49, 58, 250.]

MACDOUGAL, D. T. 1925. Reversible variations in volume, pressure and movement of sap in trees. *Carnegie Inst. Wash. Pub.* 365: 1–90. [5, 73, 101, 102, 103.]

———. 1926. The hydrostatic system of trees. *Carnegie Inst. Wash. Pub.* 373, 125 pp. [110.]

———, J. B. OVERTON and GILBERT M. SMITH. 1929. The hydrostatic-pneumatic system of certain trees: Movements of liquids and gases. *Carnegie Inst. Wash. Pub.* 397: 99 pp. [110, 148.]

MADER, E. O. 1934. Studies on the effect of bordeaux mixture on the development of potato plants. Thesis Cornell Univ. [247.]

MALPIGHI, MARCELLUS. 1675 and 1679. Anatome Plantarum (Seen only in the German edition prepared by Möbius in Ostwald's Klassiker der Exakten Wissenschaften No. 120, 1901). [4, 6, 88.]

MANGHAM, S. 1910. Translocation of carbohydrates in plants. *Sci. Progress*, **5**: 256–285, 457–479. [9.]

———. 1917. On the mechanism of translocation in plant tissues. An hypothesis with special reference to sugar conduction in sieve-tubes. *Ann. Bot.*, **31**: 293–311. [142, 147.]

MANN, C. E. T., and T. WALLACE. 1925. The effects of leaching with cold water on the foliage of the apple. *Jour. of Pomol. and Hort. Sci.*, **4**: 1–16. [49.]

MASKELL, E. J. and T. G. MASON. 1929a. Studies on the transport of nitrogenous substances in the cotton plant. I. Preliminary observation on the downward transport of nitrogen in the stem. *Ann. Bot.*, **43**: 205–231. [51, 52, 55, 60, 61, 64, 129, 199, 202.]

—— and ——, 1929b. Studies on the transport of nitrogenous substances in the cotton plant. II. Observations on concentration gradients. *Ann. Bot.*, **43**: 615–652. [199, 201.]

—— and ——. 1930a. Studies on the transport of nitrogenous substances in the cotton plant. III. The relation between longitudinal movement and concentration gradients in the bark. *Ann. Bot.*, **44**: 1–29. [192, 199.]

—— and ——. 1930b. Studies on the transport of nitrogenous substances in the cotton plant. IV. The interpretation of the effects of ringing, with special reference to the lability of the nitrogen compounds of the bark. *Ann. Bot.*, **44**: 233–267. [60, 63, 159, 199.]

—— and ——. 1930c. Studies on the transport of nitrogenous substances in the cotton plant. V. Movement to the boll. *Ann. Bot.*, **44**: 657–688. [192, 199, 243.]

MASON, T. G. 1922. A note on the growth and the transport of organic substances in bitter cassava (*Manihot utilissima*). *Roy. Dublin Soc. Sci. Proc.*, **17**: 105–112. [124.]

—— and C. J. LEWIN. 1926. On the rate of carbohydrate transport in the greater yam, *Dioscora alata*, Linn. *Roy. Dublin Soc. Sci. Proc.*, **18**: 203–205. [96, 106, 181.]

—— and E. J. MASKELL. 1928a. Studies on the transport of carbohydrates in the cotton plant. I. A study of diurnal variation in the carbohydrate of leaf, bark and wood, and the effects of ringing. *Ann. Bot.*, **42**: 189–253. [43, 95, 121, 149, 156, 218.]

—— and ——. 1928b. Studies on the transport of carbohydrates in the cotton plant. II. The factors determining the rate and the direction of movement of sugars. *Ann. Bot.*, **42**: 571–636. [31, 175, 187, 188, 192–195, 198, 249.]

—— and ——. 1931. Further studies on transport in the cotton plant. 1. Preliminary observations on the transport of phosphorus, potassium, and calcium. *Ann. Bot.*, **45**: 125–173. [60, 63, 75, 81, 121, 150.]

—— and ——. 1934. Further studies on transport in the cotton plant. II. An ontogenetic study of concentrations and vertical gradients. *Ann. Bot.*, **48**: 119–141. [192, 199.]

—— and E. PHILLIS. 1934. Studies on the transport of nitrogenous substances in the cotton plant. VI. Concerning storage in the bark. *Ann. Bot.*, **48**: 315–333. [63, 199, 201.]

MAXIMOV, N. A. 1929. The plant in relation to water. Transl. by R. H. Yapp. 451 pp. [77.]

McCALLUM, WILLIAM B. 1905. Regeneration in plants I and II. *Bot. Gaz.*, **40**: 97–120, 241–263. [222, 237, 238.]

MIEHE, HUGO. 1901. Über die Wanderungen des pflanzlichen Zellkerns. *Flora*, **88**: 105–142. [141, 170.]

MOORE, WILLIAM, and J. J. WILLIAMAN. 1917. Studies in greenhouse fumigation with hydrocyanic acid: physiological effects on the plant. *Jour. Agr. Res.*, **11**: 319–338. [222.]

MOREAU, L., and E. VINET. 1923. Sur la composition des pleurs de vignes. *Compt. Rend. de l'Acad. d'Agriculture de France*, **9**: 554–557. [6, 117, 118.]

MUENSCHER, WALTER C. 1922. The effect of transpiration on the absorption of salts by plants. *Amer. Jour. Bot.*, **9**: 311–329. [71, 72, 74.]

MÜNCH, ERNST, 1926. Dynamik der Saftströmungen. *Ber. d. deutsch. bot. Ges.*, **44**: 68–71. [10, 143.]

——. 1927. Versuche über den Saftkreislauf. *Ber. d. deutsch. bot. Ges.*, **45**: 340–356. [56, 143.]

——. 1930. Die Stoffbewegungen in der Pflanze. Jena, 234 pp. [34, 35, 36, 57, 135, 143–146, 147–149, 149–164, 169, 180, 181, 217, 247, 250.]

——. 1932. Ergänzende Versuche über Stoffbewegungen. *Ber. d. deutsch. bot. Ges.* **50**: 407–426. [164, 219.]

NÄGELI, C. 1861. Über die Siebröhren von *Cucurbita*. *Sitz-ber. d. K. bayr. Akad. d. Wiss. zu München*, **1**: 212–238. [136.]

OSTERHOUT, W. J. V. 1922. Some aspects of selective absorption. *Jour. Gen. Physiol.*, **5**: 225–230. [79, 150.]

OVERTON, J. B. 1925. Some methods for determining the tissues concerned and the path of transfer of solutes in plants. *Carnegie Inst. Wash. Yearbook*, **25**: 155. [115.]

PALLADIN'S Plant Physiology. 1926. Transl. by B. E. Livingston. 360 pp. [72, 75.]

PARKIN, JOHN. 1899. Contribution to our knowledge of the formation, storage and depletion of carbohydrates in monocotyledons. *Roy. Soc. Lond. Phil. Trans.* **191** B: 35–79. [21.]

PFEFFER, W. 1900. The physiology of plants. Vol. 1. 632 pp. Trans. by A. J. Ewart. [4, 89.]

PHILLIS, E., and T. G. MASON, 1933. Studies on the transport of carbohydrates in the cotton plant. III. The polar distribution of sugar in the foliage leaf. *Ann. Bot.*, **47**: 585–634. [171, 192–196, 220, 245.]

PRÁT, SILVESTER. 1923. Die Elektrolytaufnahme durch die Pflanze 1. *Biochem. Zeitsch.*, **136**: 366–376. [71.]

PRIESTLEY, J. H. 1920. The mechanism of root pressure. *New Phytol.*, **19**: 189–200. [79, 172.]

——. 1929. Cell growth and cell division in the shoot of the flowering plant. *New Phytol.*, **28**: 54–81. [79.]

—— and A. WORMALL. 1925. On the solutes exuded by root pressure from vines. *New Phytol.*, **24**: 24–38. [6, 117.]

PROEBSTING, E. L. 1925. The relation of stored food to cambial activity in the apple. *Hilgardia*, **1**: 81–106. [249.]

PURIEWITSCH, K. 1898. Physiologische Untersuchungen über die Entleerung der Reservestoffbehälter. *Jahrb. f. wiss. Bot.*, **31**: 1–76. [21, 140.]

REED, H. S., and F. F. HALMA. 1919a. On the existence of a growth-inhibiting substance in the Chinese lemon. *Univ. Calif. Pub. Agr. Ser.*, **4**: 99–112. [9, 237, 248.]

—— and H. S. HALMA. 1919b. The evidence for a growth-inhibiting substance in the pear tree. *Plant World*, **22**: 239–247. [237.]

REID, MARY E. 1924. Quantitative relations of carbohydrates to nitrogen in determining growth responses in tomato cuttings. *Bot. Gaz.*, **77**: 404–418. [238.]

RUMBOLD, CAROLINE. 1920. The injection of chemicals into chestnut trees. *Am. Jour. Bot.*, **7**: 1–20. [5, 93.]

Russöw, E. 1884. Über das Schwinden und wieder Auftreten der Stärke in der Rinde der einheimischen Holzgewächse. *Sitzungsber d. Naturf. Ges. Dorpat*, **6**: 492–494. (Seen in transl. by H. P. Traub, 1927, *The Minnesota Horticulturist*, **55**: 241–242.) [20.]

Rywosch, S. 1908. Zur Stoffwanderung im Chlorophyllgewebe. *Bot. Zeit.*, **66**: 121–130. [136, 188.]

———. 1909. Über Stoffwanderung und Diffusionsströme in Pflanzenorganen. *Zeitschr. f. Bot.*, **1**: 571–591. [136, 188.]

———. 1911. Über eine Diffusionsbeschleunigung der Dextrose. *Ber. d. deutsch. bot. Ges.*, **29**: 204–210. [136.]

Sachs, Julius. 1863. Über die Leitung der plastischen Stoffe durch verschiedene Gewebeformen. *Flora*, **46**: 33–42, 49–58, 65–74. [136, 188.]

———. 1887. Lectures on the physiology of plants. Transl. by H. Marshall Ward. 836 pp. [169.]

Samuel, Geoffrey. 1934. The movement of tobacco mosaic virus within the plant. *Ann. Applied Biol.*, **21**: 90–111. [212.]

Saposchnikoff, W. 1890. Bildung und Wanderung der Kohlenhydrate in den Laubblättern. *Ber. d. deutsch. bot. Ges.*, **8**: 233–242. [61.]

———. 1893. Beitrag zur Kentniss der Grenzen der Anhäufung von Kohlenhydrate in den Blättern. *Ber. d. deutsch. bot. Ges.*, **11**: 391–393. [160.]

Scarth, G. W. 1927. The structural organization of plant protoplasm in the light of micrurgy. *Protoplasma*, **2**: 189–205. [182, 195, 203.]

Schimper, A. F. W. 1885. Über Bildung und Wanderung der Kohlenhydrate in den Laubblättern. *Bot. Zeit.*, **43**: 737–743, 753–763, 769–787. [21, 42, 136, 188, 197.]

Schloesing, T. 1869. Tabac sous cloche et a l'air libre. *Ann. Sci. Nat. Bot.*, **10**: 366–369. [72.]

Schmidt, E. W. 1917. Bau und Funktion der Siebröhre der Angiospermen. 108 pp. [135, 163.]

Schroeder, J. 1871. Die Frühjahrsperiode der Birke (*Betula alba* L.) und des Ahorn (*Acer platanoides*). *Landw. Versuchstat.*, **14**: 118–146. [6, 117, 118.]

Schumacher, Walter. 1930. Untersuchungen über die Lokalisation der Stoffwanderung in den Leitbündeln höherer Pflanzen. *Jahrb. f. wiss. Bot.*, **73**: 770–823. [62, 206, 226.]

———. 1931. Über Eiweissumsetzungen in Blütenblättern. *Jahrb. f. wiss. Bot.*, **75**: 581–608. [44, 158, 211, 220, 242.]

———. 1933. Untersuchungen über die Wanderung des Fluoreszein in den Siebröhren. *Jahrb. f. wiss. Bot.*, **77**: 685–732. [112, 180, 183, 186, 187, 204–209, 211, 213, 216, 217, 220, 222, 227.]

Scott, Lorna I. 1928. The root as an absorbing organ. II. The delimitation of the absorbing zone. *New Phytol.*, **27**: 141–174. [116.]

——— and J. H. Priestley, 1928. The root as an absorbing organ. I. A reconsideration of the entry of water and salts in the absorbing region. *New Phytol.* **27**: 125–140. [116, 172.]

Simon, C. 1917. Sind die Milchröhren Leitungsorgane? Inaug.-Diss. Westfälischen Wilhelms-Univ. zu Münster. 42 pp. [42.]

SINNOTT, E. W. 1918. Factors determining character and distribution of food reserves in woody plants. *Bot. Gaz.*, **66**: 162–175. [20.]

SKAER, AILEEN M. 1931. A comparison of the loss of sugars from attached leaves and detached leaves with petioles in water, and the bearing of this on theories of translocation. Unpublished thesis for M. S. Cornell Univ. [160.]

SMITH, KENNETH M. 1931. On the composite nature of certain potato virus diseases of the mosaic group as revealed by the use of plant indicators and selective methods of transmission. *Roy. Soc. Lond. Proc.*, B **109**: 251–267. [213.]

SNOW, R. 1924. Conduction of excitation in stem and leaf of *Mimosa pudica*. *Roy. Soc. Lond. Proc.*, B. **96**: 349–374. [98.]

———. 1925. Conduction of excitation in the leaf of *Mimosa Spegazzinii*. *Roy. Soc. Lond. Proc.* B., **98**: 188–201. [98.]

STANESCU, P. P. 1933. L'influence du refroidissement du pétiole sur le transport des substances dans les feuilles. *Soc. de biol. Bucarest. Compt. rend.*, **112**: 1502. [224.]

STEWARD, FREDERICK CAMPION. 1930. Diffusion of certain solutes through membranes of living plant cells and its bearing upon certain problems of solute movement in the plant. *Protoplasma*, **11**: 521–557. [88, 139, 174.]

———. 1932. The absorption and accumulation of solutes by living plant cells. I. Experimental conditions which determine salt absorption by storage tissue. *Protoplasma*, **15**: 29–58. [80, 150.]

——— and J. H. PRIESTLEY. 1932. Movement of organic materials in plants. A note on a recently suggested mechanism. *Plant Physiol.*, **7**: 165–171. [168.]

STRASBURGER, EDUARD. 1891. Ueber den Bau und die Verichtungen der Leitungsbahnen in den Pflanzen. 1000 pp. [34, 36, 78, 91, 174.]

SUMMERS, F. 1924. The factors governing bud formation. Chap. IX. Further experiments on the ringing of woody shoots. *New Phytol.*, **23**: 116–127. [127.]

SWARBRICK, THOMAS. 1927. The healing of wounds in woody stems. II. Contributions to the physiological anatomy of ringed apple shoots. *Jour. Pomol. and Hort. Sci.*, **6**: 29–46. [24, 32, 126, 130.]

———. 1928. Studies in the physiology of fruit trees. II. The effects of ringing, double ringing and disbudding upon the starch content and cambial activity of two-year-old apple shoots. *Jour. Pomol. and Hort. Sci.*, **4**: 296–312. [41.]

SWART, NICOLAS. 1914. Die Stoffwanderung in ablebenden Blättern. Jena, 117 pp. [158.]

THOMAS, W. 1927. The seat of formation of amino-acids in *Pyrus malus* L. *Science*, **66**: 115–116. [81, 149, 200.]

TIEGS, O. W. 1928. Surface tension and the theory of protoplasmic movement. *Protoplasma*, **4**: 88–139. [203.]

TINCKER, M. A. H. 1928. The effect of length of day upon the growth and chemical composition of the tissues of certain economic plants. *Ann. Bot.*, **42**: 101–140. [181.]

Ursprung, A., and G. Blum. 1924. Eine Methode zur Messung des Wand- und Turgordrukes der Zelle, nebst Anwendungen. *Jahrb. f. wiss. Bot.*, **63**: 1–110. [154.]

—— and ——. 1925. Eine Methode zur Messung polarer Saugkraftdifferenzen. *Jahrb. f. wiss. Bot.*, **45**: 1–27. [144.]

Van den Honert, T. H. 1932. On the mechanism of the transport of organic materials in plants. *Konink. Akad. Wetensch. Amsterdam Proc.*, **35**: 1104–1112. [143, 202–204, 209, 227, 228, 245.]

Van der Wey, H. G. 1932. Der Mechanismus des Wuchsstoff-transportes. *Recueil des travaux botaniques néerlandais*, **29**: 379–496. [187, 204, 214–217, 219.]

Velten, W. 1872. Über die Verbreitung der Protoplasmaströmung im Pflanzenreich. *Bot. Zeit.*, **30**: 645–653. [42, 137.]

Weevers, Th. 1923. Ringing experiments with variegated branches. *Konink. Akad. Wetensch. Amsterdam Proc.*, **26**: 755–762. [30, 33, 220.]

——. 1924. The first carbohydrates that originate during the assimilatory process. A physiological study with variegated leaves. *Konink. Akad. Wetensch. Amsterdam Proc.*, **27**: 46–56. [190.]

——. 1928. Die Ergebnisse einiger Ringelungsversuche und ihre Bedeutung für die Stoffwanderung. *Recueil trav. bot. néerlandais*, **25^a**: 461–474. [8, 127.]

——. 1931. Aufnahme, Verbreitung und Transport der Zucker im Blattgewehe. *Recueil trav. bot. néerlandais*, **28**: 400–420. [140.]

—— and J. Westenberg. 1931. Versuche zur Prüfung der Münchschen Theorie der Stoffbewegungen in der Pflanze. *Konink. Akad. Wetensch. Amsterdam Proc.*, **34**: 1173–1178. [148.]

Went, F. W. 1932. Eine botanische Polaritätstheorie. *Jahrb. f. wiss. Bot.*, **76**: 528–557. [187, 214, 219.]

White, Jean. 1907. The influence of pollination on the respiratory activity of the gynaecium. *Ann. Bot.*, **21**: 487–499. [241.]

Wilson, J. K. 1923. The nature and reaction of water from hydathodes. *Cornell Agr. Exp. Sta. Mem.*, 65: 11 pp. [121.]

Wormall, Arthur. 1924. The constituents of the sap of the vine (*Vitis vinifera* L.) *Biochem. Jour.*, **18**: 1187–1202. [117, 122.]

Yendo, Y. 1917. Injection experiments on plants. *Jour. Col. Sci. Imp. Univ. Tokyo*, **38**: 1–46. [5, 91, 93.]

Zaccharias, E. 1884. Über den Inhalt der Siebröhren von *Cucurbita pepo*. *Bot. Zeit.*, **42**: 65–73. [8.]

INDEX

A

Abnormal movements (possibly), of fluorescein in phloem, 208, 209

of phloem contents as result of cutting, 104, 112, 134, 135, 138, 139, 147, 161, 162, 169, 170, 172, 178, 217, 218

of solutions in xylem, as result of cutting or injection, 104, 105, 109–112, 208, 209

of starvation, 52, 62–64, 81–86, 123, 124, 200

(*See also* Exudation)

Abnormal permeability of sieve tubes as result of cutting, 169

Abnormal size of sieve tubes and pores, 135, 170, 172, 180, 181

Abscission, removal or export previous to, 158, 211, 218, 220–222, 242

(*See also* Loss)

Absorption, against concentration gradient, 150, 166, 170, 171, 176, 196–198, 245

by dead roots, 77, 78, 84

retention or loss of solutes as influenced by aeration, 21, 140

by carbohydrate supply, 50, 52, 61–64, 70, 78, 81, 82, 84, 86, 123, 200

by kind of ion, 80

by light, 70, 73, 82

by rains, 49

by temperature, 119

special conditions influencing, 77–86

transpiration, influence on, 70–77

Accumulation, capacity of living cells, 79, 150

Accumulation, of fluorescein, 204 208

of ions or salts, 70, 73, 79

of nitrogen, 78, 79, 150

above rings, 52, 54, 55, 57, 60, 61, 63, 70, 86

of sugars, 100, 118, 119, 166, 170, 171, 196–198, 205, 245

Adsorption and solute movement, 142, 143

Aeration and filling or emptying of storage tissues, 21, 140

Anesthetics, effect on translocation, 162, 222

of fluorescein, 206

Ash, absorption by dead roots, 78

accumulation above rings, 54, 57, 60, 63

content as influenced by hot winds, 76

diurnal variation, 61, 70

effect of ringing on, 47–64, 130

removal before abscission, 158, 221, 222

tissues concerned in transport, 9, 55–57, 60, 70–86

B

Bark, 7, 201

separation into layers, 192–194, 196

(*See also* Phloem)

Behavior, as influenced by translocation, 1–3, 7, 13, 235–237

nitrogen, effect on, 236

ringing, effect on, 235, 236

(*See also* Growth; Hormones)

265